Dear Freedom Model Reader,

Thank you for your interest in The Freedom Model for Addictions. The information contained in this book is absolutely transformational, and we are confident it will provide you the knowledge you need to make the changes you're seeking. It encompasses more than 30 years of research and development.

If you feel you will need, or can benefit from working with a Certified Freedom Model Presenter to take you through the full course, that service is offered exclusively through Freedom Model Private Instruction which is taught one-on-one with a Certified Freedom Model Presenter remotely via video conference or in person at one of our satellite offices.

We also offer The Freedom Model for Addictions System in a residential setting at any one of our Retreat locations. Please note that The Freedom Model is proprietary to Baldwin Research Institute, Inc. and the Freedom Model Retreats (formerly Saint Jude Retreats) and no other institution, organization or individual is certified or granted permission to teach The Freedom Model for Addictions.

To learn about The Freedom Model for Addictions System, please call 1.888.424.2626.

Thank you, and until then, I send,

Kindest Regards,

Mark W. Scheeren
Chairman and Co-Author

THE FREEDOM MODEL *for Addictions*

Written by Steven Slate and Mark Scheeren
with Michelle Dunbar

WWW.THEFREEDOMMODEL.ORG

BRI
PUBLISHING

DEVELOPED BY BALDWIN RESEARCH INSTITUTE, INC.

BRI Publishing
9 Market Street
Amsterdam, NY 12010
Email: info@bripublishing.org

ISBN: 978-0-9834713-4-9 (paperback)
ISBN: 978-0-9834713-5-6 (epub)
ISBN: 978-0-9834713-6-3 (pdf)
ISBN: 978-0-9834713-7-0 (mobi)

Ordering Information:
For inquiries on bulk sales and special discounts that are available on quantity purchases by corporations, associations, and others, please contact info@bripublishing.org

The Freedom Model, The Freedom Model Retreats, and Saint Jude Retreats are registered trademarks of Baldwin Research Institute, Inc.

For information on The Freedom Model for Addictions and our additional services visit:
www.thefreedommodel.org or call **1-888-424-2626**

Layout: The Artful Editor
Copyediting: Erin Cler

Disclaimer: The Freedom Model and The Freedom Model Retreats, are divisions of Baldwin Research Institute, Inc., do not provide any services that require certification by New York State's Office of Alcoholism and Substance Abuse Services. The information in this book is designed to provide information and education on the subject of substance use and human behavior. This book is not meant to be used, nor should it be used, to diagnose or treat any associated condition. The publisher and authors are not responsible for any consequences from any treatment, action, application, or preparation, by any person or to any person reading or following the information in this book. The publisher has put forth its best efforts in preparing and arranging this. The information provided herein is provided "as is" and you read and use this information at your own risk. The publisher and authors disclaim any liabilities for any loss of profit or commercial or personal damages resulting from the use of the information contained in this book.

CONTENTS

FOREWORD

BY PETER VENTURELLI, PhD

As a university professor, I devoted thirty-four years of my life to teaching, researching, and publishing my accumulated and trusted knowledge and beliefs about major theoretical findings concerning drug use and abuse.[1] At this point in time after reading *The Freedom Model,* many of my beliefs about drug use and addiction have been turned on their head. I am confident in predicting that authors Steven Slate and Mark Scheeren have written a revolutionary book that will challenge your conventional beliefs about drug use, addiction, and recovery. The Freedom Model fully explains a simple idea that has guided Baldwin Research Institute's groundbreaking work at the Freedom Retreats for three decades, emphasizing that serious alcohol and/or drug problems are solved *by personal choice.*

Logically speaking, since personal choices cause drinking and/or drugging behavior, other personal choices can also modify or eliminate this behavior. Any attachment to a drug is created by self-action, and any lasting change of this attachment consists of reorienting your thinking about drugs and drug use. Other corresponding views that the Freedom Model begins with are the premises that as humans all of us pursue happiness with free will and mental autonomy – hence, we are not robots whose minds can be hacked into! Simply put, as the authors have eloquently stated, "The Freedom Model is simply a different way of thinking about alcohol and other drugs."

---

1. For example, one of my ongoing publications, now in the 13 edition, *Drugs and Society,* by Hanson, Venturelli, and Fleckenstein, (Jones and Bartlett Learning, Burlington, MA 2017) is a comprehensive text covering drug use and abuse.

The Freedom Model will challenge many of your beliefs about the use of alcohol and other drug substances. How alcohol and other drugs are viewed depends on past conceptions, personally held beliefs, and the extent to which we have been exposed to inaccurate and erroneous assumptions that we often believe are factual. The reader will realize that such concocted concepts as addiction and addiction as a disease, addicts, alcoholics, recovery, powerlessness over drug use, etc., etc. do not really exist in the world of alcohol and/or drug use. As I have experienced, prior beliefs regarding alcohol and/or drug use may very well be smashed to smithereens after reading through this volume.

The 23 chapters and five appendices that encapsulate the Freedom Model will inform the reader how individuals with drug habits can break free from *the shackles of erroneous and outdated "information."* This text is well written, timely, elegant in its writing, thought provoking, and convincing, resulting in a mental revolution.

In conclusion, from the research presented together with the invaluable facts and insights of authors Slate and Scheeren, what is written in this text will be memorable, satisfying, and life changing. The Freedom Model shows you how to opt out of the drug rehabilitation money-making machine's "ongoing battle against addiction," and address your problems where they truly exist: in the realm of personal choice.

Professor Peter J. Venturelli
Professor Emeritus
Department of Sociology and Criminology
Valparaiso University

ACKNOWLEDGEMENTS

Without Gerald Brown's inquisitive mind and determination to find out what was going wrong in the treatment industry, this solution would not exist today. We thank him for his bravery and boldness in founding Baldwin Research Institute, and inviting us to continue his work.

There are countless Freedom Model Retreat staff members, our Board members, and guests, past and present without whom our work couldn't have been completed. We thank you all for your contribution.

There have been many daring researchers and authors who challenged the recovery society, and whose work inspired us on the intellectual end. There are too many to name and thank here, but you can find many of them in the citations throughout the book. We encourage readers to seek out their work. Guests at our Retreats can find much of it in our library.

Stanton Peele has been fearlessly challenging the recovery society for over forty years. He compiled and made sense of mounds of research, generating groundbreaking insights in books such as The Meaning of Addiction, and Diseasing of America. We're proud to call him an influence on our work, and a friend.

Finally, Ryan Schwantes isn't listed as an author of this text, but has been integral part of BRI's development of The Freedom Model ideas and applications. In addition, he keeps our organization running smoothly, and handles far too many responsibilities behind the scenes. His contributions to the development of The Freedom Model are invaluable.

PREFACE

All people, even those who have a serious drug or alcohol problem, can choose to use moderately, and contrary to popular belief, *they can do so successfully.*

That is a bold statement, and furthermore, *it's absolutely true.* Your inherent personal freedom allows you to control your current, past, and future use patterns—whatever they have been, are, and will be. Freedom from "addiction" comes from the knowledge, without fear or doubt that you have always been in full control of your own drug and alcohol use and always will be. Your substance use is fully and completely your choice.

Now, you might be asking why the first words in *The Freedom Model* are about moderation. We started with this topic because we wanted to demonstrate to you just how revolutionary *The Freedom Model* approach is, and to set the stage for successful change. By stating that moderation is a viable option *for everyone*, regardless of the severity of his or her habit, we hopefully have gotten your attention. As you may well know, successful moderation is a heresy in the addiction/recovery world and within our culture today. There is no topic in our treatment-centered society that creates a greater division of opinion like the argument between whether "addicts" or "alcoholics" can control their use of substances and moderate. Over the years, researchers who dared to investigate moderate drinking or drugging among "alcoholics" and "addicts" have been ritualistically attacked from all corners of the addiction treatment industry and recovery landscape. It's a firestorm of a debate.

Throughout this text, we challenge and debunk every facet of addiction and recovery, such as the reigning view that moderation is impossible for some, and provide the factual backdrop for you to reclaim your sense of freedom over your own behavior. After reading this book, you will never see addiction or recovery the same again, and you will understand that both "addiction" and "recovery" are social con-structs—parts that make up a belief system that, in its totality, is an oppressive form of Western religion.

THE ADDICTION AND RECOVERY RELIGION

For those indoctrinated into the addiction and recovery religion, the first reaction to the idea of people successfully moderating their use is anger and fear. They do not believe it is possible for *true addicts or alcoholics* to control and monitor their use. They view the statement that people can successfully moderate as heresy and honestly believe the information is dangerous and even deadly because to them it provides a false sense of security. They see the prospect of moderation as the great lie that alcoholics or addicts must never allow themselves the privilege of thinking is a realistic option. And so, with this belief system and fear intact, we can easily see why you may be repelled or frightened by the mere mention of moderation. It is entirely understandable. We too once felt this way; we *feared alcohol and drugs* and all that went with them. And then, we did the research, now having devoted nearly three decades of our lives to it, and our eyes were opened.

In this book, we make many bold statements like the one above. We do so based on facts. Many of the statements will surprise you, but they will also liberate you. We challenge and break down all the myths on which the addiction and recovery religion stands. You, the reader, will be shocked and surprised to know that ending an addiction is easy and that "addiction" does not actually exist as a state of loss of control or hopelessness but only as a state of *belief* in loss of control and hopelessness. Addiction is a set of beliefs held together by myths, mysticism, and misguided ideas, as well as misinterpreted and flawed research.

Fear of substances and their "powers" is the dominant focus in the recovery society mindset. The treatment centers are its churches, the recovery zealots are its missionaries, and the addicts and alcoholics are its unknowing followers. To be a part of this religious movement, you must both romanticize and fear the mythical, supernatural powers of drugs and alcohol. You must understand that the "addicts" or "alcoholics" are diseased, weak, lost souls with no ability to stop themselves from being led by the magical pull of substances. Addiction gurus are the priests leading their flock to salvation. Finally, the court system enforces their dogma, making this a theocracy. In this religion, people talk of substances as if they were living, breathing beings bent on their destruction. For example, users say things like "Heroin calls to me," "Alcohol is cunning, baffling, and powerful," or "I'm battling addiction," just to name a few.

The religion of addiction is one of the primary causes of the increasing death rates from overdose. Opiates have existed for thousands of years, as have alcohol and a variety of substances that are heavily used today. The rates of use for these substances have historically been stable for decades in Western societies until now. As treatment has flourished over the past 50 years, so have the rates of overdose, dangerous binge usage, and heavy continuous use.

As researchers, we had to ask, has something intrinsically changed in humans that can explain the increased rates of heavy use and death compared to the generations of the past? It's not the drugs that have changed because they are pharmacologically no different than they were – today's heroin, prescription painkillers, and alcohol work much the same as the opiates and alcohol of antiquity. The only remarkable change has been in our cultural ideas, theories, and beliefs surrounding substance use. Those changes contain misinformation that causes exceptional sadness and tragedy. Behind the senseless wave of current trends in overdose and death in Western societies is the idea that "once people start, they can't stop" and that substances have the supernatural power to enslave people. With that mantra, people give up, keep using "addictively," and die in a state of utter hopelessness. It doesn't have to be this way. *The Freedom Model* changes all that.

THE FREEDOM MODEL

The Freedom Model is not a program, nor a process of recovery, nor a moderation advocate of any kind. It is not treatment, counseling, or therapy. Instead, it is a way of thinking about the choices you can and will make in your own life. It is an approach about a confused idea called addiction and recovery, and it seeks to clear the air on these constructs. *The Freedom Model* debunks all the addiction and recovery myths so you can happily choose one of three options—continue to use heavily, use moderately (whatever that means to you), or abstain—and freely choose your options based on facts and confidence, not fiction and fear. It allows you to make the pursuit of greater happiness your deciding factor.

PURSUIT OF HAPPINESS IS THE KEY

People exist in all sorts of voluntarily maintained engagements with which they are nonetheless dissatisfied – jobs, careers, relationships, living situations, and of course habits such as using alcohol and other drugs. But as dissatisfying and painful as these involvements can be, people do not move on from them until they believe they have a happier option available to them; a better job, a better career, a better relationship, or a better living situation. Until a credibly happier option is seen, they feel stuck. This applies to habits such as heavy substance use too.

From our beginnings of helping people almost 30 years ago, our approach has had a single defining theme in the *pursuit of happiness*. We have shown people that if they can develop the conviction that a change to their substance use habits will produce greater happiness, then they will happily, easily, and permanently change their habits for the better. They will get "unstuck" and move on. That is the natural way of personal change.

This should be common sense, and yet it is directly at odds with standard methods of help for people with substance use problems. The directive against any discussion of moderation exemplifies this best (which is why we chose this topic as our opening salvo). Let us explain.

"ABSTINENCE OR YOUR LIFE!" –
THE FALSE ALTERNATIVE

When you arrive for help in the addiction and recovery world you are hit immediately with a scare tactic. They say that you must never touch a single dose of alcohol or other drugs for the rest of your life, or else you will "lose control," ceaselessly consuming substances at disastrous levels. They try to make the issue a no-brainer by presenting you with a false alternative – either you abstain for the rest of your life, or get back on the fast track to an addicted-hell of *jails, institutions, and an early death* (as the popular phrase from 12-step programs puts it).

In this binary set of options, your pursuit of happiness never enters the equation. Fear and panic rule the decision-making process. Think of it this way, if a mugger catches you in an alleyway, pulls out a gun, and gives you the ultimatum "your money or your life," is it really a positive decision when you hand over your wallet? *Of course not.* It's a coerced decision, one that you make begrudgingly, and one that you regret and resent having had to make. The ultimatum of "abstinence or your life" is much the same. It is a coerced decision made out of fear, panic, and other negative emotions. It is one where your pursuit of happiness is made irrelevant.

The scientific evidence is clear, nobody "loses control" of their substance use, not even the most extreme users (see Appendix A). If you don't lose control, then you are capable of moderate use. This is a simple logical conclusion based on the facts (and it is born out in the research; 50% of former alcoholics become moderate drinkers, see Appendix E). Yet treatment providers insist on telling substance users that they have a disease or allergy that causes them to lose control over their drug and alcohol usage upon taking a single dose of a substance. They do this because it's a convenient shortcut by which they can coerce you into immediately agreeing to the substance use goal that they've chosen for you.

The difference between addiction counselors and the mugger is this – the mugger is forcing a one-time decision, but the counselors are trying to force a lifelong decision. It's no wonder this tactic fails so often. People end up miserable while abstaining, feeling deprived of joy, and eventually go back to the old pattern of heavy substance use. This becomes a demoralizing and increasingly dangerous cycle between abstinence and reckless usage for too many people.

You can be happy in abstinence. You can be happy moderating your usage. Talk to anyone who successfully maintains a change to their substance use habit without struggle, and you will find that they are genuinely happier with the change. Talk to those who struggle to "maintain recovery" and you will find that they feel deprived, like they're missing out. They feel like abstinence is a burden; it's their cross to bear.

The long-term strategy for maintaining fear-initiated abstinence in the recovery religion is to keep the fear alive. So they try to get you signed up for ongoing "aftercare" treatment or heavy involvement in "support" groups. In this realm, you are battered daily with dire predictions of what will happen if you forget how disastrous any substance use will be for you. You are warned daily against ever thinking you could have a drink or drug without "losing control." You are pressured into defining as an "addict" or "alcoholic", a handicapped person who is powerless over substances. The support you receive is in maintaining this fragile identity, and in coping on a daily level with the fact that you've been robbed of the ability to control your substance use by the *disease of addiction*.

STARTING ON THE RIGHT FOOT

Those who come to see a change as genuinely happier and more satisfying than their previous problematic style of substance use change rapidly, and maintain the change happily. This is most directly achieved by re-assessing the relative benefits of various levels of use (including abstinence). Happiness is front in center in their decision-making process. For decades now, we've seen that when we can communicate this strategy successfully, success in change follows. Panic based decisions of lifelong abstinence are a massive obstacle to communicating our message. The false alternative of abstinence or "uncontrolled use" makes your pursuit of happiness irrelevant in the decision-making process. It literally closes your mind to the sort of realizations that really power a successful change. By shortcutting the decision-making process with fear and panic, it also shortcuts the process of re-assessment in which you would have been able to develop the conviction that moderation or abstinence is truly your happier option.

Hopefully now you can see that we didn't start with this topic of moderation just to be shocking or contrarian. We started with it so that you can start off on the right foot, and immediately begin the process of imagining greater happiness in changing your habits. If that never happens, you will never be happier making a change; you will struggle, you will "white knuckle it" trying to stay sober, and you will quite probably go back to destructive styles of substance use. By coming face to face with the fact that you are capable of moderation now, you give yourself the best chance of quickly and happily changing.

Remember this though: to say that you *can* moderate is not to say that you *should* moderate. You *should* do whatever offers you the greatest level of happiness as an individual. You will gravitate to whatever level of substance use you see as offering you the greatest happiness – from heavy usage to abstinence and anything in between. For you to change, you need to figure this out. Please don't skip this process. Let go of the fear and proceed with a reality-based view.

SUBSTANCE USE IS RISKY

It is a fact that substance use has risks, and you probably already know what most of those risks are. For one example, tainted drugs of unknown purity and quality have recently led to waves of overdose deaths. It seems there is tragedy everywhere surrounding substance use. It is easy to see why the treatment zealots and recovery society jump straight to an abstinence-only model. We don't mean to downplay the dangers by saying moderation is possible. We only mean to set the record straight that "loss of control" over substance usage is a myth, so that you can approach this from a place of achieving greater happiness and long-term success, rather than making a short-lived decision based on fear and panic. It would be easy for us to try to use fear to manipulate you into agreeing to abstinence, but it just isn't effective in the big picture. What's more, the practice of convincing people to make decisions based on things you know to be untrue is called fraud. It is unethical, and can only have bad consequences in the long run.

The Freedom Model and everyone at Baldwin Research remains completely neutral on whether or not anyone should use substances at any level; it is not our job to tell people what personal decisions to make, or to deny or grant permission to anyone to use substances. As educators, our job is simply to present the truth about substance use so that people can make informed decisions about it. Here are two important truths:

1. Moderate use is possible for anyone, because loss of control is a myth.

2. Risk-free substance use is not possible for anyone.

Every action in life carries some level of risk and cost. It is up to you to be aware, and decide what level of risks and costs are acceptable to you for the return you get from substance use.

BELIEFS ARE POWERFUL

We want to make the following point absolutely clear: *as long as you are a believer in addiction and recovery, you should never attempt to moderate or use at all.* That statement, of course, makes sense, considering your adherence to the belief in powerlessness. If you believe a class of people called *addicts* exists who cannot stop taking drugs and/or alcohol once they start, and that you might be one, then any level of use *is* a bad and potentially fatal idea for you. As a believer, any attempt to adjust your substance use will be undermined by your skepticism of free will over substance use.

Free will is an absolute. Either you have it, or you don't. If you believe drugs can enslave you, abstain. If you believe in loss of control, abstain. If you believe in recovery, abstain. If you believe in addiction, abstain. But know that even with a sound rejection of addiction and recovery, you might still determine that abstinence is best for you. Many do. If that is your choice, we hope you can arrive there in the pursuit of happiness, rather than through fear and panic.

Here's the truth: drugs don't inherently contain "addictiveness" (see appendix D), and people have free will and can choose for themselves. Based on a thorough analysis of the available data provided by the National Institute of Alcohol Abuse and Alcoholism, the Substance Abuse and Mental Health Services Administration, the National Institutes of Health, and others, the fact is that more than 90% of people who have a serious drug or alcohol problem will quit or moderate, most without any professional help. This statistic is well established by addiction research but, for obvious reasons, is rarely admitted or talked about by treatment providers. Addiction and recovery are made-up constructs that promote our society's preoccupation with controlling others' behaviors, not with helping individuals navigate through their chosen habits. Just like all those who have changed their substance use on their own, you are free to choose what's best for you and your life.

Before you begin reading this book, we make one suggestion: read the entire book before you make a lifelong choice about substance use. If you have any vestige of fear or lack of confidence in your inherent ability to moderate or stop your addiction, then complete abstinence is the only safe option for you at this moment. Once you know the truth, that you are free to choose, you can make sound decisions and with a mind devoid of fear.

By knowing the facts and losing the fear of substances and their mythical powers, you can choose any substance use option available to you without the guilt or shame that keeps you distracted and stuck in heavy use. But just because you read this book doesn't mean that all the risks associated with using substances go away, it simply means you will be aware that you can change on a dime and that you need never be trapped in a single usage pattern again. The costs and risks involved in substance use are always there. This includes not only the risks to health, but also the risks to your freedom and social life. Just because you now know that you're not doomed to "lose control" of your substance use doesn't mean that others who wield some control over your life will understand this. Various people in your life may choose to impose costs on you for the sin of moderate substance use. Employers may fire you. Judges and probation officers may put you in jail. Family members and friends may shun you, and withdraw various forms of support because they disagree with your choices. This all remains a great possibility.

If you decide to moderate, you will understand there are risks associated with that level of use, but you will also know that you can choose to abstain at any time with ease. Our approach provides a path to realizing your natural ability to chart the course of your life, whereas the addiction and recovery paradigm sees all levels of substance use as a road to institutions, jails, and death. It is the difference between being free to change and being enslaved to addiction and/or recovery that clearly defines what *The Freedom Model* is all about. Whether or not the other people in your life recognize the truth about "addiction," all that matters is that you recognize the truth, and use it to make informed, effective decisions. The rest of the text will explain all the nuances of making a happiness-based choice about your future substance use.

Bear this in mind as you read the book: *The Freedom Model* does not deny the inherent dangers of substance use, and should you choose to keep using in any fashion, those risks are still there. Furthermore, if after having read the book, you still want to hang onto all or part of the addiction/recovery myths, then abstinence is your only disaster-free choice. But should you gain an understanding and embrace your free will and inherent abilities to choose your thoughts, desires, and behaviors, then you will have opened the door to a world of infinite possibilities.

CHAPTER 1:

HOW TO ESCAPE THE ADDICTION AND RECOVERY TRAP

The nation is currently amid a tragic wave of drug overdose deaths, the rate of which is rising rapidly. Alcohol-related deaths and the incidence of alcohol use disorder are going up as well. Hardly a day goes by without tragic stories in the news featuring pictures of beautiful, young people who had so much promise but lost their lives to drugs. The cause of death in these stories used to be kept secret. But now, the parents and other family members are warning others of the dangers and advocating for treatment. That's all they can do to try to help others through the loss of their loved ones. The hope is that the story of their children's deaths will serve to prevent further tragedies. It's a tough, courageous, and noble choice to be open about these deaths.

As if the tragedy of these overdoses isn't dark enough, there's an even darker side of the story that nobody sees. The news media, politicians, and activists are all using these stories to lobby for more addiction treatment. Yet what you'll often find is that the overdose victims had received every available addiction treatment, often multiple times. Their families had spent tens or even hundreds of thousands of dollars getting what they were told was the best available help, and yet their children still ended up dying. And the solution to this mess, according to the politicians, is more of the same treatment? It just doesn't add up. Something is wrong here. Why should we be calling for more of exactly what doesn't work when the evidence that it doesn't work is right in front of our faces?

ADDICTION AND RECOVERY IDEOLOGY IS WRONG AND CREATES PERPETUAL STRUGGLE

The very concept of addiction—whether it's called a disease, a disorder, or something else—says that some people (i.e., "addicts and alcoholics") are enslaved to the behavior of substance use. They cross some line where they are no longer actively choosing to use substances of their own free will but instead are compelled to use. It's also said that they are unable to stop themselves from using once they start (they experience a *loss of control*); they are unable to stop *wanting* to use substances (they experience *craving*); all of this just happens without their consent (that they're *triggered* by various things and feelings); and they're in for a lifetime of struggling with their demons (the "chronic relapsing disease" and "ongoing recovery").

In summary, those who promote the idea of addiction explain that heavy substance users should see themselves as enslaved and in for a lifelong struggle in which they'll never be fully free. This lifelong struggle is referred to as "recovery."

Throughout this book, we use the terms *recovery society* and *recovery ideology* to refer to the institutions and people who believe in and spread the concept of addiction as involuntary behavior. This includes many different versions of this concept and its related ideas, including the recovery society's recommendations on how to address a substance use problem.

We consider this recovery ideology to be faulty, based on much misinformation, and harmful to substance users. The increased rates of addiction and massive increase in opiate- and alcohol-related deaths in our country are the best evidence that this is the case. Throughout the 1980s and 1990s, addiction rates remained stable, and rates of recovery without treatment were climbing. But, at the turn of the century, the recovery society was busy rolling out fancy new neuroimaging data (i.e., brain scans of "addicts"; see appendix B), with the claim that it was proof that heavy substance users truly can't control themselves. They've even gone as far as to claim that addicts have "hijacked brains" and that drugs rob them of free will. The public ate this up because it sounded very scientific. So it finally seemed that almost everyone was convinced that addiction is a disease that permanently handicaps those afflicted.

As the public embraced the recovery society's new brain disease model of addiction, treatment became a necessity, and the industry began to grow by billions of dollars in business. Rates of addiction, rates of overdose, and rates of alcohol- and drug-related deaths started going up. None of this is a coincidence. Belief in addiction sows the seeds of self-doubt that make people feel helpless and hopeless. True believers are convinced that they don't have the ability to change and that, as the recovery society prescribes, they'll need to struggle endlessly while receiving ongoing help to battle against addiction. This entire ideology becomes a vicious trap that ensnares people in either years of unnecessary suffering or, worst case, death. This isn't speculation; it is fact.

Research in which alcoholics were given a test to gauge how strongly they believed in several common tenets of addiction, such as "loss of control" or genetic predisposition to alcoholism, showed that those who believed most strongly in addiction were more likely to relapse following treatment. In fact, this belief system was one of the top predictors of relapse after controlling for dozens of other factors, including the severity of the drinking problem (Miller, Westerberg, Harris, & Tonigan, 1996). Other research has shown that those exposed to these ideas formally in treatment subsequently had binge drinking rates nine times higher than those who were exposed to a more choice-based view and a binge rate five times higher than those who received no treatment at all (Brandsma, 1980). Heroin users binge after treatment too, as was shown by a study of over 150,000 heroin addicts in England that overdose risk skyrocketed in the weeks immediately following the completion of treatment. (Pierce et al., 2016)

It only makes sense that people would give up trying to change and dive headlong into substance use when they've been taught that quitting and sustaining it is going to be a losing battle anyway. As belief in addiction (as a true state of involuntary substance use) has exploded in our culture, so too have rates of "addiction." But as one prolific drug researcher noted, "Conversely, cultures in which people do not believe drugs can cause the 'loss of control' exhibit very little of it" (Reinarman, 2005). The false and toxic ideology of addiction and recovery is what makes people struggle so hard to change their substance use habits. It is what makes *you* struggle.

THE FREEDOM MODEL

Whereas recovery ideology says heavy substance users are enslaved and involuntarily using substances, *The Freedom Model* says just the opposite. It says that people are actively and freely choosing each time they take a dose of drugs or alcohol and that one simple thing motivates them to do so: the pursuit of happiness. There can be myriads of reasons for substance use held in the mind of the individual (pleasure, stress relief, a desire for a social lubricant), but it all boils down to substance users seeing the next dose as their best available option for feeling good. Some will say that heavy substance users find the conditions of their lives intolerable while sober so they use substances as an escape. But this is just another way of saying that they see intoxication as the happier option.

In *The Freedom Model*, we recognize that heavy substance users are fully free to change at any time and they need not look forward to a life-long struggle "in recovery." Although the brain disease model of addiction is convincing at first, it doesn't hold up to scrutiny, and neither do the other major claims about addiction, such as loss of control, inability to stop without treatment, and others (these topics will all be addressed throughout the book). "Addicts" truly are free to choose differently. When they become fully convinced that some lesser amount of substance use is the happier option, they decrease their substance use accordingly. With this change in perspective, they find that there is no need to struggle to abstain or moderate. They find that it is easily initiated and sustained.

Yes, we said it will be "easy." We know this word will hit some readers as dismissive of the struggle, pain, and suffering they've experienced. To feel addicted is *genuinely* frustrating and painful. The authors of this book have been through it. We struggled for years, and in the depths of it we even seriously contemplated suicide. However, that was a long time ago, and we're here to write this today because we found our way out of it. When we finally got over our problem, what we discovered was that it was far easier to overcome than we thought it would be. Once we really "got it," there were no more struggles to stay sober and drug free. We do nothing to "maintain recovery" or to keep us from using substances "addictively." We've had thousands of guests at our retreats over the past three decades who have had this same experience of ease moving on from "addiction." It will be easy for you too. So although the word "easy" may be unsettling to some, it is the truth, and we'd be doing you a disservice if we didn't say it now. You will eventually realize it is easy, and that is a blessing.

The recovery society has infected our culture with misinformation about substances and substance use. This misinformation is everywhere in our society: children are taught it in schools and public service announcements, our news media and entertainment is full of it, we hear it from our friends and family, and it is spread by the institutions charged with helping substance users. All this misinformation distorts how you experience substance use, your desire for substances, and your choices to use substances. Whether or not you've received treatment, you definitely have been exposed to the recovery ideology, and it can breed self-doubt within you if you believe it. This misinformation is, in fact, what makes some of you feel so helpless to change. The more you believe it, the more you feel addicted.

You *can* make whatever changes you want in your substance use habits and do so right now. If you feel like you can't "do it on your own" or that you need treatment, it's only because the recovery ideology has convinced you with its misinformation that this is true. Our goal is to lift the fog of confusion it has created and show you that you can. We're going to start right now by taking on one of its biggest myths: the idea that heavy substance users are unable to stop or moderate their substance use without treatment, support, and a lifetime of trying to "recover" from the disease of addiction.

NOBODY NEEDS TREATMENT

A popular statistic thrown around by the recovery society says that "only 1 in 10 addicts get the treatment they need." Depending on the data you look at, these numbers are accurate—only 10% to 20% of Americans who have ever fit the diagnosis of addiction get formal help (in the form of treatment, support group attendance, or a combination of both). The rest never get any formal help. The question you should be asking is, what happens to the 80% to 90% who don't get treatment? Are those people dying? After all, recovery ideology says you can't quit an addiction without treatment.

In fact, those people aren't dying. They're getting over their problems at a rate that equals and often surpasses success rates for those who receive treatment. So the claim that treatment is needed is dreadfully wrong. Nobody needs treatment for addiction. The folks who say this have a biased view. They work in treatment and see only the people who come to them for treatment. Then, in treatment, they teach those people that they'll die if they don't stay involved in treatment and support groups. Most treatment advocates are privy to only the research done on those who've undergone intense indoctrination in treatment; they are unaware of what happens in the lives of those who don't sign on to recovery ideology. They don't know what becomes of the other 80% to 90% who never get formal help. Luckily, though, this information is available.

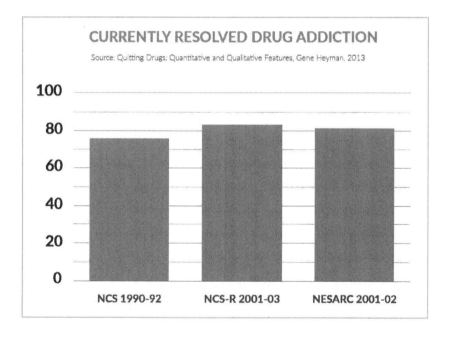

The U.S. government has conducted several epidemiological studies that surveyed tens of thousands of people to find out about their mental health and substance use histories. Every such study that's been done has found that most people, treated or not, eventually resolve their substance use problems. The following chart shows three such studies (Heyman, 2013).

As you can see, among the three studies shown here, approximately 80% of people who were ever "addicted to drugs" were not currently "addicted." That is, they resolved their drug use problems. Collectively, those studies surveyed more than 60,000 people from the general population. These studies are representative of the US population as a whole, while most addiction research uses very small sample sizes taken from a people in treatment programs.

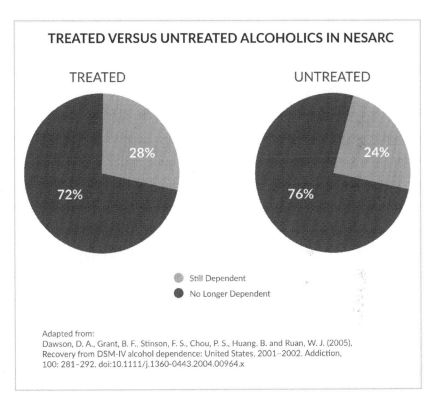

TREATED VERSUS UNTREATED ALCOHOLICS IN NESARC

TREATED

UNTREATED

28%

72%

24%

76%

● Still Dependent
● No Longer Dependent

Adapted from:
Dawson, D. A., Grant, B. F., Stinson, F. S., Chou, P. S., Huang. B. and Ruan, W. J. (2005).
Recovery from DSM-IV alcohol dependence: United States, 2001–2002. Addiction,
100: 281–292. doi:10.1111/j.1360-0443.2004.00964.x

The last study on that chart, NESARC (Dawson et al., 2005), had the largest survey group (43,000 people) and offered some of the most detailed information available. It offered data that compared treated alcoholics to untreated alcoholics. Look at the results in the chart below.

As you can see, the likelihood of ending alcohol dependence is nearly equal for both treated and untreated alcoholics (slightly higher if you don't get treatment). All of them met the diagnostic criteria for alcohol addiction, and yet it made almost no difference whether they were treated; most of them eventually resolved their problems.

What would you conclude if you took a group of people with a disease and gave some of them medical treatment and the others no treatment, yet both groups recovered equally? You'd have to conclude that both groups resolved their problems by their own power. You'd conclude that the treatment doesn't really work. And if it doesn't work, then you certainly wouldn't say that it's "needed."

Your conclusions would be correct, and they apply equally to addiction treatment. Nobody needs it, and it's important for you to realize that it doesn't "work" for anyone (in the sense of causing them to stop or reduce their drinking). There are people who will attribute their "recovery" to addiction treatment because it is part of their personal story so they assume they needed it. They are as wrong as people who take a placebo, get over a medical problem by processes of their own immune systems, and then credit the placebo for their recovery. *They would've gotten over their problem without the treatment.*

Now, remember what the treatment advocates are saying, that "addicts" can't control themselves and can't stop using substances without treatment. A mountain of evidence indicates the contrary. The studies above, as well as yearly surveys, show that over time, people naturally quit or reduce their substance use to nonproblematic levels on their own. Most "addictions" start when people are in their early 20s, and more than half of them resolve by 30 years old. Problematic substance use rapidly declines with age. When researchers crunched these numbers in the NESARC data, figuring in the trends on age, they found that more than 9 out of 10 will eventually resolve their substance use problems—treated or not. More precisely, the probability that problematic substance users will resolve their problem for various substances follows (Heyman, 2013):

- Alcohol: 90.6%
- Marijuana: 97.2%
- Cocaine: 99.2%

Although the researchers didn't offer a probability rate for heroin, we have no reason to believe it should be any different. Ninety-six percent of heroin addicts were currently resolved in the NESARC data. (Wu, Woody, Yang, Mannelli, & Blazer, 2011)

This mirrors findings from the 1970's. For example, a study on Vietnam vets diagnosed as heroin dependent found that within the first three years about 88% quit without relapse and, in a 24-year-long follow-up study, 96% had eventually resolved their problems. You should also know that *only 2% of those vets received treatment* (Robins, 1993)!

Another extremely important fact about the Vietnam vet heroin addicts is that, while the overall relapse rate was a mere 12%, those who were shuffled into treatment ended up having a staggering 67% relapse rate—that's more than five times worse. So, while the recovery society moans and groans that "only 1 in 10 gets the treatment they need," more than 9 in 10 resolve their problems—*usually without treatment*—and there are many cases where treatment leads to worse outcomes.

The idea that anyone needs addiction treatment is flat out misinformation. It hurts people by convincing them that they're helpless, thus taking away their motivation to try to change. And with the flood of data that's been released over the past few decades, the claim that treatment is needed is becoming worse than just misinformation. Treatment advocates are either willfully ignorant of this information, which is irresponsible, or they're just knowingly *lying* to the public. Nobody, *and we mean nobody*, needs what they're selling.

ADDICTION AND RECOVERY: TWO SIDES OF THE SAME COIN

The recovery society labels heavy substance use as "addiction" and defines it as a state of involuntary behavior caused by a disease. We simply call heavy substance use an activity that people have learned to prefer. But when substance users learn to view this preference as an addiction, it adds a layer of confusion that both blocks people from reconsidering their preferences and makes it harder for them to change should they choose to. The reasons for this are that these substance users are struggling to fight something that isn't there—they're trying to "recover" from a nonexistent disease.

It is imperative that we say this now and that you remember it: *Since addiction is not a disease, it can't be medically treated, and you can't recover from it.*

Let that sink in for a minute. Many of you seek out our solution precisely because *you know something is wrong* with the idea that you have a disease called addiction. However, many of you then ask us to show you "how to recover from addiction," or "how to get into recovery," or "how to maintain recovery." You're looking for an alternative *treatment* for addiction. You are still looking for some outside force to battle the nonexistent forces of addiction. This just goes to show the depths of your confusion and the stranglehold the recovery society has on our views of substance use. If your problem isn't a disease, then it can't be treated. There is no proper medical treatment for a nonmedical problem.

The recovery society and its treatment providers invented the concept of addiction whole cloth—they invented it, promoted it, and own it. You can't mention addiction without implying involuntary, unchosen behavior. They created a bogeyman called addiction that robs you of the power of choice and forces you to use substances against your will. With this concept, they created the idea that there is something to be treated, to fight, and to recover from.

There is nothing to fight and nothing from which to recover. There are only personal choices to be made. Your substance use isn't involuntary. You voluntarily choose it because, for better or worse, you prefer it. You could try to "recover" by avoiding "triggers" and working on "alternative coping mechanisms" all you want, but if you still prefer heavy substance use, you will find yourself wanting to do it and will do it anyway.

The goal of recovery puts people on the wrong path and creates obstacles where they needn't be. The concept of "triggers" is the perfect example. People become convinced that, if they, for example, see a billboard advertising beer, they'll be uncontrollably triggered to immediately start drinking. Life then becomes a quest to avoid such triggers for those "in recovery," and they live with the paranoia that something will trigger them to drink at any moment. In this way, efforts at recovery keep addiction alive by sustaining the identity of a fragile, helpless addict. Meanwhile, when people come to the realization that they prefer being sober more than being intoxicated, nothing will trigger them into drunkenness. They can be in a room full of people swilling it up, and they won't be tempted in the slightest.

Do you want to critically examine your preferences and change them or fight a bogeyman? They are mutually exclusive courses of action. *The Freedom Model* will show you how you can change your preference for substance use.

Think of it this way. If you didn't have cancer, you wouldn't spend your time getting chemotherapy. It would not only be a waste of your time, but it would be costly, cause you other problems, and take away from time that you could be using to build a happy life. This analogy shows the absurdity of the situation that even some people who disagree with the disease model of addiction still seek out treatment for it and focus on recovering from it. Mind you, plenty of incredibly intelligent people fall for the recovery trap because the addiction disease proponents have done an amazing job at mainstreaming their views.

While the myth of addiction as a disease has been repeatedly proven false by credible research over decades, the idea of "recovery" from alcoholism and addiction has remained mostly unexamined with the same critical eye—until now. This book will challenge everything you believe to be true about addiction and its stable mate, recovery. It will then provide a new way to see yourself—as a person who is fully free to change your substance use if it is unsatisfactory to you.

Once you understand that substance use is a choice and that you are in control, you can easily change your substance use. You will turn the page on this chapter of your life and move on. Some of you at this point might not think it'll be that simple—*and that's the problem.* When people are planning to come to our retreats to learn *The Freedom Model,* they often ask us to set up a year or more of weekly aftercare sessions for them. Some will even offer huge sums of money to convince us to set up this formal support system for them, but we won't do it. The idea that support is needed is a recovery society idea. It is based not only on the assumption that you are weak but, more important, on the myth that there is something you must battle. Recovery ideology states that there is a force stronger than your free will compelling you to want and use substances, that something outside of your own mind can make your decisions for you, and that some outside strength is needed to support your fight against addiction. We *can't* and *won't* support you in fighting a nonexistent thing, and we *can't* make your choices for you. What we *can* do is offer information that you can use to make new choices. Once you have this information, it's up to you to use it.

We are happy to report that most of our guests over the years have used this information to their advantage. We have the highest success rate of any program of help for problematic substance use. Sixty-two percent of our alumni choose long-term abstinence, and many others choose moderate levels of substance use. More important, they feel happy and free from the burdens of both addiction and ongoing recovery.

One way to think of *The Freedom Model* is that part of its goal is to help you return to the state of mind of those who resolve their problems without treatment. We want you to understand that you can make a change in your life because of a personal choice and preference instead of taking on an addict identity and fighting addiction. In our discussions with many people who have overcome their "addictions" without formal help, many have told us that they rejected the core ideas of addiction. They knew they could choose differently and that doing so was only a matter of finding the motivation to see less substance use as preferable.

Formal research on "self-changers" who had problems with alcohol, heroin, and cocaine found that they cited decision-making processes (i.e., "cognitive appraisal") most when discussing their path out of addiction (Sobell et al., 2001). Factors such as the presence of support were rarely mentioned; dramatic consequences equivalent to hitting rock bottom were mentioned even less. Decision making was the theme when they told their experiences and often in a positive frame. For example, one former heroin user in the study said, "I made a decision … in favor of life; that gave me strength."

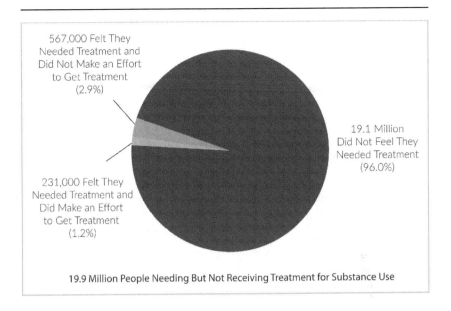

567,000 Felt They
Needed Treatment and
Did Not Make an Effort
to Get Treatment
(2.9%)

19.1 Million
Did Not Feel They
Needed Treatment
(96.0%)

231,000 Felt They
Needed Treatment and
Did Make an Effort
to Get Treatment
(1.2%)

19.9 Million People Needing But Not Receiving Treatment for Substance Use

There's good reason to suspect that those who don't get treatment don't buy-in to the whole concept of addiction and recovery. When the researchers from the Substance Abuse and Mental Health Administration (SAMHSA) asked them why they didn't get treatment, 96% of them said they "don't think that they need it."(Han, Hedden, Lipari, Copello, & Kroutil, 2015) This group of people had the symptoms of "addiction" and fit the diagnosis of addiction, yet they didn't think they needed treatment, thus showing that they rejected the idea that they were powerless and unable to stop on their own. Note that recovery ideology would say these people were "in denial" and that they can never make any progress unless they "admit they have the disease of addiction and need help." Yet they don't get help, and they do get over their problems. They get over their problems without taking on a lifestyle focused on being diseased and recovering, without the added complications of "recovery," and without "support." They are the majority of people with substance use problems who resolve those problems (both in raw numbers and percentages).

You can and will resolve your problems too. You will by your own power, just like they did. We're here to show you that you can. You are free. *The Freedom Model* is all about informing you of this wonderful truth and showing you the power you have to change.

If you get nothing else from this chapter, please remember this: the *overwhelming majority* of people who fit the diagnosis of addiction never get any addiction treatment, don't go to meetings, don't set up formal support systems, don't worry about recovery, don't think of themselves as addicted, and don't battle addiction for the rest of their lives—*nevertheless, they change.* They begin to see their options and futures differently, and then they choose differently and permanently resolve their substance use problems. So can you.

AN IMPORTANT NOTE ABOUT THE RECOVERY SOCIETY

The term "recovery society" refers to people who spread the idea of addiction as being involuntary behavior driven by disease, disorder, or other causes outside the realm of personal choice. They have many wrong ideas and explanations of addiction that go well beyond the mere claim that a "disease of addiction" exists. These ideas include myths about the powers of drugs; various weaknesses of those they classify as "addicts"; and, of course, their claims about what is required to get into and maintain "recovery from addiction." The recovery society comprises of therapists, counselors, sponsors, intellectuals, law enforcement agencies, treatment agencies, activists, and various activist organizations that spread this misinformation.

Throughout this book, we speak bluntly about how wrong these people are and how damaging their ideas can be. However, *we do not think these people are bad, intentionally evil, or involved in a conspiracy to mislead.* As you have seen already, substance users can become victims of recovery ideology and recovery society institutions, but that is not the intention of those in the recovery society; rather, this belief system that now harms people is an unfortunate consequence of historical events and missteps. It wasn't planned or orchestrated to hurt anyone. The recovery society may include a handful of bad actors just as there are in any group, but the overwhelming majority of people who make up recovery society helpers and proponents are completely well-intentioned people. They can be loving and supportive friends and helpers because they truly want to help and do care. Unfortunately, though, they are misinformed. We do not wish to personally denigrate or insult them, but our criticisms of their ideas and methods are unequivocal.

We must also note that the recovery society is not the cause of people's choices to use substances in a problematic way. People choose their substance use based on their own beliefs that it is what they need and is worth the costs. Recovery ideology can contribute to people feeling stuck in substance use and is often the major obstacle to change; that's why we focus on unlearning this ideology. However, once this obstacle has been removed, it's still up to people to seriously reconsider their preferences if they want to change.

REFERENCES

Dawson, D. A., Grant, B. F., Stinson, F. S., Chou, P. S., Huang, B. and Ruan, W. J. (2005), Recovery from DSM-IV alcohol dependence: United States, 2001–2002. Addiction, 100: 281–292. doi:10.1111/j.1360-0443.2004.00964.x

Alcohol Use and Alcohol Use Disorders in the United States: Main Findings from the 2012–2013 National Epidemiologic Survey on Alcohol and Related Conditions-III (NESARC-III), *U.S. Alcohol Epidemiologic Data Reference Manual, 10*, April 2016, NIH Publication No. 16-AA-8020. https://www.drugabuse.gov/related-topics/trends-statistics/overdose-death-rates

Brandsma, J. (1980). Outpatient treatment of alcoholism: A review and comparative study. Baltimore, MD: University Park Press.

Han, B., Hedden, S. L., Lipari, R., Copello, E. A. P., & Kroutil, L. A. (2015, September). Receipt of services for behavioral health problems: Results from the 2014 National Survey on Drug Use and Health. Retrieved from https://www.samhsa.gov/data/sites/default/files/NS-DUH-DR-FRR3-2014/NSDUH-DR-FRR3-2014/NS-DUH-DR-FRR3-2014.htm

Heyman, G. M. (2013). Quitting drugs: Quantitative and qualitative features. *Annual Review of Clinical Psychology, 9*(1), 29–59. https://doi.org/10.1146/annurev-clinpsy-032511-143041

Miller, W. R., Westerberg, V. S., Harris, R. J., & Tonigan, J. S. (1996). What predicts relapse? Prospective testing of antecedent models. *Addiction (Abingdon, England), 91* (Suppl), S155–172.

Pierce, M., Bird, S. M., Hickman, M., Marsden, J., Dunn, G., Jones, A., & Millar, T. (2016). Impact of treatment for opioid dependence on fatal drug-related poisoning: A national cohort study in England. *Addiction, 111*(2), 298–308. https://doi.org/10.1111/add.13193

Reinarman, C. (2005). Addiction as accomplishment: The discursive construction of disease. *Addiction Research & Theory, 13*(4), 307–320. https://doi.org/10.1080/16066350500077728

Robins, L. N. (1993). The sixth Thomas James Okey Memorial Lecture. Vietnam veterans' rapid recovery from heroin addiction: A fluke or normal expectation? *Addiction (Abingdon, England), 88*(8), 1041–1054.

Sobell, L. C., Klingemann, H. K., Toneatto, T., Sobell, M. B., Agrawal, S., & Leo, G. I. (2001). Alcohol and drug abusers' perceived reasons for self-change in Canada and Switzerland: Computer-assisted content analysis. *Substance Use & Misuse, 36*(11), 1467–1500.

Wu, L.-T., Woody, G. E., Yang, C., Mannelli, P., & Blazer, D. G. (2011). Differences in onset and abuse/dependence episodes between prescription opioids and heroin: results from the National Epidemiologic Survey on Alcohol and Related Conditions. Substance Abuse and Rehabilitation, 2011(2), 77–88. *https://doi.org/10.2147/SAR.S18969*

CHAPTER 2:
"YOU HAVE TO WANT IT TO WORK"

S everal years ago, I (Mark Scheeren) was sitting in my AA home group, and we were all lamenting over a member who had gone back to drinking and using drugs and had died. People were noticeably upset, and some were visibly frightened. Everyone parroted the same response, "He just didn't want it badly enough."

The recovery society and addiction treatment providers, regarding their treatments, often say "You have to want it to work." This comes from the hard truth that people who don't want to quit upon entering a treatment program probably won't quit upon leaving the treatment program. What they're acknowledging is that the only way you will moderate or quit your substance use is if you *want to* moderate or quit your substance use. In this case, they are correct—*this is the entire key to making a different choice!*

Controlled research suggests that people who seem to be successfully treated had made their choice to change their substance abuse patterns *at the time they enrolled* in treatment, not after having received the treatment. Some people "want it to work" when they sign up for treatment so they had already changed before they were treated. For example, the results of a massive study of drinkers who enrolled for outpatient addiction counseling treatment showed that they reduced their average drinking between week zero, when they enrolled, and week one, when they received their first counseling session (Cutler & Fishbain, 2005). The graph below shows that this pretreatment reduction in drinking held throughout the following 12 weeks.

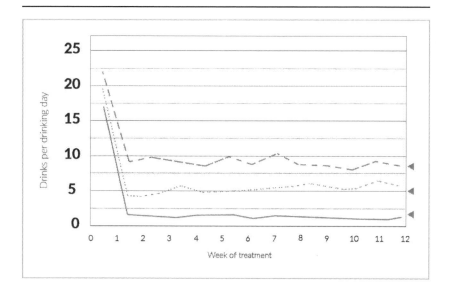

The important thing here is that the results follow the same trajectory for three different groups: those who went through a full 12 weeks of treatment, those who attended only one session of treatment, and those who enrolled but didn't show up for even one counseling session.

The average reduction in drinking happened at the same point in the study across all three groups. Drinking was decreased sharply before their first session and then hovered around that same decreased level throughout the following 12 weeks regardless of the number of sessions they attended. This shows that treatment effectively played no role in their reduction of drinking since the reduction took place *before treatment*, didn't decrease with further treatment, and didn't increase among those who didn't receive any treatment. "Wanting it to work" is truly everything. Yet treatment gets the credit for people's reduction in drinking, when this change happens because they simply changed their minds about drinking when they decided to enroll for treatment.[2]

---

2. Note: There are differences in the average number of drinks for the three groups, but this difference is a reflection of differing levels of commitment to a change. The 12-weekers were the most committed to a reduction in drinking and thus stayed most committed to attending treatment as well. Nevertheless, the more important point for this analysis is that the basic curve was identical across groups.

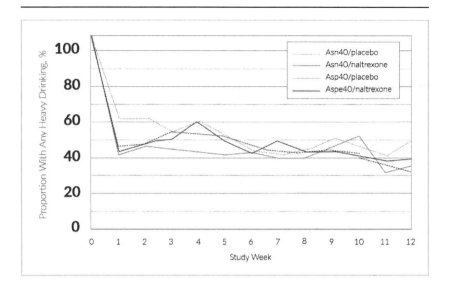

A recent study comparing naltrexone, a drug used to reduce substance cravings, to a placebo resulted in a *shockingly similar curve* (Oslin et al., 2015). You can see in this graph that the placebo groups, those people taking a pill that contained no medication, reduced their drinking as much as those taking the medication. What's more, all groups reduced their average drinking at the beginning of the study and maintained this average throughout the following 12 weeks of treatment. Again, treatment gets the credit, when in fact the receipt of treatment simply coincides with people's choice to change. Naltrexone is currently being hailed as a miracle drug for addiction, yet its success is an illusion, a misattribution. The fact that the placebo groups did just as well makes this crystal clear.

The proponents of recovery ideology continue to say you need treatment, yet they also continue to say "you have to want it to work." What they fail to understand are the full implications of this dichotomy. They don't realize that what they're also admitting when they say "you have to want it to work" is that treatment is essentially useless and can't make people reduce their substance use. There is no external force, treatment included, that can impose different wants on someone.

Changing your wants and desires is an autonomous activity, meaning you are the only one who can do it in the confines of your own mind by thinking things through and coming to see that you could be happier if you used less. No one else can do this for you because no one else can think for you. To change your desire for substance use, you must weigh the benefits of heavy use against the benefits of moderate use or abstinence. Whichever option *you come to see* as most beneficial or preferable is the option you'll truly want, become invested in, and carry out.

Treatment providers and the helpers in the recovery society have no idea how to facilitate this autonomous process, so they don't even bother addressing it. Instead, they circumvent your autonomy with fear by convincing you that you *must* become immediately abstinent and follow their program or die and that you are a helpless addict who has *no choice* but to become their ward and follow their commands. The result is that many people in this situation don't think through their options and change their wants. They may sober up for a while out of fear and obedience, but they're still left wanting heavy substance use. Eventually, it all falls apart.

While the recovery society proponents do express *some* positivity, their approach leans more toward a presentation of doom and gloom. They don't help people move on from heavy substance use with the vision of a happier, more attractive alternative; instead, they replace it with the burden of a lifelong struggle and the promise that you'll forever feel deprived. Let's quickly review what they present.

As we discussed in chapter 1, the practitioners and proponents of recovery ideology tell you that you're suffering from an incurable disease that requires treatment, a lifelong effort to battle, and ongoing support and yet will inevitably result in periodic relapses for which you'll need more treatment. So, right off the bat, they're presenting a grim prognosis. Based solely on this description of the problem and its solution, many people immediately give up and don't even try to change. After all, if it's going to be a losing battle, then why not just continue to drink and drug? Substance use is at least offering some pleasure. And if you believe you need substances to deal with stress, anxiety, and depression, then the stress, anxiety, and depression most people feel when presented with this dire prediction is enough to make them immediately turn back to substances. This is the reason the one-year retention rate of popular support groups is in the single digits and the rate of "relapse" to heavy substance use immediately following inpatient treatment is estimated to be 75% or greater (Miller, Walters, & Bennett, 2001).

There's more bad news. To deal with this "chronic disease," you're told that you'll need to take on a recovery-centered lifestyle, which entails constant work. This means that you will need to go to meetings every day; get involved in active service work outside meetings to help other alcoholics and addicts; avoid places where people drink and drug, including regular family holiday parties and weddings; avoid triggers, such as driving by that old bar or part of town where you scored drugs; avoid images of drugs and alcohol on television; make sure you don't feel stress, anxiety, anger, or depression, or else you'll relapse; work on every life issue you have, or else you'll relapse; never have so much as a sip of alcohol or puff of a joint ever again for the rest of your life because it'll turn you into an uncontrolled, substance-using zombie. And the list goes on and on.

"Recovery" demands that you strive ceaselessly to become a perfectly functioning, perfectly spiritual, and perfectly moral person, and even then, failure is considered inevitable. In an even subtler way, there is a movement that pushes the idea that you need a "purpose-filled" life to gain the resilience to not be tempted to backslide into use. Within recovery ideology, recovery doesn't mean getting over a problem and moving on; it means you will be fighting a lifelong battle that becomes even more challenging when you attach substance use to every challenge life tosses at you. In the specific case of "avoiding triggers," the desire for substance use is taken as a permanent condition to be accommodated rather than changed. This is like people with diabetes avoiding all sugar because their bodies can't handle it. That's what *recovery* means, adjusting your life to accommodate your permanent handicap. The best evidence of this is the fact that the recovery proponents regularly compare addiction to a chronic disease, such as diabetes, and say the two are alike.

Again, recovery ideologists skip right over the part where you could analyze your options and come to believe that you'd be happier with less or no substance use. So not only are you constantly working, struggling, and fighting to stay sober because your heavy desire for substance use is fully intact, but you're often doing so with the painful sense that you're deprived of the only thing that would make you happy. In group counseling and support meetings, you'll often hear people say things such as "Drinking was the only thing that ever made me feel comfortable in my own skin" or "I'm having so much trouble dealing with my brother's death, and getting high would make all that pain go away." These statements reinforce the idea that you will be deprived of something wonderful and magical if you quit. When people say they're "feeling weak and need support right now," they are confirming that they're fighting an internal battle against the bogeyman of addiction. But it doesn't have to be a battle.

You *can* feel comfortable in your own skin without alcohol, and drugs don't help anyone to deal with loss. In recovery society support groups, treatment, and counseling, you never question these beliefs about substances. You never consider that life without them could be markedly better and more enjoyable. You are simply told there is no rhyme or reason to your desire for substances and not to think about it. Instead, you are presented with the declaration that you must fight your urges to use these substances because you are an addict. If you've attended treatment programs, addiction counseling, or support group meetings, you were told that you had no choice and needed to fully invest in the recovery subculture because your handicap, the disease of addiction, makes that the only place where you can safely exist. You were told you needed to have a stress-free and purpose-driven lifestyle or you'd "relapse." But what if none of it were true? What if you could separate your use from all these other areas of your life and just ask yourself whether you still prefer it?

The recovery society and its proponents completely misunderstand addiction, and they put the cart before the horse. They tell you to quit before you figure out whether you really want to quit. They don't make quitting an attractive option either but, instead, present it as a painful and confusing option that will create a lifelong struggle. Yes, "you have to want it to work," but that's all that really matters. Yet it's the one thing that's not addressed.

THE FREEDOM MODEL:
A POSITIVE APPROACH

The approach you have in front of you now is a culmination of three decades of continuous research, testing, and experience with helping people. At Baldwin Research Institute, we've never stopped evolving our method, and it has provided great success all along. It has changed many times, sometimes dramatically. At the beginning, we used and recommended many elements of the 12 steps; in fact, we were members of AA. Our initial goal was to find which parts of AA worked, and over the years, we weeded out elements one by one that we discovered were counterproductive, limiting, or unnecessary. Eventually, it became clear that there were no elements of the disease concept and 12-step methodologies that were helpful, so we subsequently discarded all of it. Through all this, one thing has remained constant since the beginning: *we have always presented a positive vision of self-initiated, self-propelled change.*

You've already gotten some of this positive message when we told you in chapter 1 that you can and will get over your problems without a lifetime of treatment and support. We gave you mountains of evidence to back up that claim. Know this: you can make changes, and *you're going to be all right.* Nine out of ten people get over these problems, and most don't get treatment. Of those who do, only a fraction follow the treatment protocol of lifelong support. Most of the people who are successful simply move on with their lives, and so can you.

DO YOU WANT "RECOVERY"?

One of the most important discoveries we've made over the years is that shedding the identity of addict or alcoholic and focusing on creating whatever life you want for yourself is far better than focusing on "recovery." We know this confuses some of you because you think you want recovery and we're putting it down. Once you understand what "recovery" means in the realm of substance use problems, you'll decide it's not what you want.

If you've never been involved with the recovery society, its groups or treatment programs, you might think recovery is a good thing because you define it as getting over a substance use problem. But if you've been in the recovery society, you know *that's not how the term is defined.* As we described above, "recovery" is a lifestyle built around the negative *addict self-image* and focused on fighting the disease of addiction. Recovery has no end. It's a state of limbo in which you constantly fear relapse and sustain a self-image of fragility that keeps you in self-doubt and fosters permanent victimhood. This definition is also codified into official policy in language suggested by the White House whereby the term "former/reformed addict" should not be used but instead replaced with the terms "person in recovery" and "not actively using" (Ferner, 2015). Of course, in this model "not actively using" means you are still a "person with substance use disorder." Recovery keeps the bogeyman of addiction alive and well in your mind, and that's a tragic mistake.

"Recovery" is both a set of ideas (the self-image of "addict/alcoholic" or "person with substance use disorder" according to new language guidelines) and a set of actions (work to battle the disease of addiction). Both the ideas and the actions obscure what lies at the core of personal change.

Research has shown that belief in the disease model of addiction leads to "relapse" into problematic substance use (Miller, Westerberg, Harris, & Tonigan, 1996) and multiplies binge use at an alarming rate (Brandsma, 1980). As soon as people enter addiction treatment and learn these ideas, their risk of fatal overdose goes up and peaks immediately after they discontinue addiction treatment (Pierce et al., 2016). The self-image of the struggling, helpless addict taught by the recovery society increases substance use problems *and* leads people to struggle longer. The conclusion is, treatment creates addicts and alcoholics!

CORNERED INTO PERPETUAL RECOVERY

Learning recovery ideology doesn't reduce people's desire for substance use but rather engenders fear and makes them feel cornered into abstinence. Sometimes, substance users sit in that corner for a long time, dying to use substances and feeling miserable and deprived. Every now and then, while nobody is looking, they sneak out of the corner and get as high as they can until they get put back in the corner. While in the corner, the recovery society expects them to walk through a set of actions that define recovery. Unfortunately, those actions don't decrease their desires to use and often do the opposite. Many people who attend support group meetings, such as AA and NA, report that their desire to use substances is greatest right after leaving a meeting.

There is no disease of addiction, so ironically, when you focus on taking actions meant to fight it, you can only hurt yourself. Recovery ideology tells people that, at best, they can become perpetually recover*ing*, as in constantly battling addiction, with a constant threat of relapse. In our early days, we told people they could be recover*ed* (in the past tense), as in being confident that they're done with problematic substance use and no longer needing to fight it. This idea was a definite step in the right direction, to offer the possibility of a better self-image than the recovery ideology offers.

LOST IN PROCESSES

Unfortunately, we too got caught up in processes. We thought there was a lot of good in the actions prescribed in the 12-step program. In the early years of our research, many of our teachings were based directly on these activities, and everyone who worked at BRI and the retreat were AA members. We operated on the AA slogan "Do what I did to get what I got," which means that if one person goes through a set of actions and gets over his or her substance use problem, then another person should be able to mindlessly take those same actions and get the same result. How embarrassing it is for us to admit and put into print, but since we attended support meetings and spent all our time helping newcomers, we thought this activity was what *caused* us to get over our substance use problems. We would then recommend this behavior to the next person telling him or her to "go to meetings and help people."

"Do what I did to get what I got," approaches personal change like baking a cake and thus, treats people like unconscious, lifeless elements that can be physically manipulated and reformed by an external force. That's painfully wrong. People aren't lifeless matter to be manipulated. All people have free will, a positive drive, and mental autonomy. Because of this inherent nature of humans, two people can have the same experiences, but each one comes out with a different set of ideas. One person may go about helping other "addicts" and learn something valuable from the experience that he applies to his own problems. Another person may find it to be an annoying chore and gains no insight into making her own personal changes last. The truth is that, even for those who both quit substance use and helped other "addicts," the quitting came first; the activity of helping others didn't cause them to quit. There is no set of actions by which you can reliably make someone stop desiring drugs and alcohol. Meeting attendance and "service work" have nothing to do with developing a mindset where your desire for substances is reduced. They are not a recipe for success but simply temporary distractions.

Recovery ideology completely misses this point about recipes, including the "progressive" alternative approaches now coming into fashion. These alternative treatment providers acknowledge that a "one size fits all" approach doesn't work. "Going to meetings and doing the 12 steps doesn't work for everyone," they say. "There are different combinations of treatments that work for different people." Sadly, even these well-intentioned "mavericks" still hold onto the idea that people are like flour and eggs that can be transformed by external forces to make a *sober cake.* They think there are many different recipes to follow and that it's just a matter of finding the right one.

Part of our recipe for many years had been helping our guests make a plan to rebuild their whole life and find more fulfilling activities to replace heavy substance use. We called it "replacement." Since most of our guests at that time were ripe for such life improvements, we offered a focus on goal setting and self-analysis to address this need. We assumed goal setting was needed to cause a change in substance desire and use. Like treatment, we too connected substance use and other life issues in this casual way. We said things like "If you're not happy, you won't stay sober" or "If you don't have purpose, you'll continue to get high." This was a mistake. In time, we recognized that there were many guests who didn't need to rebuild their entire lives because they had plenty of fulfilling life activities on their plates already. But of even more importance, there were many guests who left with no goals and no plan who never got drunk or high again or reduced their levels of use. Based on what we believed at the time, these people should have been struggling in their "purposeless" lives. But they didn't, and we began to see that substance use need not be tied to these qualities. People could just stop or decrease their use and live exactly as they wished, with a greater purpose or without it. Besides, we're in no position to decide what qualifies as a purpose-driven life, and we certainly can't judge what brings happiness to people. Happiness is unique to everyone and exists in his or her mind.

For the people who changed their substance use habits, it was simple; once they realized that the entire construct of addiction was a myth, they moved past their substance use regardless of any other changes in their lifestyles. Just knowing they were choosing their use was enough to open the way to stopping or reducing it. That's *The Freedom Model* in a nutshell! After that one issue was resolved, they simply moved on. Some went out and created goals, and others went home and conducted their lives as they always had but now without substance use problems.

Knowing this information indicated to us what the solution is. It's not found in prescribing a set of actions, goals, or life involvements at all but instead is found in a person's direct perspective of substance use. Regardless of whether people are rich or poor, come from abusive or loving backgrounds, or have psychological problems, they have a strong desire for substance use only because they think they get significant benefits from it; that is, they use substances because they prefer to. People will stop preferring substance use only when they reassess and gain a new perspective on it and the option of changing it. There is no need to "replace" use; there is just a choice to be made regarding what level of use you believe will bring you the greatest amount of happiness moving forward.

You can't prescribe a "plan of recovery," "aftercare plan," or any other set of actions that will guarantee a change in perspective of a person's options. In fact, all those actions are nothing more than a distraction. Wanting it to work means you must genuinely want something different.

You can mindlessly help other addicts or alcoholics while making absolutely no change in how you think about substances, just like the treatment industry advocates that millions do every year. You can go to meetings thinking you're getting "support for your recovery" and sit there pining away to get drunk or high. *Where these plans of action go wrong is that they're plans of action.* They allow you to feel like you're addressing your problem, when you really aren't. They're distractions and provide a way to ride the fence on reassessing and figuring out whether you'd be happier putting heavy substance use behind you forever. Thoughts are changed by direct choice *within your own mind*, not by mimicking the actions of others, not by driving to meetings and attending them, not by seeking a purpose to replace use, and not by avoiding stress or triggers. All of that distracts you from looking at whether continued use is still attractive to you and deciding whether to continue to use and at what level. Unplug your concept of substance use from the distractions, and it becomes clear: you can choose to stop, based on whether you even like it anymore, or moderate, based on how much you still like it.

To facilitate this better, we had to strip our program down to the content that addresses that issue. Then, we had to deal with those specific issues comprehensively and throw out the distractions that didn't matter. Our guests had been telling us for a long time exactly what matters—the ideas and the facts—but we stubbornly kept the extraneous processes and actions and the concept of replacement.

Over a 10-year period, Mark Scheeren, a cocreator of *The Freedom Model*, personally conducted follow-up interviews with program graduates during which he would ask the graduates whether they had been abstinent (these interviews would later become studies conducted by outside, independent research firms). For those who were abstinent or reported significantly reduced levels of substance use, he would follow up by asking them what they felt was the most important part of the experience for them. Repeatedly, the graduates said, "You told me I had a choice." When asked whether they were doing the selfless service work that our book had prescribed or they were working to attain or had attained their goals and found greater purpose, some had, but many more were just living their lives, with no thought of those ideals, and using the resources that had been freed up when they reduced their substance use to enjoy their lives in other ways.

Please understand that we are not opposed to a purpose-driven life, but we are opposed to judging what is and isn't a "better purpose" for others. Using substances has a purpose; at its core it's to get high and be happy for a while. Some people think a life that includes substance use has no purpose, while others think a life of abstinence has greater purpose. There are plenty of abstinent people who don't purport to live purpose-filled lives. We have found these two things to be unrelated. It's not for anyone to decide whether another person's life has meaning and purpose. That is very personal to each individual and is not related to substance use at all.

We concluded that we no longer needed to judgmentally prescribe goals, actions, and processes to our guests. It became clear that our goal needed to be to help people understand that they, and no one else, were the only *cause* of their use. We saw that people could find their own avenues to purpose and happiness in their lives (especially after they came to grips with the fact that they were choosing their use).

Once people understood their inherent power of free will and choice regarding substances, they naturally moved on with their lives; there was nothing they needed to artificially "replace" anymore. In the final analysis, all people have their own personal purpose in life, and no one else can make that purpose "better" or more "right." Any program that says you should replace drugs with "better" alternatives is prescribing nothing more than judgment that some activities are morally superior to others.

Steven Slate, a cocreator of *The Freedom Model*, worked as a presenter of *The Freedom Model* at the retreat for two years, from 2003 to 2005. (We called the presenters instructors in those early days.) A few years later, with the rise of social media, many former guests tracked him down to offer their thanks. He asked each of them what had helped, and they all said the same thing to him that Mark's guests had said: what had helped them most was learning that they had a choice and could pursue greater happiness. Many of these people who contacted him had been young adults whose families had intervened early. They didn't want to reduce their substance use at all throughout their stay at the retreat. They had been determined to leave the retreat and go back to the same extreme levels of substance use while avoiding being caught. He was shocked that they were thanking him years later, but they said things like "Yeah, I went wild for a while after leaving the retreat. But when things started to get bad, I remembered that you told me I had a choice and that I might be happier without drugs, and then I just quit. Thank you."

When Steven piloted the day class version of our service in our New York City office, he was teaching the entire process taught at the retreat, but it quickly became apparent that it was overkill. Right off the bat, he had several guests who began *The Freedom Model* while they were currently drinking, but after a few hours of classes over a couple of weeks, they quit or decreased their drinking with little or no difficulty. They hadn't even made it to the part of the curriculum that recommends particular goal-setting actions or purpose-driven processes. They had just covered the evidence showing that there is no disease and no loss of control and that they were free to change and likely would. They discussed the idea that, if they saw reducing substance use as a happier option, they would easily change. And that's just what they did. They said things like "I've been duped by treatment. But I now know it's really easy to change, and I already did it. Thank you."

In these cases, Steven happily cut the curriculum short because they had found their solution in learning just a few key pieces of information.

By now, Steven has had several students to whom he has given a single research paper from a medical journal that debunks the biggest myths of addiction and recovery. He gave them this paper just before either the first or second class. Upon reading this information, they began to feel completely free to change and then quickly did so.

We've repeatedly had proven to us that the ideas and information, rather than any gimmicky processes, were all that mattered. There is no set of actions you can mimic, no special environmental condition you can live in, no perfect set of goals you can create, no support you can garner from others, or no pharmaceutical you can take that will make you not want to use substances. They are all indirect approaches that, if you rely on them, will distract you from the simple and direct approach: think differently and make different choices.

INDIRECT PROCESSES OF CHANGE

We define indirect processes of change as any methods that don't directly address a person's preference for using substances. It's important to remember that this preference is the product of the benefits you see in substance use and its perceived value relative to the options of less or no substance use.

The most poignant example of an indirect process is the various pharmaceutical treatments for addiction. These methods target neurons instead of people's thoughts and ideas about substance use, so they are doomed to fail in changing anyone's motivation to use (i.e., preference). There are two classes of pharmaceutical treatments for addiction: those that relieve withdrawal, such as methadone, Suboxone, or nicotine replacement patches, and those that modify or block the effects of substances, such as naltrexone, Antabuse, and Chantix. Some of them act with a combination of these effects. None of them have been very successful. Let's examine one of them to see the principle in action.

Naltrexone is a drug that fills in opiate receptors in the brain so that, when opiates or alcohol are taken, the effects perceived as pleasurable are blocked and not felt, thus earning this drug the title of "a blocker." This pharmacological mechanism is well understood and verifiable.

However, researchers also claim that naltrexone "reduces cravings," and yet they openly admit they have *no working theory on a pharmacological mechanism by which the drug reduces cravings*. This claim is based solely on the observation that some people report getting fewer cravings when they are on naltrexone. These blockers are all the rage right now with fans of alternative methods of recovery. There have been plenty of naltrexone success stories in the media over the past few years in which those who have used it claim that it's as if this wonder drug "flipped a switch" that made them stop craving.

But does it really flip a switch to turn off cravings? At the beginning of the chapter, we showed a graph from a recent study comparing naltrexone with a placebo. The curve showed that a nearly identical reduction in drinking took place at intake for both the patients on naltrexone and those taking an inert placebo. This suggests that something other than the drug was responsible for the reduction in drinking (and, thus, the reduction in "craving"). It's reasonable to assume that the individuals who reduced their craving and substance use when taking naltrexone had already reached the point where they no longer saw frequent intoxication as their preferred state. What else could explain the fact that a placebo worked just as well as the drug?

Online message boards are filled with testimonials from people who took naltrexone and either felt no reduction in craving for alcohol or felt an initial reduction in craving that wore off quickly. In our review of these testimonials, we found that many expressed a sincere desire for a solution to their troubles. However, they also expressed the insight that "I don't think I was ready to quit yet." Of course, what this statement means is that they still preferred drinking. This might sound like a contradiction, but it's not. It's entirely possible and common to both want your troubles to end and continue wanting to do the thing that's causing those troubles. The reason is because people want the thing (in this case, alcohol) for the benefits they perceive they will get from it but don't want the negative consequences.

Medication assisted therapies work the same way a restrictor plate in a race car works. Now, you might not know what that is, so let us explain.

Years ago, in NASCAR racing, the executives of NASCAR wanted to make racing safer by limiting the speeds of the race cars. They did this by making a rule that all the cars were now required to have a small metal plate in the car's engine that restricts the flow of fuel, which forces all the cars to have a limited top speed. But here's the issue. If NASCAR officials would let them, the drivers would happily remove those restrictor plates because they want to win races and are willing to take on the risks of the higher speeds. Currently, even with the restrictor plates in place, all the drivers on the racecourse have their gas pedals mashed to the floorboards to wring out every bit of speed they can from the restricted engine.

And here is the parallel to pharmacological therapies: The restrictor plates did not stop race car drivers from *wanting* (craving) to go faster. They simply made race car drivers, who once enjoyed going extremely fast, frustrated race car drivers who are now forced to go slower. That isn't unlike the frustrated and deprived former heroin users who are now getting the Vivitrol shot and still wanting desperately to get high but are now frustrated. Essentially, they have self-administered restrictor plates in their brains that do not allow them to enjoy what they really want to do, which is to feel high. The effect is that they crave even more. They want, they desire, and they dream of getting high. Like the drivers and mechanics who are motivated to go faster and are willing to cheat on the racetrack by secretly bypassing the restrictor plates in their cars, we see thousands of people every day who continue to use heroin while taking naltrexone, Suboxone, or methadone. Pharmacology does not change a person's likes and dislikes, motives, or desires and cravings any more than a restrictor plate makes a race car driver a lover of driving more slowly.

Online message boards are filled with discussions by people who've been *coerced* into taking naltrexone for opiate habits (the following comments refer to a long-lasting naltrexone injection):

> I took the vivitrol shot almost 30 days ago, and i have been trying to get high for the past week, and still cannot feel a thing. im not ready to quit and im obsessing over the idea of using. i am a heroin addict and i want to feel the rush!

Another reluctant naltrexone patient describes the torture of feeling a continued desire for opiates with no way to feel their effects:

> Come on, can someone please respond to this, i have been
> on the vivitrol shot for a long time and i just am not cut out
> for this shit. i was ment to die alone thinking about the next
> come-up, I can't take it anymore. I feel like im developing
> a psychotic disorder, Btw im 2-weeks into my 3rd shot and
> anyone whos reading this and all those liers out there that
> keep telling you not to relapse because you will "feel better
> in time," thats bull f***in-shit.

They are people who, as evidenced by their resistance to addiction treatment, *don't want it to work*. Someone is coercing them to take naltrexone. While on it, they complain that they can't get high, they crave all the time, and they're losing their minds. Just because the drug blocks the flow of receptors that facilitate getting a high does not mean the drug will take away cravings.

A recent study of naltrexone for alcohol showed that both patients who were on the real drug and those on the placebo similarly reduced their craving and drinking. The fact is that those who believe it works had already figured out before they started taking the drug that they'd be happier with less substance use. Taking this drug was just a symbolic part of their decision to change. It may have provided a convenient storyline for them as well. It's comforting to think that your behavior was the result of a disease and that you needed a pill to change it. That wipes away a lot of shame. The idea that this drug reduces cravings is an illusion though. The drug didn't change these people; they changed themselves by changing their perspectives on the relative value of heavy substance use in their lives.

If we take their interpretation of their experiences as proof that naltrexone was what "worked" to reduce their desire for alcohol and then recommend that others with a strong desire for opiates or alcohol do the same, then we've missed the point of what really drove the change—"wanting it to work." If you force people suffering from a strep infection to take penicillin, it wouldn't matter whether they want or don't want the medication to work; either way, the drug would eradicate the infection. Likewise, if a drug could remove cravings, then it wouldn't matter whether someone had been coerced to take it or voluntarily took it because the drug would work regardless. But we see here that it does matter. In fact, based on the data, it's the only thing that matters. People who don't "want it to work" do not experience reduced craving while on it. Desire is a matter of the mind, not one of pharmacological processes.

We've heard countless anecdotes about paths out of addiction that are then turned into "plans of recovery." They all fall into the trap of focusing on the actions that accompanied change for some people rather than the ideas that drove the change. For example, many people become obsessed with healthy living and nutrition when they quit using substances. They take supplements, eat organic foods, and avoid unhealthy foods. They say that doing these things reduces their cravings. Steven, a coauthor of this book, ate tons of fried, fast, and sugary foods both before and several years after having resolved his substance use problem. Why didn't he "relapse" because of his poor nutrition? And why did many people, whom he's personally witnessed, who became obsessed with healthy foods quickly "relapse"? The answer is simple: what people choose to eat has nothing to do with their choice to use or not use substances.

The same is true for working out. People who've focused on physical fitness when they quit say that, if you do this too, you will get and stay sober. Some even have very scientific-sounding explanations for why it will work for you—that working out replaces the endorphins you need and those endorphins somehow translate into losing the desire for substances. Yet physical fitness and yoga classes and trips to the gym have become a common feature in most rehabs, but success rates haven't gone up. I instinctively knew this was a silly idea the day I saw a health food guru/yoga teacher show up at the retreat with a massive crack cocaine habit. Anyone who recommends these plans of action suffers from the belief that people are like unconscious matter that can be transformed by actions and biological influences. Well, your physical body can certainly be transformed this way, but your thoughts, ideas, and beliefs—all products of your mind—cannot. Your mind and its thoughts are what drive your desire for substance use. If you drink a healthy smoothie every day while retaining the belief that you need to be high or drunk to be happy, you will still have a great desire for substances.

The same is true for taking on goals and new activities as a plan of action that will combat addiction. There are correlations that show lower rates of substance use problems in people who are married, raising families, and more educated and have higher-paying careers and some involvement in organized religion and their community. It's often been pointed out that many women quit their substance use problems immediately upon getting pregnant and many men do too as soon as their first child is born. These things are all true, but the fact that they are true doesn't mean that, if people take on these things as goals, their desire for substance use will decrease as a result. You should know that, over the years at our retreats, we have seen every demographic there is, from homeless sex workers to CEOs of multimillion-dollar corporations and everything between, which is to say that we've seen people with all the factors and goal paths that correlate with less substance use problems, and yet they still have substance use problems.

Although these correlations hold across large groups, they don't hold with individuals. The college-educated stay-at-home mom with three kids who is involved in the PTA and church and whose husband makes enough money to hire a nanny for extra help will still down two bottles of wine a day if she believes that wine adds something indispensable to her life. Her thoughts about her life and whether the wine adds to it are all that matter in whether she'll keep desiring it. We've seen plenty of people who chased goals and improved their lives in many ways but still went back to problematic substance use. And we've also seen people with next to nothing going for them who easily resolved their substance use problems. What they did was change their perspective on substance use and come to believe their life would be better without it.

Many people stop using substances heavily and go back to school, start new careers and relationships, and have children. The things they do don't *cause* their change in substance use. What does is that they change their perspectives on substance use first, which then changes their desire and use of substances, which in turn frees up time and resources to pursue those things. Having a child won't cause you to get sober. Just ask anyone who grew up with parents who used substances problematically.

We recommend that you don't get stuck on plans of recovery, plans of action, or processes that aim to indirectly change your substance use. Don't look to change the physical and external as a means of changing the mental and internal. These tactics are not effective. There is no physical or external process that will decrease your desire for substances. Your desire for substances is mental; it is a product of your perspective of your various options.

If there is anything that could be called a process in *The Freedom Model*, it would be the process of mentally choosing. Every day, you make choices, and those choices are no different from choosing to change your substance use except for the fact that you've learned to see them as being relatively easy to make. Changing your substance use is a normal choice, which means that all normal internal processes that apply to normal choices, such as judging, reevaluating, deciding, or assessing, accurately describe what you're doing when you change your substance use.

Again, that you "have to want it to work" is another way of saying you will do what you really want to do. If you want to keep using heavily, you will; if you want to use moderately, you will; and if you want to abstain, you will. *The Freedom Model* is here to show you that you are truly free to change your wants and choices.

REFERENCES

Brandsma, J. (1980). *Outpatient treatment of alcoholism: A review and comparative study.* Baltimore, MD: University Park Press.

Cutler, R. B., & Fishbain, D. A. (2005). Are alcoholism treatments effective? The Project MATCH data. *BMC Public Health, 5*(1), 1–11. https://doi.org/10.1186/1471-2458-5-75

Ferner, M. (2015, March 3). Here's one simple way we can change the conversation about drug abuse. Retrieved from http://www.huffingtonpost.com/2015/03/03/drug-addiction-language_n_6773246.html

Miller, W. R., Walters, S. T., & Bennett, M. E. (2001). How effective is alcoholism treatment in the United States? *Journal of Studies on Alcohol, 62*(2), 211–220.

Miller, W. R., Westerberg, V. S., Harris, R. J., & Tonigan, J. S. (1996). What predicts relapse? Prospective testing of antecedent models. *Addiction (Abingdon, England), 91* Suppl, S155–172.

Oslin, D. W., Leong, S. H., Lynch, K. G., Berrettini, W., O'Brien, C. P., Gordon, A. J., & Rukstalis, M. (2015). Naltrexone vs placebo for the treatment of alcohol dependence: A randomized clinical trial. *JAMA Psychiatry, 72*(5), 430–437. https://doi.org/10.1001/jamapsychiatry.2014.3053

Pierce, M., Bird, S. M., Hickman, M., Marsden, J., Dunn, G., Jones, A., & Millar, T. (2016). Impact of treatment for opioid dependence on fatal drug-related poisoning: A national cohort study in England. *Addiction, 111*(2), 298–308. https://doi.org/10.1111/add.13193

CHAPTER 3:

THE QUICK ANSWERS

After reading this book, you will know that it's simple to "overcome an addiction." You can "overcome an addiction" by learning that you're free now and have been free all along to change your substance use and that there is no *addiction* to overcome. However, for most people, it's not as simple as our telling you that you're in control and then having you snap your fingers and change. If it were, we would give you a one-page pamphlet rather than a long, detailed, well-cited text. To change the beliefs that keep you feeling trapped, we offer a critical analysis of the popular mythology about addiction and substances and an alternative to it: *The Freedom Model*.

We understand that most of you want the answers to the most basic questions surrounding addiction right away. So we're going to provide those answers now in their simplest form, with the caveat that much more discussion may be needed to truly understand them and that further discussion will be provided throughout the rest of the book.

ARE YOU DENYING THAT ADDICTION EXISTS?

As we said in chapter 1, the essential component of any definition or explanation of addiction is the assertion that people's substance use becomes an involuntary behavior. The recovery society and its proponents have explained the notion that it is involuntary in many ways, and yet each of these explanations has never been proven. In fact, the research indicates that elements of choice are involved in all substance use and that it is a voluntarily, freely chosen behavior.

So, yes, we are denying that addiction is *involuntary behavior* but affirming that at the root of people believing they are addicted is the idea that it is involuntary. *However, we affirm that people use substances in troubling and costly ways and that some substance users feel as if they are compelled to use substances and can't stop.* Here, we're going to quickly refute the three most popular explanations that have been used to convince people they are "addicted." These three points are covered in appendices A, B, and D, respectively, if you would like to study them in greater depth.

1. First, recovery ideology says that addiction includes a "loss of control" whereby addicts will not be able to stop drinking or drugging once they start. *Several* laboratory experiments over the past 50 years have shown this to be false. None of these studies have confirmed the existence of such a weakness in people labeled as addicts or alcoholics. What they've shown is that, when those diagnosed to be "addicted" are given a substance without their knowledge, they don't seek out and keep taking more of it. These studies have also shown that self-described addicts will moderate and save up several doses for a binge when the supply of a substance is tightly controlled and that, when faced with offers of money or more substance, most addicts have their price and will turn down the next dose they're offered in favor of the other reward. What's more, data shows that at least half of former alcoholics become moderate drinkers. All these facts demonstrate that cognition and choice are the factors ruling addicts' behavior rather than a mysterious loss of control, phenomenon of craving, or weakness of will (see appendix A).

2. Next, recovery ideology says that repeated usage of substances causes neural changes that *force* addicts to crave and use substances perpetually, that their brains are *hijacked* by substances (as the popular saying goes). Again, extensive research disproves this claim. The overwhelming majority of *addicts* quit or reduce their substance use *despite* such neural adaptation (called "brain changes"). Moreover, the probability of addicts quitting or reducing their usage remains constant whether they have been "dependent" on substances for less than one year or more than 40 years. This fact flies in the face of the theory that more exposure to substances leads to more brain hijacking, which in turn leads to more involuntary craving and substance use. *Brain changes be damned.* People still quit and moderate despite this physical state. Here's how one esteemed researcher put it after reviewing this line of research:

> There are no published studies that establish a causal link between drug-induced neural adaptations and compulsive drug use or even a correlation between drug-induced neural changes and an increase in preference for an addictive drug. (Heyman, 2013)

The available evidence completely refutes the brain disease model of addiction (see appendix B).

The brain changes that are said to cause addiction are a completely normal phenomenon. They occur with the learning of any repetitively practiced skill or habit, yet they don't *compel* people to use their skill or continue their habit. Do you think piano players, taxi drivers, or jugglers are compelled to do these activities once they become skilled at them? Of course, they aren't, and yet all these activities lead to significant brain changes, just like repetitious substance use does. Such brain changes are the *result* of habit, not the *cause* of habit. They serve only to facilitate efficient continuation of the habit, but they do not rob the individual of free will. You might think of this in the same way that lifting weights alters your muscle tissue, and yet this physical change doesn't cause you to punch people.

3. Much is made of the role of physical dependency and withdrawal syndrome that occurs when people stop using some drugs, such as opiates, benzodiazepines, and alcohol. *Surely, people who suffer from withdrawal syndrome must be true addicts enslaved to their drug of choice.* Once again, this is not the case. Throughout history, most people who have had withdrawal syndrome simply experienced it as a sickness rather than as a compulsion to seek and use more drugs. It's true that some people do require medical help to safely weather this condition, but it is not true that withdrawal compels people to use substances (see appendix D). Furthermore, withdrawal symptoms don't need to be present for people to feel addicted, which can be seen in users of drugs that cause little or no withdrawal, such as marijuana and cocaine, and all the nondrug activities people feel addicted to, such as gambling, shopping, or watching pornography.

WHAT IS THE FREEDOM MODEL AND HOW CAN IT HELP ME?

To answer this question, first, we must explain to you the basic tenets of the recovery society philosophy. It assumes that heavy substance users are stuck with a lifelong compulsion and lack of self-control. Based on this, it assumes that, the moment you enter treatment, your goal should be a lifelong effort to maintain abstinence. This is the reason people enter into treatment dreading that they will never be able to drink or drug again. With this as a starting point, treatment's primary objective is to teach methods of resisting the desires for substance use that it says you must fight for the rest of your life. Thus, the goal of treatment is to prepare you to construct and exist in a limited world to support you in painful resistance of your desire and protect you from exposure to substance use and so-called triggers. The recovery society is trying to help you not do what you really want to do (which is to use substances heavily). This is the reason treatment programs fail.

The Freedom Model completely upends this approach. We do not assume that you will be stuck with your current level of desire for the rest of your life, nor do we assume that your goal must be lifelong abstinence from substance use. We know that your behavior is voluntary. Furthermore, we ask you to become fully informed about your abilities and the alternative ideas about substance use and addiction *before* you make any decisions regarding whether you will abstain or decrease your substance use for the rest of your life.

The decision-making process and your ability to choose are everything in *The Freedom Model*, whereas the decision to abstain is already made for you in the recovery society regardless of your liking it. When people are scared or shamed into abstinence or otherwise made to feel that it is their only option, they rarely become truly invested in and motivated to continue to abstain. *The Freedom Model* abandons this practice and focuses on allowing you to decide for yourself freely and fully informed.

You can get excited about quitting or reducing substance use, and you can like it and truly want it instead of feeling like you must do it. You can become truly motivated to make a change because you can change your preferences for substance use.

The Freedom Model works by first removing the obstacles to change and then providing insight and information that can help you effectively make new choices, leaving those choices up to you. It does all this by providing information. With new information, new perspectives, and new thoughts, you may develop new desires, do away with the painful task of fighting your desires, and easily make new choices.

HOW DO I QUIT DRINKING OR DRUGGING?

You quit by ceasing to continue using substances. Quitting is a zero-step process, and it isn't difficult. We know this sounds dismissive of the difficulties you've felt in trying to quit, and again, that's why we've provided this detailed, thoroughly researched and cited text to help you understand why it truly is simple.

Quitting isn't difficult when you really want to quit. As you think critically about your past attempts to quit in which it felt difficult, you might want to ask yourself whether you truly wanted to quit. *You either felt that you had to quit, were obligated to quit, or were cornered into quitting.* In those difficult attempts, you didn't see a life without substance use as the happier, more attractive option than a life with substance use. This is another way of saying you didn't really want to quit. When you move forward on a quit attempt without really wanting it, then it becomes a painful struggle to resist what you really want.

So the "how" of quitting is figuring out that a life without substance use is actually the happier, more attractive option. It's an internal mental change of wanting abstinence. The same goes for reducing your level of use. It's hard to reduce your substance use only when you view a reduction as less enjoyable than heavy/frequent use. The key is seeing a reduction in usage as the happier, more satisfying, more attractive option. Once you do, it takes no special technique to moderate. It also is a zero-step process. *It's easy.*

If you are using substances in a way that poses immediate danger to your health, then the right time to at least take a break and regroup is always now regardless of your level of enthusiasm about the prospect of quitting. However, we're not encouraging anyone to jump the gun and attempt to make long-term changes in the same shortsighted and frustrating way that never works. Whether you've quit already, think you need to quit right now, or plan to quit sometime after finishing this book, the key ingredient that will make your changes last is finding a way to see quitting or reducing your substance use as the happier and more attractive option—in both the long term (e.g., I'll be happy to feel healthier not get cirrhosis) and the short term (e.g., I can enjoy my life more *today* without/with less substances).

HOW DO I DEAL WITH WITHDRAWAL?

If withdrawal is an issue for you, as it can be with alcohol, benzodiazepines, and opiates/opioids (and some other classes of drugs), then you should seek medical help for withdrawal when you decide to quit. Withdrawal from alcohol and benzodiazepines is easily addressed in a matter of 3 to 14 days and opiates/opioids, three to seven days, under the care of qualified physicians.

Withdrawal from opiates/opioids is rarely life threatening, although it may be dangerous for a miniscule portion of people who have other health issues that add complications. In most cases, it can be tolerated without medical help, but there is no shame in seeking such help if you feel you need it. The help is out there, and it is effective. Just a word of caution: we recommend that you don't get duped into the long-term opiate replacement regimens that are so popular. That's the same dead-end road that ends in great frustration. You can let your detox provider know that you want to detox completely. Millions do every year, and they move on with their lives. You can too.

Withdrawal from alcohol and benzodiazepines can be life threatening. It is rare but significant enough that it's better to seek help and be safe rather than sorry. Again, medical help is available, and it works. There is no excuse for not getting this help; it is available in hospitals in every major city and certainly somewhere in every state and is usually covered by medical insurance or the state. Your local emergency room must help you with withdrawal, especially if the medical staff determines that your symptoms are life threatening.

As you will learn later, withdrawal syndrome doesn't compel anyone to want to use substances. It is a separate medical issue that can be successfully medically treated, and to that degree, it's an easily solved nonissue in the bigger picture of changing your substance use habits.

HOW DO I RESIST CRAVINGS?

You don't get cravings; rather, you *actively crave*, so no resistance is needed since it is something you choose or don't choose to engage in.

Recovery ideology has renamed *wanting substances* as "getting powerful cravings." This language distorts what's happening when a person wants to use a substance or even thinks about a substance. It leads people to believe that there is an objective force called a craving that they "get" or that otherwise happens to them. This mythical craving then becomes something to fight, resist, or prevent by some complicated means. Seen this way, it becomes something that requires strength and support or a special coping technique to overcome or resist.

The truth is that craving isn't a thing or a force; it's an activity that you choose to do. You actively engage in craving by thinking in some way *A drink/drug would feel good right now*. It feels "stronger" when your thought amounts to *I need a drink/drug right now*. And there are various shades of wanting between these extremes. To crave is to actively think that using is the preferable option. So, like quitting, dealing with cravings is a zero-step process once you know what you want. When you change your perception of substance use and see using less or none as your preferred option, then craving will no longer be an issue because you won't be thinking *I really need a drink/drug right now*.

Until you've changed your perception of substance use, you may find yourself revisiting the thought that you want or need a drink/drug right now. *All you need to know at this point is that there is no powerful craving that's forcing you to use and that, when you think you need to use, you are free to challenge that thought. You are free to ask yourself* Do I really need a drink/drug right now?

Habit plays a role because you will be more apt to think these thoughts in the situations in which you've always thought this way. If you recognize that it's just habit rather than a powerful craving thrust upon you by the disease of addiction, then you will realize there is nothing to battle or resist and the habit of ideating about substance use will naturally die.

In short, know that craving is just thinking favorable thoughts about substance use and you are free to think differently. Craving isn't something that happens to you; it's something you actively do.

ISN'T ADDICTION GENETIC?

Many of our readers as well as their family members are convinced that addiction "runs in their family" and that there is some genetic abnormality that forces them to use substances. They point to family members who've had substance use problems as proof that they're genetically fated to repeatedly use substances problematically.

This is a case where you will find exactly what you're looking for. As of this writing, the most recent data (NESARC III, 2016) shows that 68.5 million Americans, or 30% of the adult population, have fit the diagnostic criteria for alcohol use disorder at some point in their lives. That's nearly one in three people. Fourteen percent fit the criteria for addiction to drugs. This means that the odds of having relatives who've struggled with substance use problems, even in your immediate family, are extremely high. If you have at least three adults in your family, chances are that one of them will have had an "addiction" at some point. Given this statistic, the odds are that *addiction runs in everyone's family*.

Thus far, science hasn't verified a single "addiction gene" nor has it explained how such a gene would cause people to want substances. Genetic determinists have now moved to saying there's probably a "cluster of genes" that somehow converge perfectly to make people addicts. But again, they don't know exactly how this would work or whether it's really the case. As such, the question of whether genes are involved in heavy substance use is a very murky issue. But as we showed in chapter 1, even if genes are involved, 9 out of 10 people get over their substance use issues anyway. Our position is that, looking for an addiction gene or other "causes" of addiction is a fruitless quest. What's even worse is that it gets in the way of people making changes because these "causes" end up functioning as excuses for people to give up on trying to change.

Another popular cause of addiction that fits this pattern is an emotionally turbulent childhood. Adolescence is a highly stressful period of life, a roller-coaster ride of negative emotions *for most people, whether addicted or not*. So the chances are that, if you look for this experience in your past, you will find it. Since emotionally turbulent childhoods are not the exclusive domain of addicts, then it's not logical to consider them as being a cause of addiction. Again, focusing on this as a cause is a block to addressing your problems and initiating change now. Substance use, at all levels, is an activity chosen in pursuit of happiness; it's caused by the personal view that substance use will provide what you need emotionally. The way to move on from a pattern of substance use that you're constantly regretting is to change your perspective on whether it's the best option for getting you what you feel you need emotionally.

CAN I REALLY MODERATE?

Since there is no such thing as "loss of control" of substance use, *anyone* can modify his or her substance use levels and patterns—from the successful executive who drinks a little too much now and then, to the homeless man at the local bus station begging for money to get more crack. Nobody lacks the ability to use substances moderately. However, not everyone wants to moderate. Successful moderation is just a matter of finding your way to preferring moderate use more than heavy use. If you set out to moderate when you truly want to use heavily, you'll end up using heavily. This topic is so bogged down in misinformation that a quick answer will not be enough. *Just as we asked that you make no rash decisions about lifelong abstinence yet, we now also ask you to hold off on the decision to moderate until you've educated yourself fully by reading the rest of this book.*

Some of you will be afraid of this topic and not want to discuss or even consider it. Beware that this position means that you're holding onto a strategy of being scared into abstinence. You want someone to tell you that you must be abstinent and are unable to moderate. You want to feel as if you "have to" abstain. However, that isn't the case. You don't *have* to do anything. We don't discuss moderation to promote it; we discuss it because it is an option and *some people will choose it regardless of whether we discuss it.* Our position is that it's better to be open and informative about the topic than to promote ignorance and engender fear by withholding information. What's more, openly considering all options is a better way to become fully invested in the one that you want, as opposed to feeling cornered into something you don't really want.

To be clear, we are not recommending any substance use whatsoever, and we aren't giving anyone permission *to moderate. We have no authority what-*

soever to grant or deny anyone permission to do anything. We respect the fact that you make your own choices in life and will do so based on your own judgment regardless of what we say. To deny the possibility of moderation or withhold information about it would be an attempt to manipulate you and choose your goals for you. It would mean that we're not telling you the whole truth based on fear and trying to steer you in a specific direction. That's what the recovery society and treatment do. Its proponents say that heavy substance users *can't* moderate and instead will fall immediately back into uncontrolled heavy substance use after their first hit or drink. We've found that's what some people who are afraid to discuss this topic want to be told, that they can't moderate. This allows them to be able to avoid the responsibility of making their own decisions. The goal of *The Freedom Model* is for you to learn the whole truth so you can make an informed decision. Even if you know you want lifelong abstinence now and don't plan to change that decision, we challenge you to become fully informed. That way, when you make your decision, you will have done so for reasons of finding your happiest option rather than feeling fearful and deprived and believing that abstinence is your lifelong punishment.

BE PATIENT

This chapter has provided the briefest of answers to the most pressing questions people have when addressing a substance use problem and learning *The Freedom Model*. We know how frustrating and sometimes painful it is to feel addicted, and we also know that, with a new mindset, it can be extremely easy to change. As you learn more about *The Freedom Model*, you will gain a full understanding of these issues and the deep conviction that you are free to change your substance use. As you expand your knowledge, you'll eventually see that it can be an easy and enjoyable change to make.

REFERENCES

Alcohol Use and Alcohol Use Disorders in the United States: Main Findings from the 2012–2013 National Epidemiologic Survey on Alcohol and Related Conditions-III (NESARC-III), *U.S. Alcohol Epidemiologic Data Reference Manual*, Volume 10, April 2016, NIH Publication No. 16-AA-8020.

Heyman, G. M. (2013). Addiction and choice: Theory and new data. *Frontiers in Psychiatry, 4*(31). https://doi.org/10.3389/fpsyt.2013.00031

CHAPTER 4:

WHY DO I KEEP DOING THIS? WHY DO I PREFER IT?

Recovery professionals have spread the view that heavy substance use is pathological, which means it must be explained as a disorder, a disease, the outgrowth of some complex and twisted set of causes, or a compulsion meant to self-medicate that underlies psychological issues. They claim that substance use becomes involuntary for those they deem to be addicts. This claim has injected such confusion into the topic of heavy substance use that it hurts the people seeking help. While some people who come to us for help have some clarity about why they prefer to use substances, an increasing number of people are completely confused about this matter. They say "I don't know why I do this; I don't even like it." They've come to view their desire for substances as a mysterious and foreign drive.

You don't necessarily need to know every detail about why you prefer intoxication to change your preference. The majority of addicts (i.e., heavy substance users) change their preferences over time naturally and cease or decrease their substance use accordingly. They change their thinking about substances and their reasons for use in ways that aren't fully clear. If you're seeking help now, you don't want to wait any longer for that to *mysteriously* happen for you. When you want to proactively change what you're doing, it only makes sense to seek some clarity on the "why" of the whole issue; this will open the way to rethinking your reasons.

Below is a list of tangible, commonsense reasons people prefer heavy substance use even when it comes at a high cost. We're going to discuss them here, and we invite you to set aside for a while all those other complicated explanations you may believe about addiction as you read through this chapter. We would like you to consider the simplest explanation first.

The goal of this chapter is for you to become conscious of the factors that may be painfully obvious yet are rarely considered. We want you to see the commonsense explanation of what lies behind a strong desire for intoxication.

SOME PRIMARY REASONS BEHIND A PREFERENCE FOR INTOXICATION

NEW EXPERIENCES

Prior to using various substances, you hear that being intoxicated on them is enjoyable. But knowing that from others and experiencing it firsthand are wildly different things. Humans are learning machines that are satisfied by new experiences. New things are like a workout for the mind, but the newness isn't just in the first use of a substance. There are many substances, many contexts in which to use them, many ways to use them, and many ways to experience their effects. Like taking up a sport or hobby, the initial experiences are exciting, but then practicing and becoming proficient in your new activity comes with its own newness and excitement.

Newness was a factor in your substance use at one point, and there's a possibility that it still is and thus still figures into your preference for intoxication. It's not odd to be fascinated with exploring the effects of substances. It can be dangerous, of course. We're not endorsing it, but we are here today to tell you it doesn't need to be denied as a factor because this fascination is quite normal. Putting all the other perceived benefits of substance use aside, the novelty of substance use can make it seem fascinating even when it may be an otherwise unpleasant experience. Many people's initial experiences with substances are unpleasant or even painful and may include vomiting, coughing, fear, paranoia, and anxiety; yet the substance user perseveres and keeps exploring this new and exotic experience. At some point, the novelty wears off, and substance use can become rather boring; nevertheless, new-ness is a factor by which many people find substance use exciting and thus attractive for a long time.

PLEASURE—THE "HIGH"

The most obvious reason people prefer intoxication is that they enjoy the "high" and find find it pleasurable. Consider a few words used to describe the feeling of intoxication: buzzed, high, rolling, wired, lift-ed, tripping, and amped. All these words denote a special state, often elevated, a break from feeling ordinary. To leave the state of feeling ordinary for a while and feel extraordinary instead is a sensible reason to feel attracted to intoxication.

Despite all the talk about substances accessing the brain's pleasure cen-ter, this psychological part of the pleasure—*the high*—is harder to pin down biologically than you would think. Expectancy and various sit-uational and psychological factors are an equal or bigger part of the pleasure than the simple reaction of drugs triggering neurotransmit-ters. This information is explored in detail in chapters 17 and 20. But the fact is that, by whatever mechanism it occurs, many people experi-ence pleasure when using substances and it is *the* primary reason peo-ple prefer to be intoxicated.

Some substance users may avoid or object to discussing the pleasure aspect of substance use and say "It doesn't even feel good to me any-more." This certainly may be true in some cases since pleasure is high-ly subjective and other reasons may have become the main driver for the preference for intoxication. But in many cases, this is more like-ly a mantra learned from the recovery society. Treatment professionals and support group members spend a lot of time encouraging people to believe there's no rhyme or reason to their substance use and that plea-sure plays no role (e.g. "nobody would enjoy being an addict!"). They also make substance use a moral issue, claiming that it's bad because it's selfish and hedonistic. This puts substance users in a corner and makes it virtually impossible for them to admit or even consider that they drink and drug because they find it pleasurable.

Some substance users may object to talking about the pleasure of sub-stance use because they look at all the negative consequences of their substance use and find that *overall*, it's not pleasurable and in fact may be painful and frustrating at times. While it is important to look at the activity overall, it's also important not to let hindsight reasoning blind you to what drove you to the behavior in the moment. For example, even if a night of drinking leads to intense vomiting, a splitting headache, a fight with your spouse, and a terrible hangover, a cascade of awfulness that started in the second hour of your drinking, it doesn't change the fact that you found it pleasurable in the first hour of drinking. It also doesn't change the fact that you thought that drinks number 9 and 10 would bring more pleasure at the time that you took them. Mental pleasure is always a factor in people's desire for intoxication.

PHYSICAL PLEASURE

Substances do much more to the body than simply tickle the "pleasure center" of the brain, and these bodily effects are a big part of what gets interpreted as pleasurable. In an amazingly thorough decade-long study of moderate and heavy opiate users conducted in the 1970s, researchers obtained detailed reports from users about how heroin feels. Most of them described how it starts in the body with a feeling of *physical relaxation and warmth*, and then the physical comfort of this feeling cues them to relax mentally as well. The bodily sensations figure heavily into the high of opiates.

Likewise, marijuana contains cannabinoids that fill cannabinoid receptors all over the body and have the effect of smoothing muscle tissue and causing a physical relaxation. These effects on the body cue people to feel relaxed in their minds as well. In other words, while feeling physical relaxation, people give themselves permission to feel mental relaxation as well.

Alcohol also brings feelings of warmth and physical relaxation and a whole host of physical effects, including raised blood pressure and heart rate, loss of equilibrium, slowed reaction times, and loss of coordination, among others. If you think that some of these physical effects wouldn't be pleasurable, think again. Even though some of these effects challenge our ability to physically function, that could be interpreted as pleasurable. If you have you ever run in a three-legged race, you likely had a lot of fun doing it. The novelty of how the temporary handicap changes your experience is enough to make it enjoyable. It's found to be pleasurable because it's a break from the norm.

The sedative and depressant drugs slow down the body's functions. It's important to understand that those two terms refer to physical effects of the drugs even though the terms have a psychological sense as well. A drug classified as a *depressant* doesn't make you depressed in the sense of the term denoting sadness and/or negative overall mood. What is meant by calling a drug a "depressant" is that it depresses (i.e., decreases) neurotransmission (i.e., activity in your brain). In the reverse, stimulants, such as cocaine and various amphetamines, raise the heart rate and put the body into a fight-or-flight mode. They speed up many bodily functions, including neurotransmission. The slowing of neurotransmission by depressants has wide-ranging physical symptoms, and the speeding up of neurotransmission has the opposite wide-ranging physical symptoms; the physical effects of both these classes of substances can be considered pleasurable. Again, this may be because these feelings offer a break from the norm, a challenge to normal functioning, and can sometimes offer improved physical functioning. Activities such as riding on a roller coaster, playing a sport, having sex, or getting a massage put your body through unique physical experiences, which are usually considered pleasurable. Drugs are no exception nor are they special in this sense; altered physical experience is often perceived as enjoyable. This is a major factor in most people's preference for intoxication.

Are you willing to consider that seeking physical pleasure isn't all that odd or bad and that you're not some sort of monster for seeking it in substances? If so, your preference for intoxication won't be such a mystery, nor should you feel ashamed by it.

ALTERED STATES OF CONSCIOUSNESS

Because substances affect neurotransmission, they can alter sensory perception and conscious experience. Coincidentally, the desire to alter one's consciousness is an extremely normal feature of humanity, as drug researcher Andrew Weil (1986) wrote in *The Natural Mind* in answer to the question of *why people take drugs*:

To come up with a valid explanation, we simply must suspend our value judgments about kinds of drugs and admit (however painful it might be) that the glass of beer on a hot afternoon and the bottle of wine with a fine meal are no different in kind from the joint of marihuana or the snort of cocaine; nor is the evening devoted to cocktails essentially different from the day devoted to mescaline. All are examples of the same phenomenon: the use of chemical agents to induce alterations in consciousness. What is the meaning of this universal phenomenon? (pp. 18–19)

It is my belief that the desire to alter consciousness periodically is an innate, normal drive analogous to hunger or the sexual drive. Note that I do not say "desire to alter consciousness by means of chemical agents." Drugs are merely one means of satisfying this drive; there are many others. . . . Anyone who watches very young children without revealing his presence will find them regularly practicing techniques that induce striking changes in mental states. Three and four-year olds, for example, commonly whirl themselves into vertiginous stupors. They hyperventilate and have other children squeeze them around the chest until they faint. They also choke each other to produce loss of consciousness. (p. 19)

To my knowledge these practices appear spontaneously among children of all societies, and I suspect they have done so throughout history as well. (p. 20)

He also mentions yoga, hypnotism, and meditation as commonly used methods of attaining altered states of consciousness. People have sought altered states throughout recorded history, and seeking them through drugs *is no exception*. Archeological evidence exists of people ingesting alcohol as far back as 7000–6600 BCE in China, and it has appeared all over the world. Opiate use has been traced to 4000 BCE with the Sumerians. Tobacco was cultivated in 1400 BCE in Mexico. Marijuana was found with a mummified shaman from around 800 BCE in China. Coca has been used for the past 1,000 years in South America. Tea dates to second-century BCE, and both tea and coffee (caffeine) came into wider use in the 1600s. And the 20th century saw the creation of many more drugs that alter consciousness. Historically, drugs have often been used with religious ceremonies to find altered states of consciousness. Ancient religious texts are littered with references to substance use.

We are telling you this not just because it's interesting historically but because it demonstrates that seeking altered states of consciousness via chemical means has been and is a common human activity. Yes, substances have also been demonized throughout history, and they're certainly demonized today. But the targets change with the times and fashions. Heck, there was a time in Europe when leaders were afraid of coffee and tried to ban it while, at the same time, opium use was still perfectly legal, respectable, and given in drink form to children in pubs while their parents drank alcohol! If you can let go for a moment of the shame thrust upon you by society, you might see that your desire to alter consciousness with substances isn't so foreign and pathological as you've been led to believe.

There's no question here; the quest for altered states has always been a common human pursuit, and there are thousands of years of recorded history in which various drugs have been used to achieve it. This is a factor in most people's desire to use substances. You're not a special breed of monster called an "addict"; you are a normal human being.

SOCIAL FACTORS

The fact that "everyone's doing it," or at least some people whose opinions we value are using substances, can make it appear more attractive. Take note that we're not calling this *peer pressure* because that term implies that your peers compel you to use substances. In fact, this attraction to substances based on social factors occurs within the individual's mind. You may see some people with whom you want to fit in who are using substances and think that fitting in with those people is very important and that substance use is a way to achieve this goal. If you see things this way, it will add to your preference for intoxication.

This aspect of attraction to substance use is usually associated with young people, yet we see it just as or more often with older people. Many who drink are terrified of quitting because they're afraid they'll stand out at every social event. Of course, this is another way of saying they're incredibly concerned about fitting in and that they see drinking as the only viable way to do so. However, nobody has to believe this to be true. Such views are sometimes carried over into adulthood, but they are also routinely abandoned. We want to show you that you can change this belief if it's a factor for you.

It's also worth mentioning that social cues are a major part of human reasoning. If you hear someone yell "fire" and see people running to escape the building you're in, you don't stop to investigate, think things through, and verify whether there's really a deadly fire from which to run. You take the other people's actions as proof that there is and that you should run. Sometimes we prefer intoxication in the same way. We may not think about it too much. But when we see other people getting intoxicated and loving it, we assume it's really fun and we'll like it too. When others signal that it's a great way to have fun, we may be persuaded to believe it's a great way to have fun as well.

Substance use can seem like a very adult and independent thing to do. It gets wrapped up in self-images and can serve as an expression of being fun, extreme, a risk taker, hip, or macho. Depending on how much you associate it with these traits and care about maintaining them, the prospect of losing this expression of personality can be terrifying, and can play a huge role in why some people continue to prefer heavy substance use. Feeling like there's a big loss in self-image to be had by quitting or reducing your substance use can make it the more preferred option as an ongoing activity.

Strong social meanings are attached to substance use. For example, there's a forbidden fruit aspect to substance use that comes into play depending on the culture in which you grew up. Illegality or taboo can make something appear more attractive, as if it must be special if such effort is made to keep you from getting it or it's reserved for people other than you. A good example of this is found in comparing places where young people are allowed alcohol, such as in Italy, versus places such as the United States where it is forbidden until the age of 21. Italy has very low rates of problem drinking, with the young drinking moderately, whereas the United States has high rates of problem drinking, with 20% to 25% of college-age people qualifying as "alcohol dependent." In Italy, drinking isn't something so special that someone has to scheme and sneak off to do it, so it lacks the forbidden fruit meaning. In fact, it's so banal that, in some therapeutic community rehabs in Italy, *wine is even served with lunch!*

Some substance use is also seen as elite and thus more preferred. This is the same social meaning whereby people like "delicacy" foods that may not taste that good. The objective taste isn't the thing that makes most delicacies taste great; it's the cachet (i.e., the importance and elite meaning of a thing) that is so appealing. Or consider designer hand-bags versus their counterfeit versions that sell for thousands of dollars less. The counterfeits are often of the same quality and look identical, but it's not the function or look that's preferred; it's the knowledge that you've got the special bag that only the elite have. This factor is alive and well with substance use. Part of preferring some forms of intoxication, for many people, is in the fact that it's a special thing that an average peer of yours doesn't do or that you're not allowed to do. This can be seen in those who must have the latest hard-to-find designer drugs, who see heroin as something that only the brave and truly individualistic people would do, who see cocaine use as a status symbol, who romanticize rare cigars and the playboy image they evoke, and who are obsessed with getting special and expensive bottles of wine.

In the United States, rates of "addiction" in men are routinely twice as high as the rates of "addiction" among women. What's more, men's "addictions" tend to last longer. There are long-standing cultural differences between the genders that contribute to this. Particularly, for men, heavy drinking and drug use is associated with masculinity. You need look no further for evidence of this than the drinking practices found in fraternities. With this association in mind, some men may find heavy substance use attractive because it proves their masculinity.

This has been a quick review of only a few of the many ways that social factors play into people's preference for intoxication. Having thought this through, is it so odd or pathological to prefer substance use? Or might your preference be based on common, natural human tendencies?

POWER TO RELIEVE PSYCHOLOGICAL PAIN

A common belief is that intoxication can relieve stress and anxiety, depression, trauma, and all manner of bad moods and psychological pain. The image of a man who lost his job and wanders into the bar to drown his sorrows in alcohol is a common theme that we've all seen dramatically portrayed countless times. After a lifetime of exposure to this message, is it so out of the realm of possibility that the belief that substances contain *magical* psychological powers might influence your preference for intoxication?

The belief in these powers is an interesting topic. As we mentioned at the beginning of this chapter, many people come to us saying that they're forced into substance use by mysterious cravings and can't imagine any reasonable answer for why they use so much. But then, in the next breath, they start talking about how they get intoxicated to self-medicate their stress, anxiety, depression, and trauma. There's their reasonable answer, but they don't see it. It's an odd case of self-contradiction to hear people say "I don't know why I do this" and then rattle off a list of functions they think substances legitimately serve for them. If you think substances are a powerful medication for emotional problems, then of course you'll be attracted to use them when you have those emotional problems. In this case, then, a strong preference for intoxication isn't a mystery at all. If you think there's a miracle drug that'll cure all your woes, you're going to have a strong preference for it. In fact, you'd be foolish if you knew about such a drug and didn't have a strong preference for it.

Now, whether such miracle drugs exist that cure such woes is highly questionable, and we'll get to that later. Right now, we're simply looking at what factors play into a strong preference for intoxication and how belief in a drug's *wonderful* psychological powers is enough to make for a strong preference, even when the belief is erroneous. These beliefs are extremely popular in our culture today, and they're often taught to us directly by the recovery society and all its advocates. This faulty education leaves many people with even stronger preferences for drugs after rehab than they had before rehab. The belief in the psychologically comforting effects of substances isn't odd at this point; it's commonplace. This belief is a major factor in many people's preference for intoxication.

POWER TO LOWER INHIBITIONS

It is also a common belief that substances lower inhibitions, making people feel freer to speak their mind, be sexually liberated, or become calm, cool, and collected for socializing at parties and business networking functions.

Who doesn't want those benefits? Again, if you knew of a pill you could pop to give you all of this, you'd be rather foolish not to desire it. Many people start using substances at turbulent times of their lives, such as adolescence, the college years, and early adulthood when they're first living on their own, making friends, finding romantic partners, and trying to fit in. Pairing substance use with their first experiences, such as meeting and romancing a sexual partner, convinces them that the substance facilitated the experience. They then come to believe that they need to be intoxicated to get them through those tough situations. As they take on this belief, it's increasingly used in other areas, such as to *enhance* performance in work, sexual, and social situations, and can eventually be seen as a needed crutch. As this happens, preference for intoxication grows exponentially.

Again, these benefits are questionable, yet all that matters regarding preferences is that you believe in them. Don't let your preference for intoxication be a mystery to you; it's based on these kinds of beliefs.

SLEEP

Many people think they need alcohol to get to sleep. We hear this often from those who drink wine or swear by their nighttime toddy. While it may be the case that a little alcohol can help some people get to sleep sometimes, research shows that any more than a little actually ruins your sleep. It disrupts REM sleep so you don't get the good kind of sleep that's needed to mentally rejuvenate yourself (Capretto, 2015). Nevertheless, because the immediate effect of consuming a lot of alcohol can be to pass out, many people think they "need it" to get to sleep. Whenever there is a perceived need for a substance, people find an increased preference for that substance.

THE SECONDARY FORTIFYING REASONS BEHIND A STRONG PREFERENCE FOR INTOXICATION

The primary reasons discussed above factor into most people's preference for intoxication whether their preference is weak or strong. The secondary reasons we're going to discuss depend on and multiply the motive power of the primary reasons, helping people to develop a rock-solid preference for intoxication that can eventually win out over most other options and leave people feeling "addicted."

EASE AND RELIABILITY

Substance use is an incredibly simplistic activity that takes little mental effort to repeat. It is challenging, though, in some ways: drugs can be very expensive, the efforts of law enforcement and family who police your behavior can be hard to overcome, and juggling your life responsibilities with a state of intoxication that hampers your ability to tend to those things is difficult. But substance use itself isn't a complicated activity, and its effects are mostly reliable. And these facts make it an easy go-to activity and thus more attractive.

As experience with intoxication grows, novelty may be gradually replaced with reliability, which figures into your preference in a new way and thereby reinforces it. You liked it because it was exciting and new, and now you like it precisely because it isn't; it's now become completely predictable. Factor in the reality that regular substance use can often thrust a life into chaos, and the reliability of the reward found in intoxication paradoxically can become the most stable part of a substance user's life. This is a vicious cycle. But while you live in it, further substance use is the most immediate and easiest thing to do, and thus it becomes exponentially more attractive as your preference for it strengthens.

HABIT

The principle of habit formation is another aspect of the ease of repetition. We've all heard a lot of talk about how "drugs change the brain." Well, most of the changes to the brain are in fact routine neuroplastic processes that occur in the formation of *any habit or skill*. When you repeat an activity, the brain starts to specialize the wiring involved in carrying it out. This makes repeating the behavior a mentally easier task than doing something new. If you still like the activity for some other reasons, this *like* adds to your preference because not only do you like it, but it's now one of the least challenging things you can do. Again, when you're burned out because of the other chaos in your life, your habit becomes the most predictable and easiest break from that chaos.

The habit isn't made up of only the activity itself; each thought that supports the activity becomes its own habit as well. So if you think substance use is the best way to deal with stress, contemplating substance use upon feeling stress becomes the most immediate, easiest thought. Initiating other ways of dealing with stress requires more mental work. Likewise, if it's your go-to recreational activity, it's easier to think of intoxication when bored, whereas contemplating other activities requires more mental effort. All these little habits of thought add to your preference for intoxication. It can be a vicious cycle, but cycles can be broken.

We are habit machines. Our brains tailor themselves to save mental energy on repetitive activities so it can be directed elsewhere. This goes for so-called bad habits and good habits. So for now, just consider the fact that the neurological support of habits is a central feature of human life and it's a factor in your strong preference for intoxication. This factor doesn't represent immorality, badness, dysfunction, or disease; it's simply a normal factor in human functioning (as are the rest of the factors discussed in this chapter).

CROWDING OUT OTHER OPTIONS

The practical effect of increasingly spending time with people in places and activities where heavy substance use is the norm is that you're necessarily spending less time in those circumstances where it isn't a norm. For a stark example, a crack house and a workplace are usually mutually exclusive settings. As you spend more time in the crack house, you spend less time with your work friends. Whenever you break ties with a social group in this way, breaking back in appears to be scarier and harder. It's tough sometimes to pick up the phone to call or message a friend you've ignored for the past year. Does he want to hang out, or will he think you're crazy for calling unexpectedly? In comparison, calling up your drug buddy you've been with every day for the past several weeks seems easier. With this example, you can see how one activity, when repeated often, can crowd out others, shrinking your social world.

It's important that you don't confuse this example with the recovery ideology about the *triggering power* of "people, places, and things"; that's not what we're saying. What we mean is that, when you become more comfortable with those settings, they can amplify your preference for intoxication. The fear of reconnecting to the nonsubstance-related people and places can make staying among your substance-related people and places appear to be the more attractive option, and thus intoxication continues to be preferred as well. The idea of being triggered to use by certain people, places, or things as denoted by the recovery society is based on outside factors "making" you crave and use, whereas *The Freedom Model* describes habits of people based on their internal preferences to use. This is a huge distinction.

LOWERED EXPECTATIONS OF THE ADDICT/ ALCOHOLIC ROLE

If people see you as responsible and dependable, they tend to give you responsibilities and depend on you. People seen as *alcoholics* or *addicts* are often not considered responsible and dependable so people depend on them less. This can make staying in your current social role easier than breaking out of it.

Additionally, inhabiting the role of the "addict" or "alcoholic" can persuade or require others to begin taking on responsibilities that were once yours. One case where we saw this was with a stay-at-home mother whose husband never lifted a finger to take care of the kids. Talking with him didn't help, but when she began getting too drunk to take care of the kids, he was forced to do what she felt was his part. Even though it led to many other problems in the marriage, it achieved something she hadn't previously achieved by any other means. By taking on the role of alcoholic, she solved a problem she was having, and thus, staying in that role became more attractive to her. Based on this example, I'm sure you can imagine countless other ways this occurs.

Of course, few people purposely want to be unreliable and inhabit a substandard social role, but when they slip into that role by mistake, it sometimes comes with immediate, unexpected secondary benefits. They may not be aware of how it's happening, but life seems to become easier in some ways as an addict even if it becomes harder in other ways. This role can then become a major part of their preference for continued intoxication. Staying in this role may appear easier than leaving it behind.

An example of where people slip into the role by mistake, which is becoming more commonplace, is when people suffer a serious illness or injury or must undergo major surgery. They are placed on heavy doses of medications and laid up for a period of weeks or months. They may have gone from being capable, reliable, responsible people to being temporarily unable to care for themselves and their families. While being laid up certainly has its drawbacks, many people report enjoying the unexpected benefits of decreased responsibility, lowered expectations, and having others care for them. Whereas most people simply discontinue their medications and recover fully from their illness, injury, or surgery, an increasing percentage are reporting they have become "hooked" on their pain medications and are unable to come off them. While this may be in part due to the massive propaganda and misinformation being spread by the recovery society regarding opiates, personal preference still plays a crucial role. Staying sick and in pain and now "justifiably hooked" on strong painkillers is a way of continuing those unexpected benefits they experienced. Some consider their "new illness" (i.e., "addiction") to be a side effect and a continuation of their original problem. Staying laid up for these people seems much easier and preferable than working to get back on their feet.

There are also other lowered expectations with being intoxicated: you can tell people off, say what you want, and act inappropriately, and much of this behavior will be written off by others as "the booze/drugs talking." We call this benefit the "license to misbehave." Again, people don't purposely plan this out; they stumble into it and experience the benefits without realizing what's happened. Eventually, most substance users become implicitly aware of this benefit as they repeatedly get more leeway from others while they're intoxicated than they do when they're sober. This serves only to strengthen their preference for intoxication.

BEING UNAWARE OF BETTER OPTIONS

A preference for intoxication doesn't occur in a vacuum. To prefer is to like one option more than others (or from a "lesser of two evils" perspective, you hate it less than other options). Whether you like something more or hate it less, the result is that you prefer it. One manifestation of this principle arises with young and inexperienced people. They are often unaware of what else life has to offer in the way of rewards and become so impressed with the rewards of intoxication that they don't even bother to compare it to other options. Ignorance, in this case, has made intoxication exponentially preferable.

This lack of awareness of better options can be changed by seriously considering and exploring other ways of spending one's time. But until this possibility is seriously considered, the desire to be intoxicated will continue to be very strong.

LOW SELF-ESTEEM DISQUALIFIES OTHER OPTIONS

Thinking lowly of yourself and that you're incapable of successfully doing other things with your time will make any other way of living pale in comparison to a life of frequent intoxication; thus your preference for intoxication strengthens. It's a major factor in why people stay in dead-end jobs, troublesome relationships, and living in places they don't like. The fact that they don't think they are personally capable of getting a better job, finding a better relationship, or surviving in a new environment keeps them preferring substandard options. Substance use is no different; if you think you're incapable of living a satisfying life without it or with less of it, your preference for it increases.

THE "I'M AN OLD DOG WHO CAN'T LEARN NEW TRICKS" FACTOR

Some people believe that with age comes the inability to change and move on to new things. This belief leads people to mentally write off any other way of living even before they've considered it. It's the same as being youthful and ignorant of other options. It strengthens and cements a preference for intoxication. If you believe you can't do anything else (i.e., learn new tricks), it's no wonder your preference for intoxication seems so intractable; you've mentally disqualified any other options.

THE BATTLE FOR INDEPENDENCE

What happens when someone tells you that you can't have something? Of course, you end up wanting it more. This may sound like the forbidden fruit factor discussed in the primary reasons section. It is in some ways, but there are differences. The forbidden fruit factor applies to a culture or a specific age group, but the battle for independence applies directly and personally to each person. When people intervene, whether in the legal system or in the family, and say "You can't have this," they are directly trying to control you, and this strikes at your core as a free, autonomous individual. Your immediate reaction is the thought *screw you*, and then you attempt to do the forbidden activity either covertly or openly and brazenly to show your defiance, sending the message that you will not be controlled!

The unseen part of this dynamic is that it gives a new meaning to substance use. Becoming intoxicated now represents self-determination, individualism, and independence for substance users. It represents bucking the authority that's trying to control them. This is a completely different reason for use than the immediate physical pleasure of substance use. What's more, it becomes a distraction and draws substance users away from the natural processes by which they'd decrease their preference for intoxication over time. While you're asserting your independence with intoxication, you stop noticing that it may be getting boring and less pleasurable than it once was. Your reasons for use shift, and you don't realize that the only personally rewarding thing about it at that point is the way it gives a virtual middle finger to those who've tried to control you. This can increase or at least solidify your preference for intoxication.

REWARDS OF CHANGE ARE TOO DISTANT

Misinformation abounds that addiction is a lifelong battle or, at the very least, takes months if not years of misery to overcome. If you subscribe to this view, then continuing the same old pattern of substance use becomes much more attractive. This is a major factor for people who've been exposed to the recovery ideology, especially in treatment programs. If it will take years of misery to get to a better place but continued intoxication is even mildly satisfying now, then continued intoxication can appear to be the superior option and thus your preference strengthens.

The daily struggle can include emotional discomfort, such as depression and anxiety (which now often result in being dually diagnosed and medicated); a daily battle of resisting cravings; and a general sense that life will forever be miserable, boring, and full of drudgery. Add to that the even greater struggle related to the addiction battle while experiencing withdrawal. Traditionally, withdrawal has been seen for exactly what it is, a temporary medical condition that can last from three days to a few weeks depending on the substance involved and its rate of usage. However, an old theory of protracted withdrawal that lasts for months or even years, called post-acute withdrawal syndrome (PAWS) has recently gained popularity. The scientific evidence to support this theory is non-existent, but if you believe in it, then it makes sticking with daily intoxication appear to be the better option than quitting the drug that will cause withdrawal symptoms. Sadly, this view is strengthening many people's strong preference for intoxication even though they know it's coming at a high price.

WITHDRAWAL DISCOMFORT

When some drugs are used heavily and continuously over a long period, substance users may experience withdrawal symptoms upon discontinuing usage. From the most limited time perspective, in that moment, this makes further substance use more attractive. However, as mentioned above, withdrawal is easily and quickly addressed. On its own, withdrawal isn't a big deal, but when combined with several of the factors listed here, it becomes one more thing that makes further use attractive.

Withdrawal can create the illusion that the drug provides more benefits than it does. Since withdrawal can be a very painful state, substance users may become stressed, anxious, or depressed while going through it. Relieving the withdrawal by taking more of the drug then seems to relieve these symptoms. However, it wouldn't seem to provide these benefits if it hadn't created the withdrawal in the first place. That's why this factor is discussed in the secondary reasons section. This illusion exaggerates the powers of the drug, making it seem the more attractive and preferred option.

There are also practical implications of dealing with withdrawal. Many professionals see the prospect of taking a week off work to be treated as a major obstacle. They fear that others will find out or at least ask questions that put them in the position of having to lie. Some people identify withdrawal as the sole reason they continue to use substances.

If withdrawal is truly the only reason you continue using, then a trip to detox is all it will take to end the cycle; just do it! With no other reasons to use substances to the point of developing withdrawal syndrome again, your problem will be permanently solved. You can say you're going on vacation, and nobody needs to know the truth.

There are others who believe withdrawal is the only reason they keep using, but then they cycle back into heavy substance use after a successful detoxification from substances. When this happens, it is clear that this individual still has other reasons for using. He still prefers heavy substance use for reasons other than simply avoiding withdrawal. Those reasons are worth investigating

RELIEF FROM BOREDOM

Although this factor has been implicit in several places throughout this chapter, we waited to the end to discuss it because it bridges both categories of primary and secondary reasons. We've addressed it already, but it deserves another mention here because it is cited by so many substance users as a reason for their substance use.

For some young people or those who haven't been using substances long, it can be a primary reason because it's new and exciting. Substance use provides a "license to misbehave" and can lead to exciting situations as well even if those situations are troubling. Getting into trouble certainly isn't boring! However, this factor is highly related to substance users' perception of their other options. For those who believe they have nothing else available to them, it can seem the best path to relieving boredom.

For those who've severely limited their lives because of their substance use and are bored, continued use seems to relieve that boredom and thus can be a secondary reason for using. They rule out other options, or the exhaustion of the habit makes other options look impractical. As described in the sections on crowding out other options and the factor of habit, further substance use can then seem like the most efficient and perhaps only option to relieve boredom.

SHAME

Drowning in shame can be the most influential secondary reason people develop a strong preference for substance use. Such shame develops because of the social views that there's something wrong with people who prefer heavy, or even mild, use of substances that are big taboos (such as heroin and cocaine). When users believe their use has made them into a monster and permanently stained them and they've taken on an "addict identity," they may believe they have passed the point of no return. This makes continued substance use appear to be the only option. Much of the text deals with this factor because it affects so many people. We will help you to see beyond it.

THE SIMPLEST EXPLANATION IS THE MOST ACCURATE EXPLANATION

We have presented a listing of simple, logical reasons that people prefer substance use. Any of them can apply whether you have a weak or strong preference depending on how firmly they're part of your thinking. Those primary factors that represent direct benefits, such as the highs and pleasures and the power to disinhibit and relieve emotional pain, exist in comparison to other options. The less you believe that you can gain these benefits in other ways, the more your belief in these benefits will strengthen your preference for intoxication. You can change your belief in these benefits or at least their relative importance. Many of the secondary reasons are wrapped up in habit and self-perception; you can see your way past these factors as well. You've been using substances because you prefer to use substances, and *preferences can be changed*.

The point in presenting this discussion is to make obvious and bring into conscious awareness the truly simple and intuitive reasons for people's desire for intoxication. It's not helpful to overcomplicate this. Determine which reasons apply to you, but don't feel like you need to relate to everything discussed here. We want you to take Occam's razor to this issue, which is the scientific principle that says the simplest explanation is the most accurate one. So consider these questions: Do you want to get high/drunk all the time because you like the way it feels and think it provides you with myriads of benefits? Or do you want to get high/drunk all the time because you believe you have a mysterious and elusive disease or genetic factors that have never been shown to exist that have rendered you powerless?

REFERENCES

Capretto, L. (2015, August 3). Think drinking alcohol before bed can help you sleep? Not even close. Retrieved from http://www.huffingtonpost.com/entry/drinking-alcohol-sleep-impact_us_55bba1b4e4b0d4f33a02923e

Weil, A. (1986). *The natural mind* (pp. 18–20). New York, NY: Houghton-Mifflin Co.

CHAPTER 5:

CAUSES VS. REASONS

Throughout this book, we take on very specific and narrow ideas as well as broader, more abstract ideas. This chapter takes on one of the broader abstract ideas: the notion that human behavior is *caused* by some combination of biological and environmental determinants, leaving people with no real power of choice. This being *The Freedom Model*, we of course argue for the view that people are freely making their own choices. This issue is important to understand because it opens the way for people to change their lives and is essential to understanding *The Freedom Model*. Noted alcohol researcher Dr. Nick Heather once commented on the folly of deterministic theories of humanity:

> It is interesting to note that primitive man ... made the mistake of describing inanimate objects as though they were men and women; for example, the sun was personified and given the ability to plan his course across the sky. I would claim that it is equally primitive to make the reverse mistake and describe men and women as though they were inanimate objects. (Heather & Robertson, 1981, p. 21)

There is a fatal flaw in the practice of trying to understand the "causes" of human behavior in the same way that we understand the causes of an apple falling from a tree or some other purely physical phenomenon. The flaw is that people are equated with unconscious things when analyzed this way. But there's an important difference between people and unconscious things: consciousness. People have something nonphysical that guides their behavior; they have thoughts, ideas, beliefs, goals, and intentions. Most simply put, people have *reasons* in their minds for behaving the way they do. Unconscious objects have no such

ability. This distinction between people and things is crucially important. The movement of *things* is *caused* by other things acting upon
them; the *behavior of people* is chosen by themselves for various *reasons*.

Imagine you're standing on the street waiting for a bus and checking
your email on your phone when a man comes up and sucker-punches
you. The force of the punch is so strong and unexpected that it knocks
you to the ground. Your phone is lying there next to you; he reaches
down to grab it. What do you do? Try to stop him? Let him take the
phone and run away? Think about your answer.

It's safe to assume that some of our readers would let him get away
with the phone, and some would fight him for it.

On the victim's side of this experience, one part of the scenario is
caused, and another part is *reasoned*. To understand the difference between the two is to understand your nature as a human being, and how
the principle of cause and effect applies to you.

In the first part of this sequence, a physical object (a man's fist) strikes
another physical object (your body). The strike of the fist is a *cause*; the
effect is that your body is sent to the ground and your phone is knocked
out of your hand. Your attacker *caused* you to fall and lose hold of your
phone. This is an instance of pure materialistic cause and effect that
applies to all physical things.

The next event in this sequence is far different. It's the part where you
choose the movements of your body. It's the part where *reasons* come into play. Instead of being pushed around like an inanimate object, you
choose what your body does next; you have *control* over this part of
the experience.

Option 1: You like to avoid confrontation. You value your phone, but
you also think that a man who's willing to sucker punch you to steal
a phone isn't worth the fight. You think *This could get worse; he could
be crazy and have a weapon. Let it go; it's just a phone.* So you recoil a
bit and play too hurt to retaliate, letting him make off with the phone.
You chose this as the best course of action, based on specific *reasons*
held within your own mind.

Option 2: You think *Oh no, it'll be so hard to replace my phone. I can't
deal with that; he'll have all my personal information and can really screw
up my life. I might be able to take this guy.* So you reach quickly for the

phone and tussle with your attacker. You chose this as the best course of action based on your personal *reasons* held within your own mind.

Whichever way you go (and there are certainly many other options and potential reasons supporting those different courses of action), your behavior at this stage is not *caused* precisely because there are multiple possibilities available to you and it is only your own thinking/*reasoning* that will determine your course of action. Your thinking is under your own control. If we put three people (of the same physical build) into this same scenario, all three would be *caused* to have the same initial *movement* by the sucker punch (to fall and drop their phone). However, all three could then respond with completely different *behaviors* based on completely different *reasons*. Each person could have her own unique mental prediction of what actions will make her happiest with the outcome. None of the potential reactions are *caused*.

Option 3: As an example of another possibility, one person thinks *I'll look like a wimp if I let this guy push me around* and then proceeds to choose an entirely different behavior; he grabs the phone and beats his attacker senseless with it, breaking the phone in the process. His behaviors are chosen for completely different *reasons* than our first two subjects. He barely considers the phone or his safety. Instead, he thinks happiness is found in maintaining a tough reputation.

When you're in the position of being physically hit without warning, you are at the mercy of the principle of cause and effect that applies to all matter; your body will move in a way that you clearly do not choose. A trained scientist could predict how far a lifeless ball will travel when hit by calculating the various relevant factors, such as the force of the hit, density of the object applying the force, weight of the ball, wind resistance, and so on. The same goes for calculating the movement of a human body hit by another object. But there's a limit to the scientist's powers of prediction.

Whereas the scientist could predict the entire trajectory of a ball until it comes to a final resting place, he can predict only the initial trajectory of a human body to the point that the person *chooses what to think and how to react*. That part is unpredictable because it is ruled by the individual's free will and mental autonomy. Lifeless objects don't have these attributes; they belong only to the creature known as man. *A baseball can't choose to turn around and hit the batter who knocked it out of the park.*

Consider what happens when gasoline vapors contact a flame. There is an explosion of fire. The gasoline doesn't think *I'm mad; I'm gonna explode*. Nor does it have the alternative option of thinking *I shouldn't explode; I don't want the other chemicals to think I'm unstable*. It is a lifeless, mindless substance. It can't think. It can't choose. It can only be caused to do what its nature as a lifeless, mindless, unstable substance dictates it will do when it contacts some external catalyzing force, such as a flame. A hundred out of a hundred times that you put a lit match to a can of gasoline, it will ignite and explode. It has no choice.

There's good reason to parse this out. We hear endless talk about "the causes of addiction," as if people are the same as lifeless, mindless objects without the power of choice. "Cause" is a strong word that evokes simple cause-and-effect relationships devoid of choice, and the psychological establishment has used it *in this exact sense* throughout the 20th century. This is best typified by the work of the popular behaviorist B. F. Skinner, who spoke of stimuli, reinforcers, conditioning, and environmental determinism, which says that human behavior is not freely chosen but is determined by previous events. We have discussed the potential actions of two lifeless objects (a baseball and a can of gasoline) to introduce this discussion, and that may seem odd. However, our *personification* of lifeless objects was necessary to highlight the absurdity of its counterpart in psychology: the *depersonification* of human beings. What Skinner and many social researchers have sought to do is to understand human beings as if they're unconscious objects that are pushed around by the universe, with no more control in life than a feather in the wind. At worst, the behaviorists see us in the same way they see unconscious objects. At best, they compare us to lab rats, conditioned to behave in a certain way with no say in the matter.

Linguist Noam Chomsky summed this up in his 1971 review of Skinner's aptly titled book *Beyond Freedom and Dignity*:

> It is a fact, Skinner maintains, that "behavior is shaped and maintained by its consequences" and that as the consequences contingent on behavior are investigated, more and more "they are taking over the explanatory functions previously assigned to personalities, states of mind, feelings, traits of character, purposes, and intentions." (p. 18)

To hammer home the point, he cites the following from Skinner:

> As a science of behavior adopts the strategy of physics and biology, the autonomous agent to which behavior has traditionally been attributed is replaced by the environment—the environment in which the species evolved and in which the behavior of the individual is shaped and maintained. (p. 184)

Chomsky wasn't fond of this view and saw it as decidedly unscientific:

> In support of his belief that science will demonstrate that behavior is entirely a function of antecedent events, Skinner notes that physics advanced only when it "stopped personifying things" and attributing to them "wills, impulses, feelings, purposes," and so on (p. 8). Therefore, he concludes, the science of behavior will progress only when it stops personifying people and avoids reference to "internal states." No doubt physics advanced by rejecting the view that a rock's wish to fall is a factor in its "behavior," because in fact a rock has no such wish. For Skinner's argument to have any force, he must show that people have wills, impulses, feelings, purposes, and the like no more than rocks do. If people do differ from rocks in this respect, then a science of human behavior will have to take account of this fact.

Skinner thinks the only way to study man scientifically is to apply the methods meant for understanding animals and lifeless matter. Yet man has important differences from animals and lifeless matter as Chomsky points out; man has consciousness, so the science must take that into account, not reject it. Joseph Wood Krutch took aim at this same error in his 1954 book *The Measure of Man*, which was a reaction to one of Skinner's earlier works, *Walden Two*:

> Perhaps Hamlet was nearer right than Pavlov. Perhaps the exclamation "How like a god!" is actually more appropriate than "How like a dog! How like a rat! How like a machine!" Perhaps we have been deluded by the fact that the methods employed for the study of man have been for the most part those originally devised for the study of machines or the study of rats, and are capable, therefore, of detecting and measuring only those characteristics which the three do have in common. (pp. 32–33)

The deterministic behaviorist belief boils down to the idea that people do not have free will and that all behavior is determined by the interaction of past conditioning, current environment, and genetic makeup. In this view, the mind is a useless illusion. We think we choose, but we do not, according to this deterministic model of human behavior. To most readers (but not all), this will seem like an outlandish viewpoint, and you may wonder why we are spending any time discussing it. You should know that this view wasn't held by just Skinner. It was, and is, held by a great many in the field of psychology/psychiatry and by many who push the popular theories of addiction you've learned.

THE "CAUSES OF ADDICTION"

Every time you hear people talk about "the causes of addiction," they're expressing a similar deterministic viewpoint. They may not explicitly articulate their anti-freewill position or even understand that this is what they're expressing, but it's easily found in what they say *and what they don't say*. They discuss their pet theories of what causes addiction, and each of the causes falls outside your mind either in the physical or social environment; in some biological realm, such as genes or a "hijacked brain"; or in some mental disorder of which you, the substance user, are a victim. Then, they speak of combating these causes. Rarely if ever do they discuss your thoughts, beliefs, or ability to make different choices in any way. In fact, they directly claim that you are incapable of choosing to think or act differently.

The social and environmental causes of addiction are the ones most often addressed by the recovery society and addiction disease proponents, and this is straightforward to understand. They say it's the drug- and alcohol-filled environment and social circle that's causing you to use substances. It's that you have no "healthy relationships" with the right people. It's that your environment doesn't seem to reward sobriety or you have a lack of opportunities. This all causes you to use substances and be unable to stop because, even if you try, your environment will trigger you to crave and relapse.

The solution to this, from a cause-based perspective, is to create an environment that will *cause* you to stay sober. They say you need to be in a supportive environment of recovering people and to avoid so-called triggers to use, such as people, places, and things associated with your past substance use. In this new environment, you must spend all your free time with friends from support group meetings who are abstaining and avoid even the sight of a bar or places where drugs might be sold or used and all old substance-using friends.

Notice what isn't mentioned in that view: your thoughts and beliefs about substances and whether you still like to use them to the same degree and your views on whether you could be happier without substance use. No, treatment professionals don't bother with those things. The main goal is to create an environment where you won't be *caused* to use drugs or alcohol by things outside of yourself. For some of you, they'll even recommend inpatient treatment for 6 to 18 months and then moving into "sober-living" communities for even longer, where you are required to attend meetings every day and be pressured by the social environment to swear off drugs forever. They'll teach your family to be "supportive," which means that your family has to learn to be part of creating and pushing you into, and not letting you out of, the safe environment meant to *cause* you to stay sober. They see the cause of your use and the cause of your quitting as external to your mind. That is, with this theory and approach, they treat you as a passive, lifeless victim of circumstances and your environment.

Those who believe in the causes of addiction don't believe that you have any power to directly change your thinking regarding substance use, but they do think that, with the proper deterrents (threats) and reinforcers, they can manipulate you into "complying with treatment," which comprises going to meetings and counseling sessions and reorganizing your social life around this recovery "safe space" they create. So any deep talks about what you think and believe are focused on convincing you that you're powerless and that you need to let them choose where you can and cannot be, whom you can and cannot be around, and what you can and cannot do. They aim to keep you in the situation they devise to *cause* you to stay sober. This is nothing more than behaviorism and environmental determinism.

Skinner dreamed of creating a world in which behavioral scientists would meticulously design the perfect environmental/social conditions and reinforcers to cause people to behave perfectly and peacefully. For Skinner, this was only a dream, but the recovery society has tried to put this into action on a smaller scale for people with substance use problems. The fact that "compliance with treatment" is the primary problem they face when treating substance users tells you their strategy is horribly misguided. People have free will, and if they choose to think in ways that create the desire to use substances, they aren't going to comply with treatment. When they decide they'd be happier drunk or high, they leave the safe spaces, they don't call their sponsors/counselors, and they become *noncompliant*.

Then, there are those treatment professionals who obsess over *biological causes*. They are sure something is wrong with the brains of heavy substance users that will cause them to desire substances for the rest of their lives. Their solution is often a medication, such as Suboxone, methadone, or naltrexone. They believe that by manipulating the brain with a pharmaceutical, the heavy substance user will no longer desire substances. Their belief has nothing to do with pairing these drugs with any discussion or information that would help the "helpless addict" think differently. Because of the current "opioid crisis," high-level politicians along with treatment professionals and pharmaceutical corporations are currently lobbying for medications, such as Suboxone, to be handed out on demand in pharmacies. They are also furiously working to devise versions of these treatments that can be injected and will last from one to six months or longer (e.g., Vivitrol). The reason for this move from daily dosages of pills to long-acting injectable doses is that these treatments have the same problem as our previous examples of treatment have: most substance users don't comply; they stop taking their pills and return to getting high. Even those who continue to take the pills have very low long-term success rates. And even with the long-lasting versions, many people just switch to using substances whose effects aren't blunted by the pharmaceutical, or they live in the mental torture of unfulfilled desire until the injection loses its effectiveness. Desire is a product of the mind, not the brain.

Next, there are those professionals who are obsessed with the *psychological causes* of addiction. They include mood disorders, such as depression, anxiety, and trauma/PTSD. The way it's told by treatment professionals is that these "co-occurring disorders" or "underlying causes" leave substance users with an absolute need for substance use that they will continue to feed until someone other than themselves can properly treat their conditions. Here's how a doctor who works with high-priced rehabs describes the plight of people with substance use problems:

> The vast majority of people with these co-occurring disorders do not receive treatment for both their substance abuse problem and their other co-occurring conditions, which is why most treatment programs have high relapse rates.
>
> If you don't treat the co-occurring condition, then the person is going to continue to have a need to medicate, and if their prescription medications don't meet their needs adequately, then they're going to begin to self-medicate again. (Leeds, 2012)

These treatment programs enroll substance users in every kind of therapy possible, diagnose mental illness, prescribe psychiatric meds, and try to root out hidden traumas to indirectly cause the substance user to stop wanting and using substances. Modern "alternative treatment programs" have fully embraced this strategy, and yet they still have the same dismal success rates as the traditional 12-Step based programs. Compliance with treatment is yet again another obstacle in this model. These treatment professionals often can't seem to *cause* their patients to continue attending therapy and group counseling, use their "alternative coping methods," or keep taking their psychiatric meds on schedule. What's more, many people comply with all these treatment methods, yet they still find themselves desiring and using substances. In this case, when questioned, the believers in the causal power of co-occurring disorders will explain that they simply haven't found the right cocktail of meds and therapies yet.

The issue for the individual to figure out is simply this: Will further heavy substance use make me happy enough or not? The struggling individual has not mentally resolved this so, whether the "underlying causes" have been resolved or not, he may still desire heavy substance use because those conditions aren't "causes." They may be reasons to use substances for some people, but the fact that everything is going well in life may also be a reason to use substances heavily.

We need to make a note about "psychological causes of addiction" to be clear about what our stance is. Heavy substance use is absolutely a matter of psychology; people want it and choose to do it *because of how they think*. It is a matter of the mind and thus psychological. *The Freedom Model* stance is that people are free to choose to think differently and doing so will change the way they feel and behave, so in that sense, substance use is a matter of psychology. However, when treatment professionals speak of psychological causes, they are referring to mental disorders or diseases, which they believe to be out of your control and the cause of your substance use.

PROBABILITIES

There are many more proposed causes of addiction, and the fact is that none of them truly hold water. When the claim is that one thing causes another, it should be readily observable and verifiable in every case; yet it never is with substance use. Causal relationships are not subjective by nature. If we told you putting a lit match to an open tank of gasoline "causes" a fiery explosion, you could test this claim. Assuming you survived the explosion, you could do it a hundred times, and it will always result in an explosion. But if we told you that poverty *causes* addiction and you went to a poor neighborhood to survey 100 people, you might find somewhere between 5 and 20 people who currently fit the diagnosis of addiction. Why weren't the other 80 people caused to use substances heavily? Then you could go to a high-priced treatment center and find nothing but people who grew up in wealth and luxury. What *caused* them to become *addicted* if not poverty? Or say we told you trauma *causes* addiction. If you rounded up 100 people with high trauma scores, only 15 of them might also be alcoholics. This is what the research shows. Yet people confidently claim that trauma *causes addiction*, as if the individual has no choice in the matter, and is simply fated to use substances relentlessly after they've been hurt. In fact, this response to trauma is the exception, not the rule—the other 85 are not "addicted." Are they superheroes with magical powers somehow able to flout the law that trauma *causes* addiction?

These claims of causes are based on nothing more than probabilities and correlations. A reliable percentage of people with depression or anxiety problems also have substance use problems (20%). This correlation doesn't indicate that depression and anxiety *cause* addiction or even that these phenomena are related in any meaningful way. If there is a relationship, it could be that some depressed people think that getting high is a good way to deal with their depression, or they may even think it relieves the depression. Or it could be that heavy substance use itself worsens a person's life in ways that lead to depression. There could be any number of *reasons* that some people with depression also use substances heavily, but there is nothing that shows heavy substance use is a necessary result of depression in the same way that an explosion is the necessary result of putting a lit match to gasoline.

To put these correlations into perspective, consider this passage from Krutch's *The Measure of Man*:

> Let us imagine an intruder from Mars totally ignorant of earthly human nature and suspended above our earth at just the point which will enable him to perceive mass movements. It is a sweltering day in August and his attention is attracted to the area of metropolitan New York. From the center of the city long lines are streaming out toward the sea and converging at various points on what we call the shore of Long Island. The Martian observer is a competent one. He has witnessed this phenomenon on various other occasions and has carefully noted the circumstances which surround it. By now he is ready to announce a law: Whenever the temperature rises above a certain point the stream begins to flow and the higher the temperature, the heavier the stream. He has not yet plotted the curve which will give an approximate formula to express the relation between temperature and magnitude of movement. It obviously will not be a straight line because the temperature effect increases as it rises toward a certain point and then declines again. But that can wait. It is obvious now that, almost as surely as an apple falls, thousands of people go to Coney Island when it gets hot.
>
> His law is dependable enough to be relied on for practical purposes by all who are responsible for any kind of vehicular

traffic. Meanwhile, however, you and I may stay at home. However inexorable the general law is presumed to be, it is by no means certain that any given individual will obey it. You and I decide, or seem to ourselves to decide, whether or not we will do our part in making the law hold.

An individual is free, but the group of which he is a part is not. Any given man's destiny is to some extent in his own hands; but the destiny of mankind is predetermined. You or I may really refuse to go to Coney Island; but a great many people certainly will go.

If this really is true, it means for the individual at least something. It means that so far as his personal conduct and his personal life are concerned he may really and effectively behave as though he were endowed with free will; that in fact, as an individual, he is. It relieves him of the kind of despair which settles on many men when they accept what they have been increasingly taught, namely that they are simply the product of their time and their circumstances. (1954/1970, pp. 151–153)

All the claims about the causes of addiction suffer the same issues as the Martian's claim that a rise in temperature *causes* people to go to the beach. While a high temperature creates a condition in which many may think it a good choice to go to the beach, everyone is still choosing whether to go to the beach based on his or her own thoughts, preferences, goals, priorities, beliefs, and so on. The temperature doesn't compel anyone to go. The contents and powers of each person's mind are used to make him or her choose to go, not go, or not even consider it.

So it is also with substance use. Depression or poverty may be conditions in which it is probable that more people will choose to use substances heavily, but that choice is not the uniform response to depression and poverty by any means, nor is anyone forced to use substances. People can still choose their own path.

The determinists who are particularly astute will say that the causes are many and complex. They will combine the three categories of causes into one, calling addiction a *biopsychosocial* condition (biological, psychological, and social/environmental). This term accounts for all the pet causes and, more important, covers for the failure of each of these categories of causes to predict anyone's substance use habits and/or habit change. It also covers for the failures of the various treatments. When treatment for trauma doesn't affect the choice to use substances, then maybe treatment for depression will, or a better support network, or a sober-living home, or a combination of all these things and more to combat the complex of causes. You get the point, right? The biopsychosocial model is no better than the failed theories it combines. Treatment professionals claim that they are sure that the "addict" is the helpless pawn of several "causes," none of which can be proven to have a causal connection. Then, to combat these many unverifiable causes, they throw everything at addiction and hope something sticks.

There's one thing they don't try: appealing to people's innate ability to think differently about their options and make new decisions.

MIND MATTERS

Luckily, while many of the movers and shakers of psychology/psychiatry were studying everything from a deterministic point of view and ignoring the mind, there have been many others who chose to look at the human mind and the power it wields. As a result, there are mountains of evidence demonstrating that our inner life, which comprises our thoughts, beliefs, intentions, and reasoning, which all emanate from our minds, directs our feelings and behaviors. Whereas the determinists believe people need to be conditioned and caused to change by external things, plenty of evidence has mounted showing that the self-directed act of seeking and processing new information can cause dramatic changes in the way people feel and behave. The intuitive way people go through life, thinking through their problems, putting effort into acquiring information, and devising and implementing solutions, works. We don't need to wait for the universe to change us as the determinists like to tell us; we are quite capable of changing ourselves now.

Much of psychology has ignored consciousness, or mind, which has prompted many prominent psychological researchers to fight back, such as Edwin Locke, who wrote in 1995:

Acknowledging the existence and the nature of man's consciousness, that is, his identity, is the only rational base on which to build a viable science of psychology. The fundamental error of behaviorism was to reject the human mode of cognition both with respect to content and with respect to approach. Its content allowed only external events as explanations and its method allowed only the measurement of the environment and behavior. At root behaviorism represents a form of mysticism—not religious mysticism but materialist mysticism; it reflects an unlimited faith in the power of the materialistic approach to understanding man. By faith I do not simply refer to the fact that this view lacks objective evidence—rather it is advocated in clear disregard of contrary evidence. In this respect behaviorism is profoundly nonobjective. It was able to rob man of freedom and dignity only by denying the self-evident fact of his mind. Psychology should not apologize for the fact that its subject matter does not consist of inanimate matter. It should start by honestly acknowledging what man is. In short, it is time we took consciousness seriously. To insure an objective approach to the study of man, it is man's rational faculty, his capacity to think, that psychology must take as its starting point. This is the actual source of his freedom and his dignity. (p. 272)

And some of the movers and shakers have finally begun to take the mind seriously. A group of highly respected psychological researchers, led by a former head of the American Psychological Association, officially abandoned modern psychology's focus on past determinants in 2013. In their opening line, they sum up the present state of psychology:

Much of the history of psychology has been dominated by a framework in which people and animals are driven by the past. In this picture, past history, present circumstance, and inner states drive behavior, much as in a classical dynamical system the vector sum of forces operating on and within a particle uniquely determines its trajectory.

And in this 24-page paper (long for a peer-reviewed journal article; Seligman, Railton, Baumeister, & Sripada, 2013), they bring mounds of evidence to make the case for the opposite:

> We suggest an alternate framework in which people … draw on experience to update a branching array of evaluative prospects that fan out before them. Action is then selected in light of their needs and goals. The past is not a force that drives them but a resource from which they selectively extract information about the prospects they face. These prospects can include not only possibilities that have occurred before but also possibilities that have never occurred—and these new possibilities often play a decisive role in the selection of action. (p.119)

Instead of being a helpless pawn of the past, caused to behave in certain ways, they think that "prospection" is a more accurate description of how humans behave. As they describe it in this way, prospection is seeking out, imagining, and projecting the potential outcomes of various options and choosing what seems best to you. In addition to justifying this view with ample research, they call it "common sense." We agree because we believe our own theory underlying *The Freedom Model* to be similar and based on common sense. For years, we've been teaching our retreat guests that they are choosing their substance use because they see it as their best available option for happiness. The theory of prospection says the same thing.

FOCUS ON REASONS, NOT CAUSES

We've mentioned having "reasons" for behavior a few times throughout this chapter, and it's time we fully connect the dots. Cause is a strong word; it implies determinism and lack of choice. It equates human beings with unthinking objects or animals and leads people to ignore their ability to rethink their options and make new choices. Most of all, it makes people into helpless victims, hoping and praying that the "causes" of their behavior will go away or that the environment will somehow change in a way that stops causing them to want and do the same things. To the degree that people hold onto any hope for change under the cause-based view, their efforts to change are directed at finding a better environment, the right medication, or the proper therapies that will change them.

The caused-based view is not only wrong; it's impractical. There will always be "triggers" no matter where you are. You may run into an old substance-using friend, see an ad for alcohol, or suffer a new trauma or some other bout of emotional pain. If you see these things as causes, then it's off to the races with further heavy substance use.

Many readers will relate to the idea that psychological disorders, such as depression, cause them to use substances. You may have experienced feeling depressed and subsequently turned to substance use to feel better. *We do not deny your experience*, but we endeavor to explain it more accurately so you can understand it in a way that facilitates change. Is this a case of having no choice and being caused to use substances by depression, or is it a case of having learned that substance use is enjoyable and then evaluating substance use as a good option to find some happiness in that moment? The first case makes you a helpless victim of depression. The second case makes you an active chooser, which means that, with new thoughts, information, and beliefs, you are not helplessly fated to repeatedly make the same choices when life throws you curveballs.

Thinking clearly about this issue matters, and we're now going to make a hard recommendation: stop thinking about the *causes* of addiction and start thinking about your *reasons* for substance use. Causes are outside of your direct volitional control. Reasons are thoughts in your mind and under your direct volitional control. You can rethink, reevaluate, and change the reasoning that leads you to see substance use as your best available option. You can find positive reasons that support adjusting your preference for substance use if you look for them. Of course, while you're looking to address causes, your gaze is focused outside yourself at the reasons that tip the scales in favor of heavy substance use.

Addressing causes is an eternal war, each day bringing a new battle. Addressing reasons is far more efficient in ending the war in one fell swoop. Getting back to the depression example, you can try to eradicate every circumstance that might lead you into depression hoping that you won't ever be *caused to use by depression* again. This could go on for the rest of your life, or you could address the reasoning that connects depression to heavy substance use. Once you're sure that depression is no longer a good reason for substance use, it will no longer "cause" you to use substances. You will still want to address your depression, but it will no longer carry a threat of involuntary substance use.

Of course, there can be many reasons that people prefer to use substances. We covered some of the most common ones in chapter 4. Reevaluating those reasons is an individual task that will vary from person to person. To enact *The Freedom Model* as a solution to your problems, you need to understand that you are indeed free and to know that your most fundamental exercise of that freedom is at the level of thought. Then get to work rethinking your own reasons that support heavy substance use, and set out to discover reasons that support an adjustment in your substance use. Nothing outside yourself can do it for you—no person, pill, or program can cause you to change your thinking. It's up to you. *The Freedom Model* is here to provide you with the information and ideas that you can most efficiently use for this task.

REFERENCES

Chomsky, N. (1971, December 30). The case against B. F. Skinner. Retrieved from http://www.nybooks.com/articles/1971/12/30/the-case-against-bf-skinner/

Heather, N., & Robertson, I. (1981). *Controlled drinking*. New York, NY: Methuen & Co.

Krutch, J. W. (1970). *The measure of man*. New York, NY: Grosset & Dunlap.

Leeds, A. M. (2012, September 5). *Q6: Why is EMDR an important protocol in treating addicts?—EMDR with Dr. Andrew M. Leeds Ph.D.* [Video file] Retrieved from https://www.youtube.com/watch?v=C9Eqr_SqYYk

Locke, E. A. (1995). Beyond determinism and materialism, or isn't it time we took consciousness seriously? *Journal of Behavior Therapy and Experimental Psychiatry, 26*(3), 265–273. https://doi.org/10.1016/0005-7916(95)00026-V

Seligman, M., Railton, P., Baumeister, R., & Sripada, C. (2013). Navigating into the future or driven by the past. *Perspectives on Psychological Science, 8*(2), 119–141. https://doi.org/10.1177/1745691612474317

CHAPTER 6:

LEARNED CONNECTIONS

"My anxiety causes me to use."

"I was raped as a child, and the trauma causes me to use."

"My depression causes me to drink more."

"I don't like drugs. I self-medicate when I feel stressed out or sad."

"I drank like a fish after my dad died. The grief made me too weak and triggered a relapse. I won't be able to get back into recovery until I work through my issues."

"I have a co-occurring disorder that causes my addiction."

"I must keep using because I have some baggage I haven't dealt with. Can you help me figure out what that stuff is?"

—Common learned connection quotes from St. Jude Retreats guests

WHAT ARE LEARNED CONNECTIONS?

We define *learned connections* as any beliefs that implicitly or explicitly causally connect other life problems to substance use. The causation goes in the direction of a life problem causing a person to use substances. We hear about these learned connections all the time. We hear them in the news, in academia, in novels, and in casual conversation; we hear them everywhere. But learned connections are stated with the most frequency in the recovery subculture where the belief is that something outside people can *cause* them to use substances uncontrollably. We assume you have also heard statements like the quotes above, and you may even believe there is some validity to them. We certainly did.

In 1989 when our research project began at Jerry Brown's home on Baldwin Road, we believed that people needed to find happiness if they wanted to remain sober. That was a core idea of the program we were developing at the time. We promoted the idea that happiness is necessary for sustained sobriety and that one was dependent on the other. When you break one problem (unhappiness), you *automatically* break the other (addiction). For example, let's say you lose your job and become depressed. We held the belief that depression was dangerous to your sobriety and that there was an automatic causal connection between your level of depression and your drinking or drugging habits. We said that if you stay depressed, you would eventually drink or drug. Our belief held that you would not able to control that first drink or hit if you stay depressed. I can remember telling our guests that "If you aren't happy and sober, well then beware; you will be driven back to your drug of choice."

AA has its own versions of learned connections. AA states that a belief in God is necessary to recover from alcoholism. In this view, the two are mentally connected, belief in God and sobriety. Lose faith in one, and you lose the other. It also states that "character defects" will cause problematic drinking if you don't continually "work on them." It also says that "you're only as sick as your secrets," meaning you must divulge your deepest, darkest secrets to other AA members to stay sober. In the earliest days of our program development, we fell for these ideas and didn't question them.

But then I (Mark) realized something obvious. At that time, I had been sober a few years, and as I reflected on the prior years, I saw myself as I had been, an unhappy, dissatisfied person. In fact, the first two years of my sobriety were awful, but even in that depressed and lonely state, it never occurred to me to drink or drug, not once. I had made the commitment to no longer use substances, and consequently, I didn't use them or think about using them. I no longer saw alcohol or drugs as a solution to my problems. Like many people, I had trauma and abuse in my past. I was depressed for most of my life, and I had severe anxiety issues. Yet I didn't drink or take drugs once I realized that they did not have anything to add to my life anymore. Simply put, life continued to be enormously challenging and difficult for me for some time as I matured and moved on from reckless substance use. This self-evident realization, that my sobriety was not automatically dependent on my level of happiness, challenged the connection beliefs I had learned and promoted. I knew that it was time for me to investigate the learned connection theory.

As I observed the people who were coming to us for help, I began to see it more clearly. I watched just as many people become highly successful and happy in their lives relapse into heavy substance use as I saw people who were miserable and unhappy relapse. These people would say their lives got "too good" or that they have a habit of sabotaging themselves whenever they experience immense happiness and success. These people didn't fit the narrative that happiness ensures sobriety.

What most intrigued me was the many people I knew personally who had experienced immense stress and trauma (e.g., the loss of a child or spouse, diagnosis of a terminal illness, or having a severe, debilitating injury) who were not *caused* to drink and drug heavily. Most of the people I watched go through these devastating situations, including people I knew in AA, did not drink and drug as a result. Obviously, they did not believe that heavy substance use would help them with their trauma, so they didn't do it. I concluded that the theory that trauma, stress, and depression *cause* substance use must be completely wrong and that getting this right was vitally important.

HOW BELIEFS FORM AND WHY THEY ARE HARD TO CHALLENGE

When we are born, we are mental blank slates. We don't hate, we don't love, and we don't have knowledge of the world. If not for those around us, we would perish. We are completely dependent on others to learn our worldview, and from there, we develop our own perspectives.[3] This is an important point. We learn as we navigate life. We learn our values, wants, needs, talents, abilities, and eventually, entire worldview—and in the United States, that worldview includes an addiction- and recovery-centered culture. Within that recovery ideology,

---

3. Some readers may see this as being a contradiction to mental autonomy, but it is not. Our social environment provides us with many potential ideas, but we are still the choosers of what we do and don't believe.

we learn that stress, trauma, and the like cause substance use. For people who do not come from our culture, this learned connection does not exist, or they have a subtler version of it. Think about that. If not for the influence of the recovery society within our culture, very few people would ever connect stress, trauma, or any outside force to the use of substances. *If that connection is learned, that means things such as trauma, stress, depression, and anxiety are NOT automatic triggers for substance use.* And, most important to you, these connections can be unlearned.

You see, the way ideas are stated matters. If you say that stress *causes* use and that this is especially true in a special subgroup of people called *addicts* and *alcoholics*, then you have just created a powerful myth, complete with the central beliefs of that myth and its characters. The myth is then corroborated by some anecdotal evidence that seems to prove the idea true. For example, Tanya is stressed out, so she runs away and shoots heroin. Then a few days after her episode, she says, "I got high because I was so stressed out!" But is this really an inherent truth about human behavior, that everyone will automatically shoot heroin into their veins if they are stressed? Or did Tanya learn this pattern of choices in health class, on TV, through a brother who went to rehab a few years back, or from a therapist she was mandated to see after a DUI? If none these factors existed in Tanya's life, would she still believe feeling stressed automatically led her to uncontrollable heroin use and inevitable addiction? The answer is no. It would not occur to her to make that mental connection. Tanya learned the idea that being stressed and shooting up are connected; her self-doubt and well-meaning helpers validated that she's too weak to withstand this connection, and now the connection is part of her self-image and feels real. Connections like these are entirely learned concepts, not inherent, unavoidable human truths. If left to develop her own opinions, Tanya might simply find heroin to be pleasurable, but she would never see it as a solution to anything other than a desire for momentary pleasure.

There are entire societies that do not believe in these learned connections. There are people who grow up in drug-infested neighborhoods who experience a host of stressors and traumatic events and never get high or drunk in response to their struggles. As researchers, we can't arbitrarily throw out those examples that don't fit with the narrative, especially when we consider that those examples make up the majority of people. Many people experience trauma in their lives, and all people experience stress, pain, and sadness throughout their lives. Yet most of them do not drink or drug problematically. Rates of addiction/alcoholism would be significantly higher if these problems did cause substance use.

The operative word in the theory is *cause*. If stress *caused* Tanya to use heroin, then she has no recourse; she is doomed every time she feels stress, *not just some of the time, but every time!* That is the defining characteristic of a *cause*—it's a one-to-one relationship. If people are caused to use, they are powerless not to use, every single time. Choice has no role in the matter. They are automatons. This is exactly what the current thinking is in the treatment industry and our society.

But Tanya is not an automaton; in her case, she used stress as a *reason* to use. She does not understand the serious implications of labeling her reason as a cause. Reasons are not the same thing as causes, as we discussed in chapter 5. Reasons require humans to think, to *reason* with their minds, and to search for the value and benefits of a choice. To use reasoning powers is a defining characteristic of the human mind. Even though she feels helplessly caused to use, she is still choosing to do so. And worse, she's doing it with a belief system that ensures she'll keep making the same choices no matter what the outcome.

We know substance use is a personal, internal decision everyone makes and addiction is a self-created habit. But, like our guests, we too struggled with simple explanations because we did not understand that these learned connections were contrived concepts. We didn't fully understand at that time that substance use was a choice based on the relative benefits we personally saw in such habits. These learned connections were fabricated explanations used to explain why good people chose patterns of substance use that ended disastrously.

In the absence of a good explanation for something troubling (like addiction), people either mine for the truth through logic and extensive research, or they latch onto whatever is most visible regardless of its logic. Humanity has done both since the dawn of time. For example, the belief that depression can cause substance use is just as fictional as saying that villagers' sins caused a drought. But beliefs are incredibly powerful and can lead people to believe and behave accordingly. Oftentimes, beliefs are an attempt to explain situations people find troubling or inexplicable.

THE HOPI

The Hopi, a Native American tribe in the Southwestern United States, conducted a ritual for millennia to ask the gods for rain in times of drought. They also conducted the rain dance annually in August, the Southwest's driest time of the year. They would place snakes (some venomous) in their mouths as they danced the rain dance. After the dance, the snakes were released in four directions to carry the message of the need for water to the gods at the four corners of the world. To a Hopi, this belief system and ritual ensured enough rain would fall for their continued survival. As time has passed, knowledge of the reality of meteorology and its weather patterns, jet streams, and moisture dynamics has made its way into their culture. Thus, the annual rain dance has become more of a historic ritual than a plea for rain. With knowledge, came a change in technique and beliefs (Laubin & Laubin, 1989).

To a turn-of-the-century Hopi Indian, little to nothing about meteorology was known. The lack of scientific facts did not stop the need for an explanation as to why, when, and how water fell from the sky. Water was central to their lives, so they developed beliefs and rituals around it. The fact that they later learned that rain never came because of their dance finally freed them from the anxiety that for centuries pervaded their days. However, in the days prior to their newfound knowledge of meteorology, they truly believed the dance provided water. So, to a Hopi at that time, it was a fact, not a belief, and this "fact" gave them answers they desperately needed to keep a sense of hope and security for themselves and their families.

Learned connections and the constant attempts to "treat the underlying causes of addiction" are the recovery world's rain dance. To explain people's drive to get high and drunk, the recovery culture has created its own belief system, its own myths and magic. In that belief system, followers believe that their depression, stress, or trauma automatically causes their substance use, which in turn allows them to escape responsibility for the sometimes horrendous and embarrassing consequences of that use because they do not believe they choose to continue use in this problematic and heavy pattern. And because a belief is held sacred by the people who hold it (especially if it is reinforced by their culture and actions), they accept it without question—*and it becomes true to them and those around them.* Once this belief has been emotionally absorbed as fact, anytime those people feel stressed, depressed, or overexcited and anxious, they will automatically feel the urge to get drunk or high. The same pattern applies to feeling jealous, manic, sad, or whatever emotion or thought has been learned to *cause* use. The Hopi believed in the dance to provide water for life, and our culture believes in learned connections as the causes for substance use. Our culture believes that external events, feelings, and circumstances force people to use substances and thus become addicts and alcoholics and that no act of personal will can stop it. *The comparison to Hopi mythology makes it easy to see the parallels, and hopefully, you are beginning to see the grave error in this theory.*

CAUSES VS. REASONS (REVISITED)

As we discussed in chapter 5, there are two perspectives on the origin of human experience: you can think of thoughts and behaviors as being "caused" by something, or you can see thoughts and behaviors as being freely chosen.

It is crucial to understand this fact: *a cause is finite and completely predictable; it doesn't require any reasoning to occur.* For example, quietly walk up behind someone, clap your hands loudly behind his head, and he will blink involuntarily. This response is hardwired in the nervous system from birth. The blink is a reflex caused by the loud noise. The person did not *think, I should blink now.* The *thinking part* of the response is missing, the part called reasoning. Reasoning is thinking about your wants and/or needs and then deciding that something is an appropriate action to take in response to something else. In this case, reasoning does not take place in the process between the loud noise and the blink and thus, demonstrates causation.

Recovery ideology states that your behaviors (choices) regarding substance use are reflexive and involuntary and, more specifically, behaviors that our society does not view as acceptable, positive, or productive are "addictive behaviors" and the people who engage in them are out of control. Addictive behaviors are enacted with no thought (i.e., no choice or reasoning) and have no basis in personal beliefs and developed preferences. Your addiction in this skewed view is *caused* by stress or trauma or other outside factors with no input from your mind. Yet a behavior such as heavy substance use *needs thought* to occur because heavy substance use is not a simple, involuntary reflex such as blinking; it's a complex behavior that requires many steps to do. When you contrast the choice to go to a crack house with an automatic fear response, such as startling at a loud noise, the recovery ideology can be seen for the mythology that it is.

This causal theory also doesn't account for the many people who have substance use problems but didn't have a troubled childhood and don't feel depressed, anxious, or mentally ill. They are confused as to why they use substances problematically:

> I don't know why I do this! My childhood was great. I have a loving supportive wife. I've always been successful in my career. And I'm so proud of my kids. Everything is great except for my drinking. I can't imagine what is causing me to do this. Maybe I have some repressed or hidden trauma. I really don't know.

The recovery ideology of "underlying causes" has these people completely confused. According to the Surgeon General's 2016 report on addiction, 60% of people with addictions do not have mental illnesses. (Surgeon General, 2016) What then are the causes of their use? It's a good question, but it's the wrong question. You can ask why they *choose* to use, because there are no *causes* of addiction. People aren't caused to behave in any way. They choose to behave in the ways they believe will get them what they want in life. Even without mental illnesses, people choose heavy substance use.

Nevertheless, you constantly hear that stressful circumstances cause people to use, and therefore, support, such as seeing a therapist or attending 12-step meetings, causes people not to use. Meanwhile, your personal enjoyment of the substance as a *reason* for using is ignored. This thinking renders you a perpetual victim of circumstances. You are like a leaf blowing in the wind, unable to choose where it lands. But ask yourself, are your behaviors *truly* involuntary? Do you really believe there is no reasoning behind your choices to get drunk or high or engage in any other behavior that you freely choose? Take a moment now to think about it. Aren't you able to think for yourself? Can you see that there are many reasons for your use? What are your wants and desires? Don't they play a role? Aren't you exercising your inherent thinking capabilities, autonomous mind, and free will to pursue happiness?

You can't have it both ways. Either you're free, or there's a web of causes at play. Yet the most popularly cited cause—co-occurring disorders/mental illnesses—is present in the lives of only 40% of addicts/alcoholics. Everyone says the solution to addiction is treating these mental illnesses, yet 60% of addicts do not suffer from mental illnesses. So why should we think that removing this suffering necessarily causes people to sober up? It obviously doesn't. There is no amount of addressing causes that will help because nothing *causes* heavy substance use. There are no causal connections; there are only learned connections held together by nothing more than belief.

WHY DO YOU USE? WHAT IS THE REASON?

By saying that stress, negative life circumstances, and other underlying issues don't cause substance use, we don't mean to suggest that the conditions of your life have no bearing on your decisions for your behaviors; they certainly do. People are influenced by multiple factors when they choose their thoughts and behaviors, but these things become *reasons* for their choices, not the *causes* of their choices. And that is the point here! Please understand that this is not simply a matter of semantics; the choice in wording matters. Every time you say that this or that causes you to use, you should be saying this or that is your *reason* for using. People do consider the other elements of their life when choosing, but they mislabel that process as causal rather than a reasoned choice for use. A *caused* event is involuntary, but a *reasoned* event is voluntary, under the direct control of the individual. Are you beginning to see why this is so important?

In his book *Addiction: A Disorder of Choice*, addiction researcher Dr. Gene Heyman (2009, p. 103) offered a great example to demonstrate the difference between voluntary and involuntary behaviors by outlining the difference between a wink and a blink. Blinks are for the most part reflexive, and most of the time people blink without thinking of a reason or purpose for doing it. Blinks are usually reflexive, automatic responses to loud sounds, dryness, or irritation of the eye or other threats to this delicate organ. Blinks have purpose, but they are a hardwired response with no *consciously* held purpose. Winks are the same physiologically and neurologically as blinks, yet they *always have a conscious purpose*. People wink to flirt, to let someone in on a joke, or to let someone know they agree. Winks are governed by the costs and benefits people see in them; it might be socially acceptable to wink at someone in one setting, whereas it would get you branded as a weirdo in another setting, and people usually assess the value of the wink before doing it. As you can see, winks are different than reflexive, involuntary behavior.

Now that you know that a caused or reflexive action is an involuntary event, you can see that your choice to use substances, like any other choice in your life, is not involuntary. You know that every choice you make is based on thought and reasoning. Thus, stress cannot *cause* drinking like a reflex causes something, but life's stress can certainly be a *reason* to drink if you see drinking as useful and appropriate when you are stressed. Whatever your situation and circumstances, you have always been in control, and you have always used your free will to search for happiness. So the question is this: Has your search been fruitful, or has it come up short? Have your choices made you feel better? Has mentally connecting these problems with substance use helped you? Would different choices make you happier? That is the issue that is most important as you move forward in your life.

You now face a crossroad. Will you continue to believe in the learned connections, or will you embrace your power of choice that's been hidden by those connections?

SOME EVIDENCE TO CONSIDER

If life's problems truly *cause* heavy substance use, then we should at the very least see a massive correlation between addiction and other mental illnesses . According to the latest statistics available from the Substance Abuse and Mental Health Administration (SAMHSA), 43.4 million American adults have mental illnesses. Of that group, 8.1 million also have substance use disorder. That means that only one out of five people with a mental illness also has a substance use problem (18.6%), whereas the other four out of five do not respond to a mental illness by using substances heavily (Center for Behavioral Health Statistics and Quality, 2016).

A weak correlation like this should have you questioning the idea that a mental illness forces people to use substances. No jury would be swayed by such paltry evidence, and you shouldn't be either.

Beyond this weak correlation, there is more data that further reinforces the point that other mental illnesses don't cause heavy substance use, nor is a mental illness an obstacle to ceasing heavy substance use. When addictions and other mental illnesses are compared, you can see that addictions are the shorter-lived problems. For example, the National Comorbidity Survey 1990–1992 showed remission rates for drug addiction were more than double the remission rates of all other mental illnesses (about 75% of those surveyed got over their addiction, whereas just over 30% got over their other mental illnesses; Heyman, 2009, pp. 73–75). How could so many people recover from addiction and not recover from the other mental illnesses that supposedly caused their addiction or were believed to be tied closely to it? For the causal connection to be valid, then logic holds that people wouldn't get over their addictions *until and after* they got over their other mental illnesses. Yet data consistently shows that this isn't the case.

In a similar survey, National Epidemiologic Survey on Alcohol and Related Conditions (NESARC), 2001–2002 (Lopez-Quintero, 2011), where further data was collected and addiction recovery rates were identical, researchers found that addicts with other mental illnesses were *no less likely to recover from their addictions* than those without mental illnesses.

The NESARC researchers also specifically analyzed the mental illnesses most common to addiction treatment patients:

> Mood disorders included DSM-IV primary major depressive disorder (MDD), dysthymia and bipolar disorders. Anxiety disorders included DSM-IV primary panic disorder (with and without agoraphobia), social anxiety disorder, specific phobias and generalized anxiety disorder.

And they found that:

> No association was observed between mood and anxiety disorders and dependence remission for any of the substances assessed.

So not only was there no evidence that conditions such as depression, bipolar, and anxiety (stress) *cause* people to "stay addicted"; there was also no correlation found. Let's sum up what we've presented here:

- Only one out of five people with the mental illnesses said to "cause addiction" have addictions.

- The rate of remission from addiction is twice as high as the rate of remission from other mental illnesses.

- Addicts who have other mental illnesses ("co-occurring disorders") are just as likely to recover from addiction as those without other mental illnesses.

If you want to see your emotional problems as the cause of your heavy substance use, you can certainly make that choice, but you would be holding onto a belief that is false. If you accept the data just presented, the only logical conclusion is that your choice to continue heavy substance use is causally independent of the presence of other mental health issues. The question for you personally then becomes whether heavy substance use is a proper and useful response to your emotional problems. That is, does heavy substance use effectively help to relieve your emotional issues in a way that makes it worth the costs involved?

BUT WHAT ABOUT MY SPECIFIC PROBLEM?

The data presented above spoke in broad strokes about mental health issues, so some of you may still be holding onto the idea that your specific mental health issue, disorder, or illness is more unique and truly forces you to use substances. Let us now give you some more-specific data.

Our friend Dr. Stanton Peele covered the area of trauma succinctly in a 2011 article for *Psychology Today* in which he examined the data commonly used to promote the trauma/addiction connection. He noted that, while high trauma scores were correlated with addiction, we still shouldn't conclude that trauma *causes* addiction. He noted that about 3.5% of those with high childhood trauma scores become IV drug users and 16% become alcoholics. But then he asked readers to look at the other side of this, specifically that 96.5% of those with trauma don't inject drugs and 84% don't become alcoholics. If the numbers had been presented in the inverse like this, you'd never have assumed that people are forced by trauma to use substances heavily.

The Anxiety and Depression Association of America (ADAA, n.d.) noted the following:

> About 20 percent of Americans with an anxiety or mood disorder such as depression have an alcohol or other substance use disorder, and about 20 percent of those with an alcohol or substance use disorder also have an anxiety or mood disorder.

Again, this leaves us with the fact that 80% of people with anxiety and mood disorders don't connect them to heavy substance use. The ADAA also advised that "those with anxiety disorders may find that alcohol or other substances can make their anxiety symptoms worse."

Since stress is a common daily problem, experienced by literally everyone, and not a formally diagnosed mental illness or disorder, there are no specific statistics about it. But in analyzing this issue you might refer to general addiction rates. While everyone experiences stress, only a minority of people use substances in a way classified as "addicted." Furthermore, most people, more than 9 out of 10, get over their addictions and presumably have high levels of strees at the very moment in life that they choose to cease using substances "addictively" (since their lives are often in a state of wreckage from past problematic substance use when they quit/reduce).

It also helps to consider a wider context. Most of this data looks at only Americans. The United States has one of the highest standards of living in the world, but if you look at third-world countries where many drugs are produced, cheaper, and in abundant supply, you will see far lower rates of addiction. How can this be, when people who live in those countries face so many more stressful events and conditions than we do? Either we as U.S. citizens have it harder than they do, or we have contrived a false connection between stress and substance use.

Other problems require the same logic. For example, we had a friend who began heavily smoking crack when her cat died. She blames the death of her beloved pet as the *cause* of her crack use relapse. Of course, millions of people lose their pets every year, and while it's painful, most of them do not smoke crack as a result. So the causal connection of these two events is nonexistent. However, this connection can feel very real to those who've been led to believe that when facing any adversity, they'll be uncontrollably driven to substance use. Letting go of the mythical causal connection between such events puts you back in the fully conscious driver's seat of your own life. You can then focus on your reasons for substance use (i.e., the benefits you see in it and whether it still works for you) and make your choices accordingly, with no sense of compulsion.

This brings us to the conclusion that there are no causal connections between these problems and heavy substance use. Now that you're aware of the facts, you no longer have to believe you're doomed to a lifetime of addiction because of your other life problems. You can be freed from the panic you may feel when you suffer emotional pain because the pain no longer needs to be taken as a sign that you'll be forced to use substances heavily. Furthermore, you don't have to try to live the impossibly perfect lifestyle that shelters you from all potential problems and emotional pain under threat of relapse. This knowledge will help you to see your substance use choices more accurately as choices that are fully your own rather than as reflexes over which you have no control. This knowledge effectively restores your freedom from the bogeyman of addiction!

WHAT YOU REALLY NEED TO KNOW

There is no direct causal connection between "underlying causes" and substance use. Instead, the link is your belief that substance use is a useful and proper response to life's problems. Are you willing to question that belief? If you do question it, you might find that your substance use has not and does not solve life's problems. Substance use doesn't erase memories of traumatic events; doesn't relieve the negative emotions of stress, anxiety, or depression; doesn't resolve any losses that you've suffered; and doesn't mend broken relationships, bring back loved ones who've died, or get you back your lost job or career. It certainly doesn't replace any of your personal failures with success, nor does it give you back any time that you regret wasting. Far from being a solution to any of these problems, it can often cause more of them or worsen existing ones. On top of *not solving any of these problems*, heavy substance use comes with its own set of costs. If you discover this truth for yourself, then you will have no *reason* to use substances in response to these problems and thus you will have *no desire* to use substances in response to these problems.

If you never consider this truth and instead continue to see these problems as *causes* of substance use, then you will continue to feel pushed into substance use in the face of life's problems. Unfortunately, the popular method of addressing the underlying causes of addiction upholds the false idea that life's problems are in fact *causes*, which distracts people from *the reasons for using substances held in their mind*. So while you furiously try to make sure you never have any problems so you won't be caused to use substances, you are implicitly accepting the premise that you will be forced to use whenever you suffer. That is, you are ensuring that you will feel caused to use substances again in the future.

The only connective tissue between these problems and further substance use is the beliefs you hold in your mind. You can change those beliefs. We provide information directly relevant to these beliefs later in the book (chapters 17 and 18), which you can use to critically analyze the popular belief that substances can even temporarily relieve negative feelings. Drugs and alcohol do no such thing pharmacologically. They provide physical sensations that can be interpreted as pleasurable, and that is basically all they do by their chemical action. All the emotionally medicinal powers we think that substances possess are illusions. At best, intoxication can be used as a distraction, but it does not numb a single emotion. This illusion of emotional relief is what makes the learned connections so insidious. Since the substances never even temporarily solve the problems we've been led to believe we need them for, we often feel worse after using them for these purposes and then believe we must need yet another drink, another pill, or another shot of heroin to really do the trick and deal with our demons. It becomes a vicious cycle that feels impossible to escape when you're in it, yet the cycle can be broken easily just by learning the truth and breaking the learned connections.

WE AREN'T DIMINISHING OR DISMISSING YOUR PROBLEMS

Troubled childhoods, current emotional problems, and other negative situations, such as poverty, joblessness, and loss, can all create a climate in which heavy substance use appears to be a comforting option. We completely understand that to be true. Being in the wrong place at the wrong time leads to situations in which heavy substance use appears to be a comforting option as well. We get that too. You can now understand that either your past or current problems may have *influenced* your thinking about substance use without believing that they *directly caused you to use substances.* You can look back at your past and say to yourself *Given my circumstances and what I knew at the time, those were the choices I thought I had to make. I thought those underlying issues caused my use, but now I know I can change that view.* And once you see that you can change the way you see these issues and how they relate to your choice to get drunk or high, you can forgive yourself for any bad outcomes and move on.

The Freedom Model is about giving you the information that can help you make new decisions now and in the future. The fact is that, right now, whatever problems you have in your life, you are still fully free to use whatever amount of substances you think proper or make the decision to not use them in those same circumstances. You don't need to be problem free to be substance free. You can and will have problems in life—it's simply the nature of being human. And now that you know you can separate your normal human issues from the singular decision to use or not use substances, you are now free from the learned connections that kept you trapped in the past. You are in the driver's seat.

Looking for causes won't help you determine your course—looking for a new destination will.

Now, it is time to move on, to disconnect your traumas, stress, and depression from your use of substances. You can choose to use if you want to use or choose not to use if you don't. Keep that issue isolated, and then make separate choices about these other normal human struggles. Doing this will go a long way in your being free and will massively simplify solving various life challenges. It's always easier to work on one problem at a time than it is to attempt to sort through two or more problems that have been erroneously connected to each other.

THE THREE BUILDING BLOCKS OF FREEDOM

The previous couple of chapters may have seemed at times to have unnecessarily delved into some intellectual nonsense from academic-level researchers and philosophers, but hopefully, by now the relevance is clear. Those intellectuals with an anti-freewill stance led the way for the recovery society to focus on "causes of addiction" rather than reasons for substance use. When you hear those claims of causes, you are now armed with the knowledge that they're built on a weak philosophical and scientific foundation that undercuts them all. You can now confidently focus on reasons rather than causes.

To further your understanding of yourself as a freely choosing being and bring clarity to how and why you choose as you do, we will examine the building blocks of freedom, three uniquely human attributes:

- *The Positive Drive Principle* (PDP) provides motivation to act. It is readily observed that every one of us is pursuing happiness at every moment. This motivation gets channeled into whatever we see as our best option at any given moment.

- *Free will* is our ability to choose our own actions, which we do according to our perspective of our available options.

- *Mental autonomy* is our mind's separation from circumstances, other people, and other outside forces. It is the fact that thinking takes effort that comes from within us and is an independent activity.

121

With deeper understanding of these attributes, you will increase your problem-solving abilities and swiftly deal with your substance use issues. As you may have noticed, these three attributes have been implicit in this discussion of causes versus reasons. They make up the backbone of *The Freedom Model* and point to the way out of the recovery society trap.

REFERENCES

Anxiety and Depression Association of America (ADAA). (n.d.). Substance use disorders. Retrieved from https://adaa.org/understanding-anxiety/related-illnesses/substance-abuse

Center for Behavioral Health Statistics and Quality. (2016). *Key substance use and mental health indicators in the United States: Results from the 2015 National Survey on Drug Use and Health* (HHS Publication No. SMA 16-4984, NSDUH Series H-51). Retrieved from https://www.samhsa.gov/data/sites/default/files/NSDUH-FFR1-2015Rev1/NSDUH-FFR1-2015Rev1/NSDUH-FFR1-2015Rev1/NSDUH-National Findings-REVISED-2015.pdf

Heyman, G. (2009). *Addiction: A disorder of choice.* Cambridge, MA: Harvard University Press.

Laubin, R., & Laubin, G. (1989). *Indian dances of North America: Their importance to Indian life.* Norman, OK: University of Oklahoma Press.

Lopez-Quintero, C., Hasin, D. S., de los Cobos, J. P., Pines, A., Wang, S., Grant, B. F., & Blanco, C. (2011). Probability and predictors of remission from lifetime nicotine, alcohol, cannabis, or cocaine dependence: Results from the National Epidemiologic Survey on Alcohol and Related Conditions. *Addiction (Abingdon, England), 106*(3), 657–669.

Peele, S. (2011, December 5). The seductive (but dangerous) allure of Gabor Maté. Retrieved from http://www.psychologytoday.com/blog/addiction-in-society/201112/the-seductive-dangerous-allure-gabor-mat

Surgeon General. (2016, November 16). Executive summary [Text]. Retrieved from https://addiction.surgeongeneral.gov/executive-summary

CHAPTER 7:
THE POSITIVE DRIVE PRINCIPLE

W e consider the following observation to be self-evident: every one of us, in everything we do, is just trying to achieve and maintain a happy existence.

As simple as that statement is, it's turned out to be the most important insight we've had over the past three decades of running our retreats. It's important for understanding heavy substance use habits, and it's important for making changes in substance use habits. We call it the Positive Drive Principle, or PDP for short, and define it as simply a drive to pursue happiness. We aren't the first to make this observation; great thinkers over the ages have noted it frequently.

> All men seek happiness. This is without exception. Whatever different means they employ, they all tend to this end. The cause of some going to war, and of others avoiding it, is the same desire in both, attended with different views. The will never takes the least step but to this object. This is the motive of every action of every man, even of those who hang themselves.
>
> —Blaise Pascal, French mathematician, physicist, and philosopher

> Man aspires to happiness, and he cannot help aspiring to it.
>
> —Jacques-Bénigne Bossuet, 17th-century French bishop and theologian

> Man comes into the world having implanted in him inerad-
> icably the desire of happiness and aversion from pain. See-
> ing that he acts in obedience to this impulse, we cannot de-
> ny that personal interest is the moving spring of the indi-
> vidual.
>
> —Frédéric Bastiat, economist

> The object of rational wish is the end, i.e. the good or the
> apparent good.
>
> —Aristotle, *The Nicomachean Ethics*, 350 BCE

The PDP is what motivates every person into every action. You may be thinking *Why are they talking about this principle now?* Frankly, the recovery ideology that is entrenched in our culture has convinced too many people that there is no rhyme or reason to their substance use habits. About half of our retreat guests (often those older than 35 years and who have tried to stop in the past) tell us "I don't know why I do this; I don't even like it." Incidentally, the more exposure people have had to recovery ideology and treatment programs, the more likely they say and believe such things. They then go on to list all the neg-ative consequences of heavy substance use, saying "Why would I do this when it costs me my …" (e.g., marriage, freedom, license to drive, health, or job). All the "help" they've received has led them to become hyper-focused on the costs, the apparent irrationality of their behavior, and the shame of it all. They live in complete bewilderment as to why they continue to drink/drug; they've accepted it as the de facto thing they'll just keep doing because they believe they are driven by sickness, disease, or a mental disorder. They think they are engaging in behavior they don't want to be doing, and they are confused and feel helpless to change it. This confusion keeps people from seeing their way out of these problems and moving forward.

Yet, if you ask substance users why they initially began using a sub-stance, the answer in most cases is the pursuit of happiness—for the high, to loosen up in social situations, to blow off steam, and so on. Even when the answer is "to fit in," it can clearly be traced back to a pursuit of happiness. People want to fit in so others will like them, and they want to be invited to parties and to socialize with others, both enjoyable elements of life. Most young people readily admit that these happiness-based reasons are why they use substances.

But again, some portion of people with more long-term, heavy substance use habits have become so bogged down in the costs of substance use and the shameful identity of being an "addict" or "alcoholic" that they've become blinded to the fact that they're still pursuing happiness with this activity. They've been taught (through interactions with people who negatively judge their habits) that they're *not supposed to like using substances the way they do*. They've been taught that they should express nothing but shame, remorse, regret, self-pity, and all manner of negative feelings about substance use. They've been taught that they should show that they hate it and wish they weren't doing it.

So, when we ask these people why they do it and the answer is "I don't know why I do it; I don't like it," we move to another question: Then, why don't you just stop? The answers we hear to this question tend to be more revealing and fruitful. These longtime substance users say they have too much stress, anxiety, or depression. They say they can't imagine being the only one at a party not drinking. Or they say they'd be just plain miserable without it. The thing is that both questions—why do you do it and why don't you stop—are asking the same thing. So the answers to the second question are essentially the answers to the first. Saying that you don't stop because you're afraid you won't fit in is the same as saying you continue so you'll fit in. Saying that you don't stop because you'll be miserable without it is the same as saying that you continue because you think you need it to be happy.

ALL CHOICES ARE MADE IN PURSUIT OF HAPPINESS

It's important to recognize that all choices are made in the pursuit of happiness and that there are no exceptions. The PDP is easy to see in choices that our society sees as positive or at least benign. If people follow a dream career, we know they are pursuing happiness. They may struggle to achieve success in a career in which the odds are against them, such as becoming a politician, an entrepreneur, or an artist, yet we know they dream of happily succeeding one day and that the pursuit of happiness drives them to toil, struggle, and persevere in the face of rejection and failure. It's obvious that when people scrimp and save to buy a home, take an extravagant vacation, or get a fancy car, they are pursuing happiness. If they endeavor to succeed in a sport, or study a difficult topic, or to achieve straight As in high school, it's clear that they enjoy the challenge and are pursuing happiness.

Then, there are the benign daily activities, such as buying that four-dollar cup of gourmet coffee (i.e., your *triple venti, half-sweet, nonfat, caramel macchiato*). Why do that when you can get a cup of coffee with the same amount of caffeine for a dollar at McDonald's? You spend the extra money because you see a benefit; it's likely you believe the gourmet cup tastes better so you enjoy it more, and thus, it makes you happy. The same could be said of those who cook gourmet meals instead of getting by on easier-to-make, equally nutritious food. The PDP can be seen when you choose to watch one television show instead of another because you prefer one more than the other and think it will be more entertaining to you, thus making you happier. You can even see the PDP when people do small favors for each other. They do them to see a smile on someone else's face, knowing that they helped that person and, of course, finding happiness in the self-image of being a helpful, loving, generous person. The PDP is behind every one of these choices.

You can also see the PDP at work in many behaviors that people think they "have to" do, such as going to work. You don't *have* to go to work. You could abstain from that and couch surf or go homeless. Many people do. However, those who go to work see benefits in working, most obviously, the benefit of getting paid for their efforts and then using that money to trade for all the things they think they need to live a happy life.

COSTLY BEHAVIORS ARE A PURSUIT OF HAPPINESS TOO

When it comes to choosing things that others see as being not so good or benign—things that are too costly, irrational, or risky—many people have a hard time seeing happiness as the motive. They think the person making those choices must be sick, dysfunctional, or inherently immoral. The prime example here is heavy substance use. As you saw earlier, there are plenty of reasons people prefer substance use, and they all boil down to a pursuit of happiness. But then, there's that nasty issue of the costs and consequences. And indeed, often in hindsight, many people don't prefer their heavy substance use. The outcomes can be costly monetarily, legally, mentally, emotionally, socially, and physically. With experience, these costs become predictable, and people often contemplate them before they choose that next drink or hit. The prevailing thought is that no one would freely choose such destructive behaviors. This is the argument we hear most often in favor of the idea that there is a state of involuntary behavior called addiction.

It's time we thoroughly break down that argument and challenge it. What it's really saying is that, if a behavior or choice is extremely costly, then it must be involuntary. Another way of saying this is that it's impossible to make an irrational choice so that, if a behavior turns out to be irrational, then it must have been compelled rather than freely chosen. When stated this way, you can see how absurd it is.

First, to be rational, that is, to think through your potential options logically and determine which one will bring about the best results, takes effort and, in some cases, an enormous amount of effort. All people, addicts and nonaddicts alike, fail at this task several times a day! Plants and animals have it easy. They don't have to think things through to survive and thrive, but people do. Life is full of irrational decisions, and the challenge is to continually gain knowledge and wisdom to make better and more "rational" decisions throughout life. When people cite irrationality as proof that a behavior is involuntary, are they really saying that it's impossible for humans to freely make irrational choices? The truth is that irrationality isn't proof of disease; it's proof of humanity.

Second, and more important, it's not odd for people to pay a high price for the things and activities they believe will make them happy. You don't need to look far for examples of this in everyday life. Just consider the costs of owning a big house. Most obvious, bigger houses have a higher monetary price, but the higher costs don't stop there. They have higher property taxes and cost more to heat and air condition. The time and physical and mental energy costs to maintain a larger home are massive. It takes enormous effort to keep up extra rooms, such as a den, media room, finished basement, extra bedroom, home office, laundry room, and so on.

Contrast this with a modest apartment. Instead of a big 30-year mortgage, you could pay a small monthly rent. There is no property tax, no lawn and landscaping for you to maintain, no gutters to be cleaned, and no extra rooms to decorate, furnish, and keep clean. If something goes wrong structurally or with the plumbing or HVAC system or the paint starts to peel, you don't have to worry about getting it fixed. You don't have to make any decisions about hiring help, contractors, or repairmen. Your landlord handles all these issues, and the costs are already figured into your monthly rent. You needn't spend much time, effort, or mental energy on these things. Furthermore, you have no insurance or liability to worry about if someone slips on your steps and decides to sue or some other unforeseen event happens on the periphery of the property. What's more, you don't have to worry about property values decreasing or the housing market softening and having your home become worth less than you paid for it. You take no such risks by renting. It's simply much easier being an apartment dweller, as one comedian put it:

> I went to the Home Depot yesterday, which was unnecessary; I need to go to the Apartment Depot. It's just a bunch of guys standing around going "Hey, we ain't gotta fix shit."
>
> —Mitch Hedberg, comedian

Now, given the fact that modest apartments are much less costly and require much less attention and have virtually none of the risks of big houses, why does anyone buy those big homes? Are they sick and diseased? After all, their decision looks irrational once you consider all the risks and costs they're taking on by making it. They're locking themselves into 30 years of paying for a home and limiting their ability to move somewhere else should they feel a desire to do so. They don't have to take on any of the negative consequences of home ownership. What causes them then to continue homeownership despite experiencing negative consequences? Why do they take the risks involved in homeownership when they could choose the less-risky, "healthier option" of renting an apartment?

If society looked at the homeownership versus renting a modest apartment situation in the same way it views heavy substance use, then everyone would say the homeowner is sick, diseased, disordered, or dysfunctional. Everyone would say that homeowners must've been traumatized so that now they're self-destructive and self-sabotaging. Everyone would say homeowners must have underlying issues of stress, anxiety, and depression that cause them to seek comfort in the immediate gratifications of living in a big home.

Of course, this analysis would be absurd. Some people like to rent a small apartment; some people like to own big, luxurious mansions; and then, there's a whole range of options that people prefer between those two choices. Everyone sees benefits in these various options that make one look better than the others, resulting in the desire for such a home and the willingness to pay the associated costs. People see things they believe they need to make them happy in a home, and then they pursue the home that they think meets their needs. They may wish the costs were lower to get the benefits they want, but nevertheless, they freely and willingly pay the price to get what they prefer.

People's preferences for substance use are no different. They have their own perspective on the benefits of substance use, and they will pay whatever the price is to get those benefits if they think it is the option that best serves them. The PDP is how we sum up this fact. People take actions to achieve happiness, and they do so according to their own unique perspective. If you are putting effort into something, it's because you see it as the best available and viable option to achieve/sustain a happy existence. If you truly didn't want to do something, then you wouldn't do it. You are driven to always pursue happiness; everyone is.

HAPPIER OPTIONS

We've used the term "happiness" here, and we know that many people's reaction to this is "You think I'm happy doing this? I'm not happy. I'm miserable drinking/drugging like this!" There's no better way to sum it all up. Life is a pursuit of happiness, and every choice people make is aimed at having it. What we can do to reach a better, more sensitive understanding of this is to point out the nuances. Happiness is relative, and the term as it is used here doesn't refer just to states of pleasure, bliss, and joy.

Happiness comes in degrees. It refers to minor satisfactions as well. Jail is a miserable place to be, and when I (Steven) was there, I found happiness in the tiny weekly delivery of low-quality snacks that we could order from the commissary. Overall, I hated my situation in innumerable ways; as you can imagine, there are considerable downsides to being imprisoned. I wanted to be free. When I got those snacks, it was better than not getting those snacks. Getting a steak dinner would've been even better, but that wasn't available to me. So I found happiness in some cookies and candies that would've been the cheapest things on the shelf at an inner-city bodega. Some other guys preferred to order ramen soups with their commissary budget, which they didn't eat but instead used as currency for other things. They were happy enough with the food served in the mess hall at the prison. I generally starved because I was so disgusted with the food. It often contained fish, mushrooms, white sauces, or other things I don't eat. I was so hungry and repulsed by the meals I was given that I once fished a piece of cake out of the trash that another prisoner had thrown away. I was extremely happy to get that cake even while I was hating myself and being embarrassed at having taken it out of the trash in front of everyone.

One example that might illuminate the fact that people are choosing what they see as their happiest option is voting. Many people regularly complain that they hate both candidates in presidential elections. "They're all crooks," they say. But then they get in that booth and vote for one of them. Who would freely choose to vote for a crook? They see this as a choice between the lesser of two evils, and they "hold their nose" while pulling the lever. Yet, in seeing one as less evil, they essentially see that candidate as the better one. We can't overlook that these people could also completely abstain from voting. That they cast a vote at all shows that they think there's some personal value to be gained by taking part in the process. We can only assume that they think they would've missed out on sufficient benefits by abstaining and that this was the available choice that they believed would make them feel better—even if they can list off 50 things they hate about the candidate they chose.

You choose what you see as the happ*ier* option, and the key to understanding this is in the *ier* tagged onto happy. It doesn't mean that every choice you make is fantastic, it doesn't mean these choices don't come with high costs that you wish you didn't have to pay, it doesn't mean you won't regret these choices later, and it doesn't mean that they are your ideal choices. It simply means that among what you see as your available options in the moment when you choose, those choices are the better ones according to your own judgment. They are the happ*ier* options.

I (Steven) met with a friend's daughter recently who is in her early 20s and going nowhere fast. She had been kicked out of her home, was using and dealing lots of drugs, and was spending most of her time with people who regularly got into trouble with the law. As we talked, it became clear that she had no ambition, didn't think she could achieve much, and was regretful and ashamed that she hadn't gone to college and felt that opportunity had passed her by. She had no vision of any other lifestyle that could make her happier than the one she was currently living and that she clearly knew was fraught with risks and costs that would eventually catch up to her. Even when her parents took her on a vacation with them to a luxurious ski resort, she was miserable the whole time because she didn't have any drugs with her. Being high on drugs every day had become her entire definition of happiness. Being without drugs had become her definition of misery.

I know her situation well and saw myself in her. The truth is that she has a family who would support her in chasing any goal. They would invest in her and support her endeavors. She has many opportunities to live differently; she just doesn't see it that way. Her perspective is based on reasons that are pitiable, such as low self-esteem and a limited perspective on happiness because she hasn't yet achieved much. Despite having had a relatively average middle class upbringing, she believes she needs drugs to deal with the pain from her childhood. I know how painful and stuck it feels to believe those things, and if I could snap my fingers to make her change those beliefs and move forward or give her a pill that achieved the same, I would do it in a heartbeat. But I can't, because it's a matter of personal perspective. The power of the mind is such that even when she's on vacation amid many enjoyable activities that most other people would jump at, in her mind, they don't compare to drugs, which she sees as the happ*ier* option. She spent her time on that vacation seeking out a drug dealer, spending all her money on very weak drugs, using them quickly, and then existing in misery for the remainder of the trip.

The desire for any choice doesn't exist in a vacuum. It exists in relation to our view of other options. It's important to realize that the people who feel extremely attached (i.e., "addicted") to a habit see the option of changing the habit as a miserable state. They see it as one of loss and deprivation and of being deprived of benefits that are essential to their happiness. In the case above, she experienced time not under the influence of drugs as absolute misery. With this perspective of their options, people happily pay a high price to continue the habit whenever possible and will go to great lengths to maintain it. We've all seen this in the desperate behaviors of some substance users.

Not every reader will feel this attached to substance use. Many don't feel like they must have substances all day, every day. Some feel they "need it" after a hard day's work, whereas others feel like they can take it or leave it every day throughout the week but see a Saturday without a 12 pack as misery. Some feel they need it when they are upset, stressed, or sad and view going without it in these situations as a serious loss. Everyone's perspective is unique. *The greater the difference between the benefits people see in substance use and the benefits they see in going without it or less of it, the more desperate they will feel and behave.* What is normally called an addiction, that is the desperate and costly behavior and mixed emotions over substance use, isn't an entity unto itself. It isn't a disease, a brain state, or any other "thing." It is simply a perspective on one's available options, a belief that heavy substance use is the happi*er* option. It is a matter of mind.

When we're looking at random instances of substance use, we are looking at clearly momentary choices made in pursuit of happiness. The people who get badly hung over from an odd night of heavy drinking simply look at that as a poor choice they made to drink too much. They don't feel addicted nor that they will be doomed to this outcome every time they drink. But, if this begins to become a pattern of regularity, people begin to feel as if they might be out of control. They look back and feel as if they haven't chosen it because it seems that any kind of thinking or deliberation happens less often before they jump into these habitual choices.

Indeed, they often aren't thinking much more than *I want a drink/drug right now.* There is no noticeable deliberation going on in that moment. There is no conscious comparison between having a drink and not having a drink that they engage in at that moment. However, *that doesn't mean the desire isn't the product of deliberation.* The deliberation happened on an earlier date (or many earlier dates), and they concluded that, in such and such circumstances, the drink is what makes them the happiest. The repetition of reaching this conclusion and acting upon it turned into a belief that drinking is better than not drinking in specific situations. The situation could be labeled as "parties," "stress," "sadness," or "boredom." But that gets filed away as a *preference* to drink in such situations. Of course, it could be unpacked and deliberated again at any time. But that would be a new choice, and for the deliberation to come out differently, that is, for you to see not having the drink in a certain situation as the happier option, you would have to think it through differently than you have in the past. You would have to end up seeing greater happiness in not having the drink for it to become your new preference.

Sometimes, there's quite a bit of thinking that happens before people make the same regretful, habitual choices. Habitual users tell themselves not to use; they think of the costs: spending too much money, upsetting loved ones, or risking arrest or their health. But, then, they still make the decision that they see as so irrational and costly, which leaves them feeling even more confused. *The issue is this, and don't forget it: while you're looking at costs, what you've failed to do is reassess the benefits of your various options.* You still see the option of substance use as giving you the happiness you need even though it's costly. An equally important but often overlooked element of this perspective is that *you still see the choice of not using substances as not providing the benefits you need.* You still see not using as a loss, a deprivation, and a downright miserable option in that moment even though you realize it would free you from the costs of choosing substance use.

OUTCOMES DON'T REVERSE MOTIVES

We all know that hindsight is 20/20, meaning that after our decisions are made and have fully played out, we can see things clearly. What you thought was a good decision 10 years ago, 10 months ago, 10 days ago, or even 10 hours ago may look like a horrible decision right now. When everything comes crashing down from your substance use, it's easy to look back and say "Why would I have done that?" as if the motive for the substance use is some kind of mystery. Many think something sinister is going on and that they couldn't possibly freely make such a choice. Or they hold up the bad outcome as proof that they clearly can't be pursuing happiness. "After all," they say, "I'm not happy *now.*" The reasoning boils down to this:

- I would never choose for things to end badly.

- This choice ended badly.

- Therefore, I didn't really make this choice, and it wasn't driven by happiness.

This would be like saying after a sports loss that the team didn't want to win the game or, after some giant marketing failure, saying that the greedy corporation didn't want to make money. Need we hammer this point home any further? Bad things happen even when you intend for the best. Just because you don't like the consequences of your substance use now doesn't mean you weren't pursuing happiness when you chose to use.

Some may also conclude that they're "self-destructive" or "self-sabotaging" because they've repeatedly made choices that turned out badly, as if they intended a bad outcome. Well, if they're truly self-destructive, then why are they regretful now? Shouldn't they be happy that it all blew up in their faces if their intention really was to self-destruct? The logic falls apart quickly when you look at it this way. Don't get stuck in these traps; all they do is keep you from realizing the truth, that you're trying to achieve happiness with your substance use.

THERE'S ONE DIRECTION OF MOTIVATION: TOWARD HAPPINESS

What about using substances as an escape? Many people think that substance users are running from pain and that this is far different than pursuing happiness. They say substance users aren't using for any sort of pleasure; they're using simply to deal with depression or feel normal. The word "pleasure" (with a hedonistic connotation) is being used to represent all of happiness here, while it is simply only one type of happiness. What's more, averting pain is a form of happiness. Aren't you happier without pain than you are with pain? Better is better, and moving forward is moving forward. If you think of emotions as being on a continuum, with horrific pain on one end and blissful happiness on the other, then any decrease in pain, even if it's a move toward "just feeling normal," is a movement toward happiness.

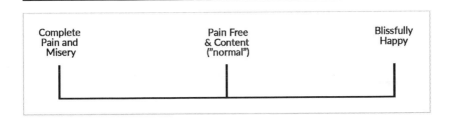

| Complete Pain and Misery | Pain Free & Content ("normal") | Blissfully Happy |

Now, in reality, there is no middle state that's devoid of feelings. You always feel something, and if you move rapidly from intense pain to no pain or from intense pain to mild pain, you will experience some happiness. How could you not? Feeling better is feeling better. For example, many people say heroin users don't use it to be happy; they use it just to feel normal. As a former heroin user, I'll (Steven) say that, when I woke up in withdrawal and, after begging, scrounging, and stealing to get a hit, I finally got one and a reprieve from my dope sickness, I was happy as hell. Did I like the overall state of my life? No, I hated it. Did I like coming out of painful withdrawal? *Of course I did.*

To feel "normal," whatever that means when people use it when they refer to their motivation to drink/drug, is a happ*ier* state than the pain, discomfort, sadness, or whatever abnormality from which people feel they need to escape.

While discussing outcomes here, don't fall into the trap of thinking that outcomes determine the motive. If, after hustling enough money to get a hit, I had ended up getting ripped off with an inert substance that turned out not to be heroin and I remained in the same painful state of withdrawal, the PDP would still have applied. Even though my disappointment at getting ripped off would have immediately moved me in the direction of greater misery, my motive would still have been the pursuit of happiness. I wanted to feel better even though that wasn't the outcome. The same goes for if I had bought a tainted bag of heroin and then died of an overdose. The *motive* would have been to move toward greater happiness although the result was the opposite.

HAPPINESS IS SUBJECTIVE AND A MIXED BAG

It's obvious that different things make different people happy depending on their perspective of the benefits. Our house versus apartment example made that clear. However, to add more depth to this idea, let's look back at our example of being in heroin withdrawal.

We have seen people during heroin withdrawal experience happiness. How can that be? Well, they were proud to be enduring the pain and not turning back to heroin for a quick fix. They had it set in their minds that there was a greater goal being achieved by enduring the pain. They looked forward to "getting over the hump" and being free of the withdrawal cycle.

There are many cases where people happily endure physical pain and, in a sense, enjoy it. Distance runners regularly experience this phenomenon. It's not just when they finish the race that they feel happiness; they also feel it while struggling to keep running. The same goes for mountain climbers. Graduate students experience it while in complete mental exhaustion as they burn the midnight oil to complete their master's thesis.

Happiness isn't all or nothing either; it's a mixed bag. We often see people who are battling a serious, life-threatening illness experience happiness. We see people on their deathbeds happy to be able to tell their visiting relatives how much they love them. We see it in the worst conditions on earth, in prisons, concentration camps, refugee camps, and after natural disasters. We see people working toward happiness in these situations, trying to find a scrap of progress amid utter devastation.

People even work toward happiness in depression, and this case might be more illuminating than anything else. Depression, as researcher Martin Seligman discovered, is caused by *"the belief that your actions will be futile."* (Seligman, 2006) Depressed people believe they are powerless to change their circumstances. They believe their efforts won't make anything better. As they continue to believe this, they increasingly withdraw from life until they won't even get out of bed. Since they believe that trying to improve their life will fail, they see it as the less-happy option; such efforts are all cost with no benefit. Severely depressed people's inaction—*literally not leaving their bed*—is a choice they make to ensure they don't sink any lower. They make this choice to avoid beating themselves up later for trying and failing. But even in this stagnant avoidance of deeper suffering, they are pursuing happiness. In this hanging on, they are pursuing happiness. The avoidance of pain is their trying to remain as close to happiness as possible.

They find that happiness in not sinking lower and in hanging on in stasis waiting for the day when things will by chance get better and it seems that effort and action will be worth trying.

WHY IS RECOGNIZING THE PURSUIT OF HAPPINESS SO IMPORTANT?

You must be scratching your head right now wondering why we would spend all this time and energy going on and on about the pursuit of happiness. If the pursuit of happiness is behind *everything*, then what significance can it have here? The answer is far more important than you realize.

Recovery ideology and its proponents have portrayed addiction as a disease for one major reason: to short-circuit any decision-making process and scare heavy substance users into stopping. In their opinion, you are incapable of arriving at the conclusion that it is worth making a change, and you are immoral and spiritually bankrupt (if you don't believe that, read through the bible of addiction that serves as the basis for every major concept of and approach to addiction, the *Big Book* of Alcoholics Anonymous). So, in the same way a preacher tries to scare people into behaving in ways that are moral and righteous with tales of fire and brimstone, the treatment professionals, sponsors, and the like try to scare people into abstinence with tales of the ravages of the disease of addiction and what will happen if you commit their version of a sin, which is having a single drink or hit of a drug.

Heavy substance use is different from diseases in an important way. *Diseases are all bad.* There's not an ounce of good in a disease. People may suffer diseases and come out with good experiences. They may value life more, be more grateful, learn patience, overcome fears, build character, and find other silver linings in the experience of fighting a disease. But these good experiences aren't inherent in the diseases or the inevitable result of diseases; these good things are the result of human beings' natural capacity for optimism and learning. People actively generate the good things to make their experiences worthwhile. It's a case of life giving them lemons, and their choosing to make lemonade.

Heavy substance use, on the other hand, is not a case of life giving you lemons. *Heavy substance users see benefits in substance use, so they desire it and actively seek to use substances to acquire the perceived benefits. Cancer sufferers do not see a high in having cancer (or stress relief, lowered inhibitions, etc.); thus, they do not desire cancer and most certainly do not actively seek to acquire cancer by furiously ingesting carcinogens. This distinction is massive.*

While people certainly can and do make choices that inadvertently lead to disease, nobody is ever motivated to acquire diseases (except for a handful of people with some strange ideas). They don't get sick so they can learn to be more grateful, patient, and appreciative of health and other blessings. They get sick by accident, not by direct choice. Diseases are *all bad* and completely unwanted, with no perceived direct benefits. As soon as you know you have a disease, you want the disease gone. Most people diligently follow their doctors' orders and readily undergo procedures and surgeries meant to remove the disease from their body or ease their suffering. The recovery society tries to engender this same readiness to change and follow doctors' orders by portraying addiction as a disease. They try to convince you that you must stop using substances, but it doesn't work. People continue to desire substances, so they white knuckle it, trying to resist their desires with willpower until they crumble and go back to heavy substance use again because that's truly what they want to do.

This choice to use substances then gets called a "relapse" into the disease. This terminology is dangerously misleading because, again, it overlooks the real issue that you want to use substances because you see sufficient benefits in doing so. In distracting you from the real issue, the disease model keeps you from working through whether heavy substance use is your happiest option. Those who push the disease model are like parents who tell their children the answers to long-division problems without walking them through the steps to discover the answers themselves. When the day of the big test comes, they don't know how to solve the problems. So, while you may accept someone else's conclusion that you should stop using substances, it isn't the same as reaching that conclusion yourself.

The PDP says that all human behavior is driven by the pursuit of happiness and that, when you choose to do something, you do so because you see it as your best available option. This concept is vitally important because the only way you will stop desiring heavy substances and change your behavior is by seeing more happiness in the change than in the using. You must reach that conclusion yourself because, as Aristotle said, "We desire in accordance with our deliberation."

Nobody can deliberate for you. People can give you an answer—that you should never touch a substance again—but giving you the answer empowers you no more than your parents giving you the answers to the long-division problems. You have your own answer. The conclusion that you arrived at some point in your life—*that heavy substance use is what you need to be happy*—is sitting there in your mind, untouched, unaltered, and creating a desire to use substances. It is a strong conviction, and as the French economist Frédéric Bastiat said, "No conviction makes so lasting an impression on the mind as that which it works out for itself."

Here's what usually happens when you're a true believer that you've got a disease and that you just need to comply with the treatment and accept the lifelong battle of your disease. You go to all the meetings, all the counseling, all the sober parties. You change people, places, and things. You avoid triggers. You run off to a meeting or call a sponsor at the slightest thought of using substances. You spend every waking moment "working on recovery," but something keeps nagging at you. The desire to use keeps popping into your mind. You feel deprived. It's a daily struggle. You get "overpowering cravings," and you crumble, going straight back to heavy substance use again. The thing that has been nagging at you is your own foregone conclusion that heavy substance use is what you need to be happy. It's the preference that you built and that you haven't changed because you skipped right over it and started fighting a nonexistent disease.

Perhaps you are one of the many struggling substance users who don't believe addiction is a disease. We get many guests at our retreats who agree that it is not a disease. Maybe you believe one of the alternative yet equivalent models of addiction in which it's not a disease but still involves a distinct lack of control. No matter; your results are the same. If you think trauma is causing your substance use and you set out to battle your trauma, the principle is the same—your conclusion that heavy substance use is what you need to be happy still goes unchanged. It nags at you while you focus on the red herring of trauma. Dealing with your "underlying causes" and "co-occurring disorders" plays out the same way. Trying to "increase self-control" or solve the problem through nutritional supplements and macrobiotic diets, yoga, meditation, exercise, and alternative support groups are methods that equally miss the point.

All those theories focus on battling an imagined cause of substance use. In fact, there are no causes to be battled; there are only reasons held within the mind that underlie your preferences and choices. By ignoring reasons, these methods never allow you to address the conclusion you came to that heavy substance use is what you need to be happy, thus leaving your desire intact. They leave you preferring heavy substance use by distracting you from reassessing its relative perceived benefits. It is true that some people accidentally determine that they no longer prefer heavy substance use while employing these approaches. These people got it despite the "help" they received.

Determining whether your current substance use makes you happy enough or you'd be happier with some level of change is everything. Once you arrive at the conclusion that your former style of substance use is not your happiest available option, the desire to continue it will literally melt away. That's why understanding the PDP is so important. Once you accept that your behavior is in pursuit of happiness, you can get on with discovering your happiest options. Substance use becomes a choice like any other choice when you see it this way. It might be an emotion-laden and a complicated choice that takes some serious unpacking and reexamination, but it is a choice nonetheless.

FEAR ALONE ISN'T ENOUGH

For some reason, many people naturally gravitate toward fear of consequences to try to change their substance use. Hearing all that we just said, they will say "Yeah, I remind myself of the consequences all the time, that I know this is going to make me miserable, but then I go ahead and do it anyway. It doesn't work; I can't make the choice to stop." Many will say they wish they would suffer a health scare, arrest, or some other kind of extreme cost of substance use to make them stop. Many people will try to build a bigger mental list of the costs to battle their desire the next time they want to drink or drug.

The risks, costs, and consequences of various choices obviously play a role in the decision to change. If heavy substance use were a costless activity, far fewer people would choose to stop it. However, and this is important to recognize, for the most part, heavy substance users are aware of its costs, and yet they persist in it. Many suffer near-fatal overdoses, arrests, and all manner of disastrous outcomes from their substance use, and yet they persist. What this says is that they still believe it is worth the price they're paying. Not only that, but they also often believe that quitting is costlier than continuing because quitting represents losing all the benefits they believe they'll get from continuing to use. This being the case, a narrow focus on the costs of continued heavy substance use will not tip the scales in favor of change.

Occasionally, fear may help people *initiate* change by sparking the thought of *I've gotta stop the destruction*, but this fear is often short lived. The PDP shows us why. Motivation goes in one direction only, toward happiness, so it's determined by where you see the most benefits. If you don't see change as more than just a reduction in costs and instead as a route to increased benefits and thus happiness, then you will revert to thinking that resumed substance use is worth the costs. So, if you see sufficient benefits in heavy substance use, you will be motivated to do it. That is, you will want; desire; or, as the popular terminology goes, *crave* it. This part of our perspective, your view of the benefits of heavy substance use versus your view of the benefits of a lesser amount of substance use, is what creates your motivation for the latter. Focusing on costs alone doesn't change your view of the benefits.

Remember the quotation from Aristotle at the beginning of this chapter: "The object of rational wish is the end, i.e. the good or the apparent good." By being careful to include "the apparent good," Aristotle recognizes that motivation is entirely subjective, that people choose based on what they see as the good. Finding a new good is the key, that is, changing your perspective on what your happier option is. We're not saying you should ignore the costs, but you already know what they are. So now, it's time to focus more on the benefits of your various options. Stop trying to tip the scales based on fear by focusing on costs. Tipping the scales of happiness, of perceived benefits, is what will motivate you to make new choices.

WHAT TO REMEMBER

The PDP is a description of how human behavior is motivated. It's based on an inherent, immutable drive toward happiness, which then gets directed into specific behaviors/choices based on your view that those behaviors/choices are your best available means of acquiring the most happiness in that moment. So the one-line definition for you to remember goes like this:

> The Positive Drive Principle (PDP): the principle that humans will always act to move in the direction where they perceive the greatest happiness.

Although the PDP drives all human behavior, it is particularly important to recognize and remember regarding problems of personal behavior. When you're dealing with things that are out of your direct control, such as diseases, natural disasters, other people, institutions, and physical circumstances, then other principles may be more important, looking for "causes" may be more important, any number of things may be more important. But with personal behavior, there are no causes; there are only reasons. To overcome any behavioral issue, such as substance use, people must look at what makes them think the problematic behavior/choice is their happiest option and whether they have happier options at their disposal. This is the only way to become motivated to act differently.

People judge their options comparatively. That is, they don't just want things in isolation; they want them because they're seen as better than the other things they think are available to them. This is common sense but needs to be highlighted particularly with substance use because, for some reason, when people try to quit because of shame and social pressure, they tend to look at the costs and benefits of substance use alone without fleshing out a fuller view of the other options: less or no substance use. If you fall into this trap of focusing on only one option, then you will not be able to see quitting/decreasing your substance use as a happier option. By failing to see more happiness in change, you won't develop lasting motivation to change. From there, you'll either work very hard at resisting further substance use and be miserable, or you'll continue heavy substance use and be miserable now that you're hyperfocused on its high costs.

Fear alone is not enough to motivate you to make a lasting change in the substance use habit. Remember the PDP, and you can look for positive reasons to change. Heavy costs can spark the feeling that something must change, but it won't fully materialize until you change your view of what your happiest options are.

If you subscribe to the cause-based view of human behavior and addiction, this entire lesson will be moot. If you recognize the PDP, you open the way to discovering your happiest options.

We have now provided a commonsense view of what motivates human behavior. Later, we examine two more aspects of humanity that allow you to redirect your PDP, free will and mental autonomy, giving you a full construct on how to initiate change. If you accept that *The Freedom Model* is true, you know that

- there are no causes of human behavior, only reasons for it held within the mind of the individual making the choice;

- you are motivated to use substances heavily by your view that it is your best available route to happiness; and

- you have the freedom to rethink things, reevaluate your options, arrive at new visions of happiness, and make new choices.

Then, you will change your goal from fighting an addiction or battling "causes" of your behavior or resisting your desires to a goal of discovering what level of substance use would make you happiest by your own judgment. If you should discover that you can see change as genuinely happier (and not just less costly), you will then effortlessly change, never to feel mired in "addiction" again. To achieve this end, you will need to shamelessly accept your current level of substance use and recognize that you have truly seen happiness in it. It will require you to be open to rethinking all your options. These are all mental efforts and take only a willingness to think things through critically. These efforts take no strength, so they won't be "hard" in the sense that we often think "overcoming an addiction" is hard because the addiction is simply personal preference based on personal beliefs. The only limit to how quickly and easily you can change these beliefs is how openminded and critical-thinking you're willing to be.

We know that many of you will have your doubts. You think *It can't be this simple.* You may feel that your substance use must be out of your control, that there must be a deeper, darker truth to why you feel stuck. If you didn't believe this, then you wouldn't have sought any help. It is essential that you rediscover your freedom and forever do away with the addict self-image that creates these doubts. The following chapters will explain why you feel this way and how you got there so you can eventually shed this destructive self-image. We also know that some of you will express immediate full agreement and want to jump ahead to see how to reevaluate your happiest options. However, we've often seen this state of agreement quickly followed by more doubt—*but isn't it genetic, but don't I need to increase my self-control and willpower, but what about my underlying issues.* Please be patient as we cover all the necessary ground to set the stage for your success. The lessons here are the result of decades of research and direct experience in communicating these ideas, and while it is true that you already have all the power it takes to change, our job is to make sure you fully understand the path to change.

REFERENCES

Seligman, M. E. P. (2006). Learned optimism: how to change your mind and your life. New York: Vintage Books.

CHAPTER 8:

THE ADDICT/ ALCOHOLIC SELF-IMAGE

We've discussed the reasons behind a strong preference for substance use, explained the difference between causes and reasons, and most important, introduced you to the power of the Positive Drive Principle (PDP). These concepts are the foundation of *The Freedom Model*, and if we discard the failed theories of recovery ideology, the conclusion should be getting clear: *substance users want to be intoxicated because they prefer being intoxicated.* They believe substances have various benefits that serve their needs, so they freely choose to use them. Like any other behavior, as people repeatedly engage in it, it becomes easier to keep repeating and thus more attractive to repeat than to change. Thus, people build a preference for substance use and mindlessly keep repeating it. It isn't any more complicated than that. People view using substances at their current level as better than using less or no substances. The same processes that underlie your use could also change the habitual desire and behavior. That is, you could rethink the benefits of using versus not using and then make new choices and new habits; then, the change feels normal and natural and takes no effort to maintain.

Unfortunately, some substance users start to think they've got a weakness or handicap called an "addiction." The more these substance users learn and believe the hype about addiction, the more helpless they feel. They transform from a fully capable person into a helpless person, which keeps them from implementing the very simple, innate powers they have to change. As they become true believers in addiction, they're effectively hobbled by this destructive self-image.

For those of us who've escaped this destructive set of views, it's hard to watch. It's like seeing a man with fully functioning legs who's become convinced that he can't walk, and now lives confined to a wheelchair. It's only his beliefs that keep him hobbled. Sadly, though, his loved ones also believe his legs don't work, so that, when he occasionally stands up, they scream in horror, telling him to get back into the chair or he'll surely fall and hurt himself. When everyone around him believes the illusion, it's hard for him to convince himself otherwise even though he sometimes does venture out of the chair and walks.

We'll describe the full process of how this illusion is generated in the next chapter, but for now, please open your mind to the idea that powerlessness over drugs and alcohol and your own behavior is an illusion and that it comes about through logical errors and misinformation.

EVERYTHING CHANGES ONCE YOU SEE YOURSELF AS ADDICTED

It's hard to quantify in data exactly what changes when people see themselves as addicted, but it's a general sense of defeat that creeps into their entire existence. Their spirit withers and fades as they accept their fate. The authors of *The Freedom Model* have experienced this state of despair themselves. Mark had quit drinking for over a year but was trapped in the recovery society because of court mandates. He was in outpatient programs where counselors worked daily to get him to conform to the disease view and to see himself as being in for a life-long struggle with addiction even though he had already willingly quit on his own. As he thought of this lifelong struggle, it brought him to the point of hopelessness.

Michelle took on this identity even before taking her first drink or drug. She was told at a young age that she had inherited the "alcoholic gene." Her father and both his parents had been diagnosed as "alcoholics," and several other relatives had severe alcohol and drug problems. When she was 10 years old, after her father had been mandated to attend AA meetings, a well-meaning AA member told her that they were "saving a seat for her." She took her first drink at 12 years old and liked it, but she had already felt the sting of shame and guilt. Her fear of the immense, supernatural powers of alcohol and genetic predisposition to alcoholism was ingrained and reinforced throughout her adolescence so that, when she began "partying" in high school, she drank "uncontrollably." Once in college, she progressed rapidly from the weekend warrior to a daily heavy drinker and drug user and struggled with severe depression.

Steven experienced it too. He'd been a multidrug user and used heroin on and off nasally for a few years before treatment. He hadn't behaved in the desperate ways of an "addict" yet and knew he would never inject drugs. But within a week following his stay at an inpatient treatment program (a program that featured seven 12-step–based sessions a day) he began injecting heroin and stealing from his family to support his drug use, and he became the desperate junkie stereotype that the addiction treatment providers taught him to become. He remembers vividly being told in rehab that "You're not done yet. You'll be shooting up soon. They all do." And that's exactly what he did. Prior to this treatment, the idea of shooting up was foreign, and he never considered it an option. That point is important for you to know. Consequently, once he crossed that line, his spirit was crushed. This was the beginning of five years of hell for him as the fatalism of his new *addict* self-image ate away at his life.

We see people with crushed spirits like this every day. One of the worst symptoms is that they go from simply wanting or liking intoxication to *needing* it. Again, they don't really need it; they've learned that they need it through the "help" and "awareness" offered by the recovery society. They go from thinking substance use is something they like now to feeling like it's a compulsion they'll be stuck with for the rest of their lives. They don't independently come up with this new way of seeing their preference for substance use; the recovery society teaches it to them.

These teachings directly affect the plight of people with substance use problems. Research has shown that belief in the disease model of addiction increases binges and relapses. After treatment, people interpret all sorts of things as dangerous triggers that can cause them to use, and they walk around paranoid that they'll be triggered to *fall off the wagon* at any moment. A common story heard in support meetings goes like this:

> You have to be on the lookout for triggers at all times. I was sober for 10 years, and then I went to a wedding. I stayed away from the bar, and everything was fine. But then dessert was served. I ate it, but it tasted weird, then I found out it was tiramisu, a cake that contains alcohol. I started craving and couldn't control myself. I went right over to that open bar and started drinking. That cake kicked off a relapse that lasted almost two years before I got back into recovery.

These stories tell the tale of an *expectancy response* (placebo effect) learned from the recovery ideology. That person was taught that she had an "allergy to alcohol" that would cause her to crave and drink uncontrollably once she'd had so much as a drop of alcohol enter her system. The result was that, because she believed in this idea, when she did ingest some alcohol, the belief kicked in and caused her to feel weak and compelled, and she acted out what she'd been taught. She blamed the cake, but the real culprit was the belief.

The same sorts of expectancies are being set up now with opioid painkillers:

> I was never really a drug user other than a joint once in a while at a party. But then I injured my back loading a truck at work and the doctor put me on painkillers. I was afraid, and I even asked if they were addictive. I had friends who got hooked on those pills. But the doctor told me I'd be fine. Then I started to feel weird when I didn't have my prescription for a day, and I realized I was addicted. I started using more and more of them, going to different doctors to get them, and then I started buying heroin when I couldn't get more pills. It's been five years of this hell.

This man believed the ongoing media hype about painkillers, and as a result, he was effectively "addicted" to them even before the doctor had prescribed them and he had taken a single pill. He had a set of beliefs similar to our drinker above. He thought these pills had the power to enslave him into continuous use. So, when he took them and felt a little odd, panic set in as he thought *They got me; I'm addicted!* and the addict self-image was cemented.

There is no such thing as an addictive drug although there are drugs that can lead to withdrawal syndrome. Recovery society ideas such as "addictiveness" matter even in the case of withdrawal syndrome, which many think is a fully physical phenomenon that produces irresistible cravings. In fact, it's not; there is a massive cognitive component to it that is ruled by belief. Mountains of evidence demonstrate that opiate withdrawal is easily tolerable and doesn't produce cravings or compel further opiate use in most people. But some people *learn to think of themselves as "hooked" or addicted*, and then they feel opiate withdrawal as a compulsion to use more opiates. A simple change in perspective turns a sickness that normally feels like the flu into an otherworldly force that makes you want, need, and pursue opiates at all costs. (see Appendix D)

REALITY, INTERPRETATIONS, AND FEELINGS

One of the few valuable things to come out of 20th-century psychology comes from those working in the field of Cognitive Behavioral Therapy (CBT). Theorists and researchers from this school found that *feelings are the result of how people interpret the events and circumstances of their lives.*

For example, the feeling of stress is "the interpretation of an event as signaling harm, loss, or threat" (Sayette, 1999), here's how it can play out. When, for example, you face the *reality* of failing at some task at your job, you may *interpret* that event as signaling that you will soon be fired (i.e., you will suffer a loss). As soon as you interpret it this way, you *feel* stress. On the other hand, you could also interpret it as a sign that your boss will choose to give that responsibility to a coworker, thereby freeing you to concentrate more efficiently on the tasks more suited to your strengths. In this case, you now see it as signaling a potential *gain* rather than a loss. Because of this *interpretation*, you feel no stress and maybe even a little excitement. The interpretation of reality is the mediating factor of the feelings that will follow.

All feelings work this way. They are the result of your interpretation of reality. When you interpret an event as an injustice, you feel anger. When you interpret an event as beneficial, you feel happy. When you interpret an event as signaling that your choices are productive and beneficial, you feel pride and confidence. When you interpret an event as signaling that you have no power to change a bad situation, you feel sadness and depression.

Although they can be hard to sort out, all feelings people have come from their thoughts and interpretation of reality. As demonstrated above, different interpretations are possible and will result in different feelings. Sometimes, your interpretation of reality may be objectively wrong. For example, you may buy a new home and think that signals a bright new chapter of your life when the reality is that the home is riddled with mold and other problems that will bog you down in unwanted expenses and work. Instead of being joyful, the purchase of the new home turns out to be a dark and trying chapter of your life. Your initial elation turns to anger and sadness as you slowly discover a more accurate interpretation of the reality of the situation. It works the other way too. Maybe you were anxious and stressed that you were getting in too deep and wouldn't be a good homeowner, but then it all worked out. It's your interpretations that determine your initial feelings even if they don't accurately reflect reality.

There are two feelings we're primarily concerned with in helping our readers understand: strong desires and the feeling of being powerless to change those desires. You feel a desire for substance use because you see it as providing something beneficial and as a viable route to those benefits. This is the PDP in action. If this desire rises to a feeling of need, it's because you see it as the *only* thing that will provide the benefits you believe you need. This desire can then be complicated by what you learn from those *helpers* entrenched in recovery ideology.

Your desire or preference for substance use can become a source for other feelings. If you interpret it as a normal, harmless desire, you won't feel much. But if you interpret it as an addiction or compulsion, you will then feel addicted, compelled, and unable to stop without help. If you hadn't learned to interpret it this way, you'd feel free to change it. It's only your belief system that holds you back.

Your preference for substance use changes once you learn to think of it as an addiction. It goes from something you feel you genuinely like and voluntarily choose to do to something you feel you are compelled to do with no rhyme or reason. These beliefs lead you to interpret other normal events and thoughts in troubling ways that result in feelings of pain and helplessness. The following table sums up the way many

things are felt/experienced before and after learning to think of yourself as addicted:

Event to Be Interpreted	Before Addict Self-Image	After Addict Self-Image
Preferring intoxication	It's what I like to do.	I don't like it. It's what I'm compelled to do.
Momentary desire for substance use	Something I may or may not choose to do as I think it through.	A powerful urge or craving that's hard and sometimes impossible to resist; proof of my addiction.
Withdrawal sickness	Tolerable consequence of ceasing substance use that sometimes requires medical help for safety.	Intolerable compulsion to continue using.
Being in the presence of substance use	An occasion where I may or may not choose to use.	A dangerous triggering situation where I might be compelled to use.
A single drink or hit	A single drink or hit.	A guaranteed uncontrollable binge of use that may never end.
A single drink or hit	A freely chosen drink or hit	An involuntary "relapse" or "slip."
A night of heavy substance use	An isolated choice, limited to one night.	A relapse into addiction.

Event to Be Interpreted	Before Addict Self-Image	After Addict Self-Image
A passing thought about substance use	A harmless thought or memory about something that's been a big part of my life.	A powerful craving or urge that's tough to resist. Sign that I have a long battle ahead of me.
Stressful moments	Normal life problem.	A trigger that will lead to relapse if not properly handled.
Angry moment	Normal occurrence of life.	A trigger that will lead to relapse if not properly handled.
Sad/depressing moment	Normal occurrence of life.	A trigger that will lead to relapse if not properly handled.
Using substances to blow off steam	Momentary avoidance of a problem.	Self-medication for the underlying issues that cause addiction.

Seeing yourself through the lens of disease and dysfunction, you become a helpless, handicapped victim rather than an empowered chooser. But if you change your beliefs and interpretations, once again, you can change these feelings. A drink becomes a drink, stress becomes stress, and choices become choices.

Although you *feel* addicted—and we realize this is a painful and terrifying feeling—the *reality* is that you aren't addicted. You are now and always have been fully in control of your substance use and capable of decreasing or quitting it when you want to decrease or quit. You're not doomed to continue living with the dread and sense of powerlessness you may currently be feeling.

SELF-IMAGE MATTERS

The way you see yourself—your self-image—has powerful implications. Some of you may not have directly experienced addiction treatment and recovery ideology, but the addict/alcoholic identity its proponents foster is deeply entrenched throughout our society. So we now ask you, have you come to see yourself this way?

Recovery ideology compounds the problems of people with strong preferences for intoxication by teaching them to identify as helplessly addicted. This self-image is damaging, so one of our main tasks in this book is to show that the beliefs underlying the addict self-image are factually incorrect. This is so you can either make sure you avoid taking it on, or change it if you've already come to believe it.

The quickest route to changing starts with realizing that you aren't really addicted and that your use is just a preference. You can reject the recovery society belief that you are helpless and need to be coddled. From there, you can reassess substance use and thereby change your preference for it. With the power of the PDP, you don't have to struggle to change and fight an addiction; you just need to see that you can be happier by making an adjustment to your substance use.

Addiction is a matter of perspective, not a state of being that compels you to drink or drug. *Remember, you don't have addiction. Nobody does. What you have is a strong preference for substance use that you've learned to interpret as a compulsion.* As real and as strong as the feelings of being addicted, powerless, hopeless, and unable to change are, they are merely the product of your thoughts and desires and not a reflection of an objective state of involuntary substance use. The next chapter will give you some understanding on how you may have learned to see yourself this way.

REFERENCES

Sayette, M. (1999). Does drinking reduce stress? *Alcohol Research & Health*, *23*(4), 250–255.

CHAPTER 9:

LEARNING THE ADDICT SELF-IMAGE

N ow that you understand the destructive power of the addict self-image, it is important to gain insight into how it is acquired. If you ask yourself *Why am I this way?* then this chapter will provide your answer. Once the confusion is cleared up, you will be free to develop a new, more accurate and thus empowering self-image.

Recovery ideology directly teaches the addict self-image, and that's obvious when you're required to identify as an addict/alcoholic to be compliant with treatment and in support group meetings. But there is also a set of easily observable social processes that teach people to take on the self-image and role of the addict. So whether you've been in-doctrinated into this belief system in a treatment program or not, there are many ways you can be persuaded to take on this damaging self-image. Let's review the ways people learn to see themselves as addicted and subsequently feel powerless and handicapped.

THE PLAYGROUND EFFECT

There's a common process whereby normal mistakes and missteps end up feeling like extraordinarily terrifying disasters. We call it the play-ground effect, based on a common example most people have experi-enced or seen.

If you've brought a child under your care to the playground, you've probably seen this happen. He's being rambunctious and running around with the other kids like an animal until he falls and bangs his knee. He might stop to nurse the wound for a few seconds, and then he jumps back up on the jungle gym. Perhaps he's a little more careful, but he happily goes on with his playtime. He doesn't feel like this incident is a disaster. *But there's another way this scene can play out.* You may look on in horror terrified that the child suffered a severe injury. He looks up, makes eye contact with you, sees that you are terrified, and starts bawling.

In that moment, the look on your face told him "this is a disaster." He then began to experience the minor injury *as a major disaster*. If he hadn't made eye contact, he'd have been fine, although maybe a little bruised. But now he feels more pain, and he's screaming, crying, and thinking he needs to go to the hospital, and the outing to the playground is ruined. His entire experience was changed when he learned to see this incident as a disaster. This interaction and its effects are what we call *the playground effect*.

The playground effect follows people into adulthood too. Much of how people define their problems and themselves is based on how others define them. It's clear how this occurs in treatment programs. People arrive in treatment with various self-images. Many (not all) feel as if they're fully in control even if they realize their substance use is the source of problems. They're like the child on the playground; they realize there's an issue but don't think it's the end of the world—yet. Then the counselors "confront their denial" and demand that they see their problem through the tragic lens of recovery ideology. They present it as a binary choice between seeing things their way or facing jails, institutions, and a tragic early death.

Treatment providers give you dire warnings and teachings about how you will be dealing with addiction for the rest of your life. They get in your face and demand that you admit you are "powerless" to control your substance use. They implore you to see it as an incurable, chronic brain disease. They have all the misconstrued props and stories needed to convince you to see your fate as tragic and your problem as insurmountable.

The fact is, research repeatedly verifies that addiction is the most short-lived of all "psychiatric disorders." *It isn't chronic* and people don't normally deal with it for the rest of their lives (see appendix C). So their dire warnings and the picture they paint of the condition are exactly like the paranoid parent on the playground; they are instantly jumping to an unrealistic worst-case scenario. What makes this even worse is that their position lends them credibility; some have medical credentials and many letters behind their names, and their air of superiority convinces many people to take them very seriously. It's no coincidence that overdose and binge rates peak right after treatment. They send people out into the world with the belief that they can't control themselves and will fall apart. This all injects a massive dose of panic into the situation. Panic, by it's very nature, cannot be the source of calm, logically reasoned long-term decision-making. It is the source of rash, scatterbrained, unfocused, fear induced short-range decisions.

The results are often shocking. People go for treatment to be helped, to improve their condition, but they leave a wreck. Binge rates and relapse rates go up following treatment; people's behavior often becomes more desperate, more reckless; they become fragile and live on edge, always suspecting a relapse is just around the corner. They tend to struggle harder and longer than those who haven't received treatment. The dynamic is clear; treatment implores you to see your situation as a disaster, and it often becomes just that.

While the direct teachings of treatment programs are the most visible way substance users learn to think of themselves as hopelessly addicted, they aren't the only way they learn this. What's less clear are the subtle ways the playground effect happens. The chatter, the gossip, the people who stop inviting you places and act like you're crazy or can't be trusted. You notice this. Their fright becomes your fright. You question yourself. You've heard about addicts. You begin to think that maybe you are one. It starts as a dull anxiety and eventually becomes a state of constant panic. Someone makes a seemingly benign comment: "Oh, you're having a wine with lunch? Won't your kids be getting home from school in a couple of hours?" They've now highlighted a truly benign choice as something dark or sinister (it really isn't sinister though; in the Mediterranean, some people have a glass of wine with every meal and are no worse for the wear). You think *What the heck is that supposed to mean?* And it starts to gnaw at you. *Am I bad mother? Oh no—I'm an alcoholic!* Had nobody highlighted the glass of wine, it would've been uneventful. But now it's been given new meaning; it's something disastrous.

The playground effect comes into play whenever a concerned friend, relative, or acquaintance sees your substance use as *an addiction* and conveys this to you in some way. It might be conveyed with a direct talk, with criticism or sarcasm, or with disapproving looks and hushed chatter that you realize is directed at you. Then the freak-out begins, as you take their cue to see yourself as an addicted monster. What's usually coming from a place of loving concern can be harmful and sow the seeds of crippling self-doubt that can last for years or, sadly, a lifetime. These people are the loving and overconcerned parent on the playground, and you are the naïve child who follows their lead into a damaging panic spiral.

In a formal group intervention, the playground effect is taken to the nth degree. The substance user is coerced to sit in a room while all her loved ones spout dire predictions of the devastation she'll face if she doesn't get treatment. And where this isn't just a prediction of the inevitable consequences of substance use, it's also a promise that the loved ones will do something to ruin her quality of life. The professional interventionist says he's seen a thousand other people just like you die so you'd better take this seriously. At this point many substance users begin to take it so seriously that they believe their problem is worse than it is. *Like the child on the playground, if they had been allowed to interpret their issues at face value, they'd seem more manageable to them. But after an intervention, your issues redefine you as hopelessly doomed.*

Heavy substance users have a strong preference for substance use. Their natural, untainted interpretation and experience of this strong preference is usually that they love getting high or drunk. Their substance use may be causing considerable problems, and they recognize this. But they really don't feel out of control or addicted until they learn to reinterpret that preference as a compulsion or addiction. They could change their preference, but this power to change gets hidden under all the self-doubt they learn and panic they feel. Don't believe us? Consider what happens when diagnosable addiction goes unnoticed—when "addicts" don't see themselves as such.

College is an interesting environment where the playground effect on drinking is rare. In our culture, drinking in college is extreme, and it's a rite of passage of sorts to engage in this drinking. In fact, it's so extreme that it's estimated that approximately 25% of college-aged individuals fit the diagnosis for alcoholism (SAMHSA, 2014). They get wild, they cause trouble, and they get fall-down drunk regularly. This is the accepted norm and isn't considered dysfunctional by most.

University students are surrounded by peers who see nothing wrong with this style of drinking. The parents aren't there to hover, disapprove, and freak out. Many administrators simply look the other way, understanding that this drinking is just a part of college life. In short, the playground effect is noticeably absent from this environment. Most college drinkers never get the message that their wild drinking is dooming them to a life of alcoholism.[4]

Like the child happily running around on the playground, they usually take their knocks without much ado. Although they fit the diagnosis, most of them never seek help because they haven't learned to think of themselves as needing it. Most never see their drinking as a big deal so they quite naturally outgrow it. After 22 years of age, this style of drinking begins a rapid decline such that, by 30 years of age, only 6% to 7% fit the diagnosis (SAMHSA, 2014). With no one to send the message that they're doomed to a life of alcoholism, they don't blow things out of proportion; most naturally tire of this drinking and move on with their lives.

Ironically, many of the parents who send their children to rehabs have been through a stage of "addiction" themselves and naturally outgrew it. We hear it all the time from callers seeking help at our retreats. Typically, they caught their college-aged son (or daughter) with some drugs, or he got in trouble at school for drinking. They immediately shipped him off to a rehab. He gets out and either escalates his use, or they suspect he's used drugs again (even if no real problems have occurred because of it). So they look for more help and call us. They tell us things like "It's serious; he's gonna die; addiction runs in our family, and I wanna nip this in the bud. My father drank a lot, and when I was in college I had a huge cocaine problem." Then we ask the parent, "So how did you quit doing cocaine?" We've gotten this same answer back so many times that it's absurd: "Well, I got out of school, moved out on my own, and it just wasn't as exciting as it used to be and cost a lot. I gradually did it less and less until I just decided I was done with it."

---

4. We'll note that this trend of looking the other way is currently changing; as the recovery society is setting up services in many colleges in recent years called "recovery campuses" or "sober dorms," and acknowledge that within a few years, this longstanding example may become obsolete. Such is the rapid growth and reach of recovery ideology.

They're convinced that their son's problem will end tragically and that he's unable to stop despite the fact that they had a big drug habit at his same age and *easily stopped it without professional help* or a lifetime of meetings. No one had intervened with them, and yet they turned out fine. But not only are they intervening and teaching their son that he's an addict with an incurable disease; they're also ready to put him right back into another rehab the moment he so much as takes a puff off a joint. We have seen many of these cases get worse and worse because everyone blows it out of proportion, and sadly sometimes, the college student ends up becoming a 40-year-old child who has spent 20 years in and out of rehabs. These cases are the most direct example of the playground effect—a paranoid parent observing a child, but they're both a little older now and the playground is a college.

To be crystal clear, we're not saying there isn't a legitimate problem in any of these cases. What we're taking issue with is how the problem is defined. The parent in our last example probably didn't define her cocaine problem in her youth as an addiction at the time. She defined it as "using too much cocaine." She decided to cut down to use the money she was spending on cocaine for something she cared about more, such as paying rent, a car payment, or electric bill or whatever her other needs and desires were. Her definition allowed for a simple, straightforward solution. What the observers in our other examples are doing is defining *drinking too much* as *involuntarily drinking and needing professional help to make sure you never drink again*. They're defining it in a way that is both inaccurate and unhelpful and leaves the individual living in fear, self-doubt, and panic. This redefinition compounds the problem. It is directly analogous to the bump on the knee being redefined as a life-threatening tragedy that requires a trip to the hospital, and it goes a giant step further in prescribing a *lifetime* of daily effort to avoid playgrounds altogether.

DEVIANCE, SHAME, SHOULDS, AND JUSTIFICATION

Heavy substance use is deviant behavior, and by this, we mean only that it is outside the realm of normal, culturally accepted behavior. Most people think it's bad or morally wrong. To the degree that people value being normal (i.e., not deviant) and being accepted, they may take on our culture's view that heavy substance use (or even mild use of a taboo substance such as heroin) is bad. Yet they prefer it and continue to do it. The next logical step upon realizing this is for them to think *I am bad because I want to do a bad thing*. This is shame. Or they think *I shouldn't want this* or *I shouldn't do this*. This is more shame. Then they get the message from others that their behavior is wrong and bad, that they shouldn't like it or do it. This leads to even more shame.

Some substance users also begin paying a heavy price for their substance use. They spend money they need for other things. They get into trouble, they disappoint their loved ones by choosing a high or drunk against the loved one's wishes, and they clash with those who disapprove of their behavior. These consequences can be very personally upsetting. They feel a need to explain their continued substance use to others and themselves. *Why would I keep doing something that's causing so much pain?*

The answer that's most immediately satisfying is "I can't control myself." They've heard about addiction, and they've been concerned, wondering whether they might be addicted. In a moment of pain, it begins to make sense. It reduces the cognitive dissonance, the shame, guilt, and pain for at least a moment and allows them to not completely hate themselves. They think that people can't be good and want something bad at the same time, yet they know they do have good intentions. So it seems like the only way to reconcile these facts is to conclude *I don't really like it; I don't really want to do it; I must be addicted.*

When others are badgering you to justify your choices to them, it just doesn't seem right to say "I do it because I like it." It also may not seem accurate anymore if you've concluded it's a bad thing and you couldn't rationally like a bad thing. So substance users say they don't like it and that they can't control it. Sometimes, they really believe this; sometimes they don't. But either way, this explanation serves a function: it reduces any altercations and comforts them.

These painful circumstances that many substance users experience make the idea of involuntary substance use believable. You know that you don't want to hurt the people around you or get yourself into trouble, yet you're doing it with your substance use. The idea of being addicted—of *having to* drink and drug—seems to make sense of your clashing wants. When substance users use "addiction" to explain their behavior and its unwanted consequences, they stop feeling so bad for at least a *moment*. It is in these moments that people learn to feel addicted.

Thankfully, this clash of wants doesn't have to be interpreted in this way. Conflicting wants are a normal part of life. Maybe you want to be at your daughter's basketball game, and you want to make enough money to secure your family's future. So you stay working late on a project instead of going to the game. How do you explain this when she's upset? "Sorry, honey, I *had to* work." This smooths it over by making it feel like an injustice to both her and you, as if you were forced to keep working. But you weren't. You wanted to work just a little bit more than you wanted to go to the game (you "preferred" this choice) because you saw more long-term joy that would be the result of work. Explaining this can be hard, but it makes you feel like the empowered decider making the tough choices rather than making you both feel like victims and helpless pawns of a cruel universe.

When you choose to get intoxicated while knowing it will conflict with some other want, you are also choosing the option you think will bring more happiness. Within our culture, choosing to get intoxicated is viewed to be an uglier choice than choosing to work late, but in principle, it's the same. When making that choice, you may think that you need to be high or drunk to feel comfort and happiness, and you're choosing to pay the price for it. You know it will upset a loved one, or leave you without money for rent, or whatever the price may be, and you're willing to pay it. If you begin acknowledging this (rather than going to the *comforting but incorrect* "I have to do this" explanations), it brings the value of your various options into focus. It keeps you aware of the perceived benefits and the trade-offs and makes you better able to eventually understand when the trade-offs are no longer worth it.

INCENTIVIZED HELPLESSNESS

Once people begin to see you as an addict, you are expected to conform to the recovery ideology or face sanctions in some way. If you express disagreement with its views, your loved ones will now see you as falling backward even if you are completely abstinent. If you simply cut down your drinking to moderate levels, they will see you as a ticking time bomb or believe that you must be hiding the true extent of your drinking.

This creates an incentive for you to parrot the recovery rhetoric whether you believe it or not. You must do this if you want to keep your family off your back, but there can be more than just annoying and unpleasant nagging on the line. Your family may have been taught tough love and may threaten to withdraw love, emotional support, and material/financial support of all kinds if you aren't actively "working on your recovery" by attending meetings, addiction treatment sessions, or therapy.

If you choose to use substances at all and you parrot the recovery rhetoric, you can get somewhat of a pass from your family by explaining that your substance use is a "relapse" into the "disease of addiction" that was "triggered" by the stress they caused you. So you get to use, get forgiven for it, and get to blame it on them, and often, you retain whatever support you're getting by talking the talk of *working* on recovery.

This is an enormous incentive for people who don't intend to quit using substances at all to start using the recovery language. You lose for sure if you don't, but you can also win a lot if you continue to talk the talk. The problem is that you might start to believe it and begin to truly feel powerlessly addicted.

If you attend treatment, whether inpatient or outpatient, you learn that disagreeing or questioning recovery ideology in any way results in confrontation. You also learn that those who talk the talk get more privileges in treatment (trips off-site of the rehab, visitation and communication privileges, friendship with staff, etc.). They also get glowing reports sent to family, courts, and probation officers. Dissenters do not get these benefits. They may even get bad reports or recommendations to courts or families that their treatment should be extended. They are said to be "in denial," and it is predicted that they will relapse.

When coercive arrangements are in play, there can be a lot riding on whether you agree to start identifying yourself as a powerless addict or not. Jail time, driver's licenses, professional licenses (e.g., a doctor's license), housing, child custody, marriages, and whatever other myriad things the legal system, parents, and spouses control can be on the line. To win, you must talk the talk. Thus, these arrangements incentivize you to start speaking like an addict, and in the process, you just might start believing your own press.

We don't intend to give the impression that everyone who goes to treatment becomes a diabolical liar, flipping the script to his or her advantage; nor do we intend to suggest that people are helpless victims of these circumstances. These incentives are just one more factor that makes identifying as an addict seem like the only rational choice at the time. The system encourages substance users to see themselves in this way. The incentives combined with the recovery ideology, the playground effect, and the emotional puzzle of shame all play off each other to create a trap that's easy to fall into.

LEARNING ADDICTION FROM CULTURE

Some readers of *The Freedom Model* may have no direct experience with the recovery society treatments or meetings, so they may wonder how much of this can apply to them. You may think *Nobody taught me to feel addicted; I just feel it because I really can't control myself.* We would ask that you think over that belief system carefully and where it may have originated. You'll come to realize you've been exposed to recovery ideology your entire life.

How many movies and television shows have you seen that include an addiction story line? You probably couldn't count them even if you tried. The sad part is that they all fit the same mold. A character is using drugs, and other people warn him he's addicted and out of control, to which he says "I can control it; I can stop whenever I want." Then the substance user is mocked for saying this and said to be "in denial." He refuses treatment, and disastrous things happen. He realizes he's powerless. He goes to rehab and starts a life focused on recovery and struggling to avoid temptation for the rest of his life. Sometimes, the story line also features supporting characters who stay in denial, refuse treatment, and die. You've been learning *addiction* your entire life. It shouldn't have to be mentioned, but this story line plays out in countless novels, songs, plays, news stories, memoirs, et cetera. And the media only presents stories that fit the mold. If a person resolves their substance use problems without struggle or without treatment, as most people do, it's said they're "not a real alcoholic/addict." Those stories aren't sexy either and therefore unfit for dramatization. Furthermore, because of the dominance of the recovery ideology in our culture, the people who overcome their problems on their own usually keep quiet about their problems and struggles.

For nearly 100 years, there has been a direct push to portray substance use this way in the media. In 1944, an Alcoholics Anonymous member with a public relations background (Marty Mann) started what is now called the National Council on Alcoholism and Drug Dependence (NCADD), an organization whose aim is to spread the disease model of alcoholism (and later, drug addiction). The organization openly brags about the decades they spent waging a propaganda campaign to change the public's perception of substance use problems. They convinced playwrights and filmmakers to write substance use problems into their work, along the template of 12-step views. They also bragged about getting Hollywood stars onboard for public awareness campaigns and politicians, such as President Eisenhower, onboard to make the disease model of alcoholism/addiction the accepted and politically correct way to view problematic substance use. It's no accident that you've learned to think it's a possibility that your drinking or drugging is involuntary. Many people have worked very hard to create "awareness of the disease of addiction."

Please note, we aren't saying this was/is a nefarious plot to ensnare you into believing a falsehood that would ruin your life. The recovery crusaders mentioned above and all the helpers and loved ones who helped you learn to feel addicted were most likely motivated by an honest desire to help. But their views are wrong, so they've mistakenly helped you to become ensnared in misinformation that can ruin your life. These ideas are dangerous when believed, and the next section contains a glaring example of how these ideas can distort your experience.

THE MYTH OF ADDICTIVE DRUGS

One of the earliest and most widespread drug scares was about the addictive power of opiates. Opium, morphine, heroin, and opioid painkillers are believed to have the power to enslave people by creating physical dependence and withdrawal that compels people to keep using.

It is true that routine daily use of these drugs creates a condition in which a withdrawal sickness may be experienced when you stop using them. But over thousands of years, millions of people have been physically dependent on opiates, and they detoxified without treatment. At its worst, the physical symptoms of this withdrawal are identical to the flu. For example, it's well documented that people come out of hospitals after surgery and go through morphine withdrawal every day, and yet they don't feel compelled to seek out drugs. This is because they don't think of themselves as addicted.

Sociologist Alfred Lindesmith (1968) carried out a famous study of opiate addicts in the 1940s and found that the dividing line between those who become addicted and those who do not is a matter of belief and learning. He cited case after case where the turning point into addiction came when a well-meaning friend or doctor noticed that the opiate user was going through withdrawal and said two magic words to him: *you're hooked* (p. 78).

He outlined a process whereby the user is introduced to the idea of "being hooked," starts fearing he may be a "junkie" or "dope fiend," and then uses more opiates with this idea in his mind. The drug effects then get reinterpreted as something he needs, that he can't go without. This seals the deal on his learning to feel addicted. Those two words—"you're hooked"—kicked off this whole process. Without the idea they represent, his experience of withdrawal would've been drastically different.

This brings us back to the playground effect. Flu-like symptoms become interpreted as an irresistible need for opiates. Essentially, a common cold is made into a fatal cancer by the introduction of a fatalistic concept. Lindesmith also observed that those who were more aware of the idea of addiction, such as doctors, were more likely to "get hooked." Meanwhile, those recreational users who were naïve to this idea or those who didn't realize the medicine or elixir they were taking was an "addictive" opiate were less likely to get hooked or have trouble stopping.

The work of another researcher, Norman Zinberg (1984), confirmed the subjective nature of opiate withdrawal. He was invited by the U.S. government to study the soldiers addicted to heroin in Vietnam. One of his most interesting observations was that when the men were sequestered to their barracks and going through withdrawal, their symptoms varied by barracks. In one, you might find that all the guys might be vomiting and having diarrhea. In another they might be stone

166

faced, quiet, silently going through joint pain, sweats, and headaches. In yet another, they might be screaming and writhing around in pain, visibly "jonesing" and begging for drugs. In each barracks, these soldiers were all collectively influencing each other's perceptions of withdrawal pain. They were all getting the same symptoms as their bunk mates, and these symptoms varied dramatically by barracks.

Objectively, heroin withdrawal is like the flu. Subjectively, it can become completely terrifying depending on what you believe, what kind of expectations and panic through which you filter the pain, and the cues you take from others about how bad and unbearable it should be.

Opiate addiction is the smoking-gun case of addiction, proving that people truly become enslaved by the drug and unable to stop without treatment. Some opiate users learn to feel compelled to seek drugs by withdrawal because they learn that opiates are "addictive" and that they are "hooked" or addicted. But most opiate users don't learn to feel compelled to seek drugs, so they don't feel this need. They just feel sick when they stop taking them. This is where the most evidence has accrued that the ideas and beliefs rule, not the drug. Again, countless millions of people have (and will) go through opiate withdrawal without feeling compelled to seek out more opiates, and the main difference between them and those who "got hooked" is simply perception. Feeling addicted is a matter of believing you're addicted.

It's not a difficult logical leap to understand how the learning process Lindesmith described can apply beyond withdrawal. Convince someone that stress will make them need a drink or a joint, and they may learn a reaction to stress that feels just as strong and compelling to them as withdrawal pain feels to the "junkie." The same can go for any of the other circumstances, emotional states, and life problems that the recovery society connects to heavy substance use. As we described in chapter 6, when you come to believe in these connections, they become very real for you.

OVERCOMPLICATING THE PROBLEM

For some reason, society puts substance use into a special class of behavior and thus believes it must have complex causes. When substance users start pondering questions like "What caused this, what happened to me, why am I this way?" they enter a land of confusion that makes them feel more helpless.

Sometimes people develop this belief system on their own. They think something like *Why am I this way? I came from a good home, a loving family. I wasn't abused or neglected. We always had everything we needed growing up.* Searching for some negative experience or cause leaves them more puzzled and hopeless. It seems like an unsolvable mystery, so they continue using as is, with no hope of changing.

This often happens in interactions with others. It pains them to think that you are willing to pay such a high price for the effects of drugs and alcohol. They consider the behavior so irrational that it couldn't possibly be freely chosen. So they start asking "What is it? Are you depressed or something?" and posit all sorts of "underlying causes of addiction." They present the notion that it must be complicated, and substance users buy into it. It's the playground effect again.

The answer to "what happened to you" is simple. You grew to like and prefer substance use based on a variety of the straightforward reasons laid out throughout this text. Then you started to learn to see this preference as an addiction by a variety of the processes laid out in this chapter.

LEARNING HELPLESSNESS THROUGH FALSE FAILURES

One of the least understood ways people learn to feel helpless is by the disappointment and shame felt after half-hearted attempts to quit. When people try to quit because they "have to" or "should"—that is, out of a sense of fear, duty, obligation, or being cornered in some way—then they aren't usually fully invested in this choice. Since these attempts are largely motivated by fear of consequences, those trying to quit don't see happiness and joy in moderation or abstinence, so it's hard for them to follow through because the proper motivation to change just isn't there.

When these people go back to using, it's seen as a failure by everyone, including themselves. But can you truly fail at something you didn't really want to do? Is it fair to call it a failure? Unfortunately, many people interpret these "failures" as a lack of *ability* to stop. As the failures stack up, the substance user feels more and more helpless. She thinks *I've tried so many times; I just can't do it. I'm an addict, through and through.*

Some people have experienced some "success" in their previous quit attempts, maintaining abstinence for weeks, months, or even years. Many were hanging on, white knuckling it, trying to *willpower* their way through resisting their true wants. Some were happy about it and didn't feel very deprived, but then they went back to using substances and felt like a failure. This is how recovery beliefs become a self-fulfilling prophecy. If you think in terms of addiction, powerful cravings, triggers, slips, relapses, and losing control, then everything gets distorted and confirms itself, deepening a sense of addiction and helplessness.

Recovery ideology hides what's really going on when you choose to quit and when you choose to use substances. It appears like a little voice inside your head saying *See, you're an addict, you can't control yourself.* It turns the choice to have a single drink into a disastrous "relapse" and a "loss of control." If you weren't thinking in those terms, you would see the choice for what it is, an attempt to feel good, to find some happiness (the PDP). And if you found that it didn't produce enough happiness, you'd be less likely to choose it again. Instead, because of recovery beliefs, you end up feeling more helpless, more addicted, and more resigned to a life of disastrous episodes of substance use.

The next step after this increased feeling of helplessness is often a search for the right treatment, the right support system, the right trigger-free environment. All this distracts you from the real issue, which is that you are choosing. You will choose differently if you can come to see different choices as more rewarding. As these new attempts to "treat" and "get into recovery" from your "disease" lead to the same results, you feel more helpless. This is reason we've taken the time to examine the myths of recovery in this book because each attempt to quit using substances framed as "recovery" actually deepens your sense of being addicted and powerless.

The Freedom Model is the antidote to this learned helplessness. You can stop seeing your past quit attempts and resumption of problematic use as failures, as "losing the battle against addiction," as "relapse into the disease." They were simply choices you made in the pursuit of happiness. The thinking behind those choices was often warped by recovery ideology and misinformation; they were not the product of the disease of addiction because no such disease exists. You let a falsehood guide your assessment of these episodes. As you learn the truth about problematic substance use, you can reassess these episodes. They are not evidence that you are addicted; they are evidence that you were either confused about what you wanted or changed your mind about what you wanted.

This example of "failures" as interpreted through recovery ideology is one of many where the logical traps of this viewpoint feed and confirm themselves and make things worse. In a way, all these processes are the same in principle. We showed you how some social processes (playground effect and shaming and request for justification), direct teaching, incentivizing, emotional reasoning, and logical errors come into play to get you to the point of feeling hopelessly addicted. They would be inconsequential without the myth that there's an entity called addiction that robs people of free will.

THOSE TEMPTING "UNDERLYING CAUSES"

One trend that's coming to rule the discourse on addiction is the idea that people with substance use problems are uncontrollably compelled to use substances by their past and present emotional struggles and hardships. Granted, some people have it far worse than others. But emotional states are subjective, and nearly everyone has had painful episodes in their history, especially during childhood and adolescence. So even if your childhood was generally good, you can probably point to episodes and events that really hurt when you were growing up. If you've heard a convincing presentation of the theory that these experiences permanently scar people and turn them into helpless addicts later in life, then you might start connecting them to your substance use as "causes" of your current behavior. The seeds of self-doubt have been planted.

This same reasoning is applied to feelings of inadequacy, episodes of depression and anxiety, and more. Through the lens of recovery ideology, addicts, we're told, have these problems. Then you think *Oh no, I have these problems; I am an addict!* It doesn't occur to you that all people have those problems, so everyone who looks for them in their lives will find them.

This is a particularly thorny issue because the fact that so many substance users feel alone in their problems and that they are damaged because of them while everyone else has it all together allows this underlying causes theory to lure them into its trap. The fact is that most people have these problems, but only a small percentage of them have heavy substance use problems. Plenty of other people see themselves as damaged too, but they tend to want to keep that self-image a secret. You are far less alone than you might imagine. Don't let this erroneous belief make you feel trapped in "addiction."

Think of it this way. Have you ever seen one of the psychics on television who walks up to a person and says "I see a spirit next to you. Did you lose someone you love?" Yes, of course he did; we all have! Then the psychic says "He says he knows. Was there something you wanted to tell him that you didn't get to say before he died?" The audience member then breaks out crying and says "Yes, I wanted to tell him I love him and forgive him, and I never got to say it!" The psychic's claims are so vague and universal that they would've applied to almost anyone in the audience. That's how the "underlying causes of addiction" rhetoric works to bring people in and create self-doubt. The "causes" proposed are so vague and universal that they apply to everyone and then help cement the illusion that you are an "addict."

YOU CAN BREAK OUT OF THE ADDICT ROLE

Social roles are social. That is, they are the product of an interaction between two or more people. To create and sustain a role, both people need to believe in it and play along. For example, in a mentor/mentee relationship, the mentor must see herself as having something to offer the mentee, and the mentee must see himself as having something to gain from the mentor's advice. Then the mentee needs to ask for advice, and the mentor needs to offer it. If either of the parties doesn't see him- or herself in the role and the exchange of advice doesn't occur, the roles cease.

Likewise, to be in the addict role, some people need to see the substance user as helpless, *and the substance user needs to agree to see himself as helpless too and less than those other people.* It's easy to take on this role because so many people see substance users this way, suggest this to them, and try to tell them who they are and how they should think and behave. Regardless of whether other people see you as an addict, you can reject this role. It may cause problems in some social interactions, but you don't have to play along.

Substance use can be very problematic. It can be dangerous and even fatal, but it's never involuntary. You have learned to see it this way by various processes, some of which are obvious, and some of which are subtle. The result of this learning is that you interpret your preference for substance use as an addiction: an involuntary compulsion. Since your feelings come from your interpretations of things, this interpretation makes you feel powerless and addicted. It is a very real feeling. It is a painful and terrifying feeling. But you aren't truly powerless, and you aren't truly addicted. You would never have felt this way if you hadn't learned to see things this way. The good news is this can be reversed by learning the truth.

Some of the information we've already provided regarding addiction is enough for some people to see through the ruse and feel free to change. Some of you will be caught deeper in the trap of recovery mythology and will want more information before you can believe that you are truly free. We encourage you to keep reading. *The Freedom Model* will provide a way out of all those tricky ideas holding you back and making you feel addicted. You are not helpless; you're being held back by nothing more than ideas. You have the power to change those ideas. You have the power to reject the role and self-image of the addict/alcoholic.

REFERENCES

Lindesmith, A. (1968). *Addiction and opiates*. Chicago, IL: Aldine Publishing.

Substance Abuse and Mental Health Services Administration (SAMHSA) (2014). Results from the 2013 National Survey on Drug Use and Health: Summary of National Findings, NSDUH Series H-48, HHS Publication No. (SMA) 14-4863. Rockville, MD: Substance Abuse and Mental Health Services Administration. Retrieved from https://www.samhsa.gov/data/sites/default/files/NSDUHresultsPDFWHTML2013/Web/NSDUHresults2013.pdf

Zinberg, N. (1984). *Drug, set, and setting: The basis for controlled intoxicant use.* New Haven, CT: Yale University.

CHAPTER 10:
CONSTRUCTIVE SELF-IMAGES

The addict self-image is an incredibly destructive thing. It is disempowering because it denies your ability to change and leaves you looking instead for a way to compensate for and cope with an imagined handicap. We have shown you that the main premises of addiction are not empirically supported and in fact are contradicted by the available scientific evidence. We have explained the myriad ways you may have been persuaded into taking on this addict self-image and how that has distorted your experience into one of feeling unable to change. We've given you a far better explanation of why you've been using substances problematically, with the Positive Drive Principle (PDP) and by explaining the reasons behind a strong preference for substance use. With all this, we're aiming to show you that you are fully free to change and that any obstacles are purely mental; that is, they are matters of beliefs, thoughts, knowledge, and the like.

Even if you dislike and reject the label of addict or alcoholic, you may still have a self-image that is synonymous with what these labels represent. That is, you may see yourself as being saddled with powerful urges, impulses, and cravings that you are too weak to overcome. You may see yourself as hardwired to need substances to feel normal. You may see yourself as having a genetic deficiency that causes you to crave and lose control. You may see yourself as being unable to resist temptation. You may see yourself as morally deficient in some way that causes your heavy substance use or as having personality and character traits, which cannot be changed, that always lead you back into heavy substance use or other "addictions"—*an addictive personality*. You may see yourself as being fundamentally incapable of being happy without heavy substance use and as needing an "escape" that only substances can provide. Worst of all, you may have no working theory on why you keep using substances problematically, *yet you believe there's something fundamentally unchangeable about you that causes it.* Whether you agree with the labels of addict or alcoholic, it's the harboring of this negative self-image that causes you to feel so discouraged.

A substantial body of psychological research has demonstrated that your fundamental beliefs about yourself wield massive influence over your life. This research demonstrates that, by changing the way you think and see yourself, you can literally change who you are. At the same time, the idea that people are born with genetically predetermined personality types, character traits, levels of intelligence, and talents has been accepted by our culture. This set of beliefs casts people as unchangeable. However, in recent years, it is being challenged by researchers who've shown that people can and do change.

Researcher Carol Dweck focused her efforts on investigating two different fundamental mindsets that reflect this divide. For more than 30 years, she researched the effects of what she calls the *fixed mindset* and the *growth mindset*.

1. The fixed mindset is the belief that you are born with traits that are "carved in stone" and unchangeable or "hardwired," as many describe it.

2. The growth mindset is the belief that you are a flexible, growing, and changing person and that with effort and practice you can change much about yourself.

She found that these *mindsets affect motivation and the level of effort people are willing to expend on overcoming obstacles as well as the goals they choose to pursue.* The answer to why this happens is very logical because those with a fixed mindset believe they either have the ability to do something or they don't. As soon as they struggle, they take it as revealing a weakness or lack of ability. They give up quickly on tough problems because their fixed mindset tells them they've hit the limits of their ability and, since abilities can't really be changed, there is no point in trying (Dweck, 2000).

Most of Dweck's research was done with students, specifically, looking at their mindsets regarding intellectual ability. She measured this using tests with word and math problems and the like. The growth-mindset students she identified put in extra effort when encountering test problems above their educational level because their mindset tells them that effort changes you and grows your abilities, and so it is worth trying. To the individual with the growth mindset, tough problems represent exciting challenges and opportunities for growth. In contrast, the students with the fixed mindset had a radically different reaction to test problems above their educational level. For them, any extra effort or struggle signals that they've reached the limits of their abilities. The next thought in the individual with a fixed mindset goes something like *I just don't have the brain for math* or *I guess I'm just not smart enough to do this.*

In addition to affecting immediate performance on such things as academic tests, Dweck found that mindsets also have longer-term implications for students. Those with growth mindsets increased their IQ scores over time, whereas those with fixed mindsets did not. Then, at various stages of their school careers, she saw that the growth-mindset students chose to enroll in advanced classes and to take on bigger and more challenging goals. Meanwhile, as the fixed-mindset students progressed through school, they tended to take the easiest classes and choose goals that they were already sure they could achieve. She called those goals "performance goals" because they're chosen for the purpose of demonstrating known abilities. On the other hand, growth-mindset students were choosing challenging goals that would grow their abilities.

Failure isn't too scary nor is it a blow to the ego when you have a growth mindset; it's an opportunity to grow and learn. But when you have a fixed mindset, it's terrifying because it reveals your inherent, immutable weaknesses and shortcomings. Failure hurts when you have a fixed mindset, so you shrink your life, sticking to only what you know so that you won't diminish your fragile ego.

One of the most interesting elements of this line of research was that students who started out with lower IQ scores but a growth mindset eventually outperformed those higher-IQ students who had a fixed mindset. Part of the problem was that some of those high-IQ students had been told that they were "gifted" and, in the process, were taught and took on the fixed mindset. After all, the entire notion of being gifted rests on the idea that *some people just have it and some people don't.*

So, when students who see themselves as "gifted" and thus of fixed abilities, struggle, they'll experience the struggle as reaching the limits of their giftedness. This is a sad state of affairs because their intelligence is laid to waste by a mere belief system (and a faulty one at that).

The fact is that people can grow and change many things about themselves. The influence of our mindset isn't just limited to intelligence and educational achievements. It's related to many things. For example, Dweck (2006) has also conducted research that demonstrates the effect these mindsets can have on how people approach their social and romantic life. In these realms, the fixed mindset leads again to quick discouragement when difficulties occur in people's relationships, leaving them feeling like they just aren't good at making friends or that a romantic relationship simply "wasn't meant to be." Further goal choices are affected too. In the same way that fixed-mindset students stop taking academic risks to guard against failure, in their social lives, they react to rejection by decreasing their efforts at making friends, thus protecting themselves from further social failures. Of course, this also wipes out the potential for social successes (you can succeed at what you don't attempt). In contrast, those with the growth mindset become more outgoing and better at coping with rejection just like they're better at coping with academic failure. What's more, they work to overcome difficulties in romantic relationships and seek partners who challenge them to grow, whereas those with a fixed mindset look for someone who will blindly praise and worship them and more readily dissolve such relationships when difficulties appear.

This mindset research isn't an anomaly. For several decades, research in the areas of perceived self-efficacy, motivation and goal setting, and attribution (how you explain your own failures and successes) has all pointed to the same conclusion: that how you see yourself matters. We take all this as empirical support for the idea of "self-image," which we already described in our lesson about the destructive nature of the addict self-image. Think back on how feelings of panic and helplessness started to set in whenever you started to think you might be an addict/alcoholic. You know those ideas dragged you down. But what's most important now is that you consider the possibility that you can embrace a more positive self-image. When you do, it will unleash your inherent freedom and power to change yourself.

YOU CAN CHANGE YOUR SELF-IMAGE WITH KNOWLEDGE

The statistics we gave in chapter 1 were meant to start the process of showing you that you are capable of change. The most vocal recovery activists never stop spreading the message that the "chronic disease of addiction" forever hobbles "addicts", and that they're unable to resist the lure of heavy substance use without constant involvement in the recovery society. If you believe this rhetoric, then you have developed a fixed mindset about your substance use—the self-image of an "addict" or "alcoholic." We have shown that the facts support the exact opposite—that most people change their substance use habits and they aren't living their lives focused on maintaining recovery through ongoing treatment and support. In fact, most never set foot in a treatment center, outpatient clinic, or support meeting. Furthermore, the success rates for those who receive addiction treatment are no better than the success rates for those who go without treatment. This suggests the treatment doesn't cause them to cease or reduce their substance use. Everyone who changes his substance use changes by his own power of choice, even someone who gets treatment for addiction. Furthermore, people resolve their substance use problems quicker than any other condition classified as a mental disorder (see chapter 6). In direct defiance of recovery ideology that says people "lose control" once they have a single dose of substances, more than half of former "alcoholics" become moderate drinkers (see chapter 3 and appendixes A, C, and E). So go ahead and throw out those myths that have led you to see yourself as handicapped. Use the facts to your advantage: you have no weakness, you don't lack the ability to change, and you are not addicted or enslaved to desire heavy substance use forever, and you do not use substances involuntarily. You can see yourself as a growing, changing, flexible person. You can see yourself as free to change, on your terms, when you see fit.

Another important point that Dweck demonstrated was that people can change their mindset when they have access to the right information. After learning about the power of mindsets to limit or empower students, she then wondered how she might go about persuading the fixed-mindset students to take on a growth mindset instead. She decided that giving them information about a feature of the brain called neuroplasticity might help. Briefly, neuroplasticity is a combination of the word "neuro," which stands for the brain, and "plasticity," which means malleable or changeable. The term refers to the fact that our brains are always changing and that they change in response to the repetitive actions, thoughts, and efforts we make. This means that, when we put effort into learning and growing our abilities, we do just that – we learn, grow, and change

Half of the students in Dweck's study were given a general course on the brain, and the other half were given a course that explicitly focused on neuroplasticity. The results were that the fixed-mindset students who learned about neuroplasticity changed to a growth mindset and experienced all the same gains in academic achievement and IQ score increases that come along with that hopeful self-image. The students who took the general course on the brain didn't change their mindsets. The right information can be empowering as it was in this case because it disputed the fixed-mindset students' belief that they couldn't grow and change their mental abilities (Dweck, 2000).

On the other hand, misinformation can be just as effective in changing a mindset, but in a disempowering direction when it becomes a part of your self-image. For decades, recovery ideology has centered on the idea that the brains of "addicts" are "hardwired" to make them crave substances and their free will has been "hijacked by drugs" so that they have no control over their intake of substances. This is a fixed mindset view if ever there was one. Recovery proponents present an incomplete case for this view, which includes a bunch of neuroscience jargon and colorful pictures of brain scans of addicts. Without using any logic to get there, they simply assert their faulty conclusions, confident that everyone will just believe them without question. The problem is it's all very easy to believe, in part, because people think they don't have the intelligence or knowledge to make sense of such things and that the addiction researchers must know what they're talking about. But the fact is, in this case, the *experts* are wrong. While they have found evidence that the brain changes as people repeatedly use substances, researchers haven't found anything that indicates that those brain changes compel further substance use. To the contrary, they've found that people freely quit or reduce their substance use despite having "hijacked brains" and their brains begin adapting yet again to follow their new habits. All this changing that goes on is perfectly normal. After just slightly more than a year of abstinence, the brain scans look nearly identical to the brains of people who've never been addicted. In fact, based on these findings, increasing numbers of neuroscientists are now coming out against this brain disease view of addiction (see appendix B).

There is nothing in the available scientific evidence that indicates that addicts are unable to stop using substances because of neuroadaptation (see appendix A). And in fact, there is nothing to suggest that the brain changes that result from repetitious substance use are abnormal or some sort of malfunction of the brain. This is important. *All* repetitious activities change the brain. Research has shown that activities such as learning to play a musical instrument, driving a taxi in London, learning to juggle, and learning to walk and talk, to name but a few, all change the brain. When the brains of people who do these things are compared to the brains of people who don't do these things, significant differences can be found. However, we don't say people are "hardwired to drive a taxi," nor do we assume that when someone sits down to play a song on the piano that his "free will has been hijacked by pianos." These are routine neuroplastic changes to the brain, a natural way that it adapts to make it easier for people to repeat any habitual behavior. Habits are easy to break, and new habits are easy to make when you find good enough reason to do so.

The idea that addicts are hardwired for addiction is quite simply wrong. It is not true. If you believe it, then you become just like those students with the fixed mindset. You lose hope and motivation to change, and the slightest bit of struggle is taken as a sign that you're a hopeless case who can never change. Again, there is no such thing as a "chronic disease of addiction" that you'll be fighting for the rest of your life (see appendix B), and there is no evidence that brain changes cause continued substance use (see appendix C).

CHANGING LEARNED CONNECTIONS

Another area that demonstrates where a fixed mindset can be problematic is in the recently popular belief in underlying "causes" of addiction. Those who believe the recovery ideology that says addicts will turn to substance use the moment they have to deal with any difficulty in life gain an unnecessary complication from this belief system. Every life problem now raises the possibility of turning to substances.

Of course, after instilling this belief, treatment programs then try to arm the addicts with "alternative coping methods" to employ whenever they face a life problem. Still, when difficulties arise, it becomes a tense moment of choosing between substance use and the alternative coping method. It never had to be this way. Treatment professionals, in their desperate attempt to explain problematic substance use, have taken normal life problems that literally everyone has and unnecessarily connected them to substance use. *If there were any validity to the trigger theory, we'd say this was a case of proactively creating a trigger.* This is yet another aspect of the addict self-image that needs to be obliterated. If you choose to believe you are too weak to deal with difficulties in life and problems will somehow cause you to use substances, then you will face this struggle often because many problems are unavoidable. But this "underlying causes of addiction" theory isn't true, so you don't need to make it a part of your self-image (see chapters 5 and 6). You can break this connection between substance use and other life problems and see yourself as someone who can deal with normal life problems as well as the next guy.

YOU HAVE A CHOICE

You have a choice to make: You can choose to consider the information we're offering and use it to dispel the disempowering addict self-image, thereby freeing yourself to discover your happiest choices, which will then unleash a tidal wave of motivation that can be used to change your substance use habits, or you can choose to continue to live with the self-image of the addict and prepare yourself for a lifetime of coping with your handicap.

The choice is yours because you have free will, and only you can make that choice because you have mental autonomy (that is, no one can do your thinking for you). These two aspects of your humanity, free will and mental autonomy, will be discussed in the next chapter.

Do you want a destructive and limiting self-image, or do you want a constructive and freeing self-image? It's up to you. We're here to offer information that you can use to confidently shed the addict self-image and replace it with the self-image of a freely choosing, evolving person, with multiple avenues toward happiness.

REFERENCES

Dweck, C. S. (2000). *Self-theories: Their role in motivation, personality, and development.* Philadelphia, PA: Psychology Press.

Dweck, C. S. (2006). *Mindset: The new psychology of success.* New York, NY: Ballantine Books.

CHAPTER 11:

MENTAL AUTONOMY AND FREE WILL

The pursuit of happiness is the engine behind all human behavior (it is the positive drive principle), but if you look around, it's clear that people pursue happiness in *many* ways. Where does that individual expression come from? Why does one person see her best path to happiness in heavy substance use, whereas the next person does not? The most basic answer is that all people have *free will and mental autonomy*, two aspects of human consciousness that allow each person his own unique thoughts and perspectives on the world.

Free will is simply the ability to choose, a uniquely human attribute that arises from the depth of our consciousness. People can store and retrieve knowledge of the past, develop abstract conceptual knowledge, and reason logically with such knowledge. Then, they can use all this to project the potential outcomes of several potential courses of action at any given moment. *They can choose because they are conscious enough to be aware of more than one potential course of action at any given time* (and they are not ruled by instincts like animals are). This means that you choose your thoughts and beliefs, the level of mental effort you will put into your decisions, and where to focus your attention, and, of course, through all this, you ultimately choose your physical behaviors.

Mental autonomy is another uniquely human attribute, which makes each person the master of her own mind and thus her own behavior. You are conscious of your world through your own senses and experiences, so whoever you are is made up of this collection of conscious experiences and unique vantage point. Nobody can walk in your mental shoes (or see through your eyes, as it were). This is a realm that is accessible to only the individual who experiences it. Likewise, your mind can't be controlled by other people or circumstances, but rather, you are in control of your own mind at all times. You're the only one in there.

DO YOU AGREE?

When we sit down to discuss these issues, most people instantly agree that they have free will. However, as we begin discussing whether they'd like to make a new choice about substance use, oftentimes, they have a list of exceptions that contradict their previously stated belief in their ability to make their own choices.

For example, some will say "But I can't say no to a drink in a social situation." One of two things is going on when people seriously raise this concern:

1. They literally believe that there is some overpowering magical force called "peer pressure" that robs them of the power to make their own choices about substance use and forces them to say yes.

   or

2. They want to drink in social situations but see this desire as a supposed weakness or inability to choose.

Think of it. You can't say no, but you can say yes? Saying yes is a choice just like saying no is a choice, and when we put it this way, most of you will agree, in this moment at least. But will you agree the next time you're offered a drink, or will you go back to the default belief that you can't say no? That kind of thinking has kept you from making changes that you knew would improve your life. The fact is that you *want* to drink in those social situations so that, when you are offered a drink, you say yes and choose to have that drink. This isn't bad or wrong in and of itself, but telling yourself (and others) you have no choice in the matter is wrong and leaves you feeling helpless in those moments when you begin to think a change might be in order. So, although free will is a rather obvious fact of human life, it needs to be pointed out and remembered in matters of personal behavior like this. If you want to make changes in your own behavior, you can literally do it at the drop of a hat. You have free will.

Of course, this discussion shouldn't be taken to mean that our solution amounts to "just say no." The point is that making different choices begins with recognizing that you *do* have a choice. There is no real force of peer pressure and no real force behind so-called triggers. Nor do any inanimate objects, such as drugs, contain a force called "temptation," which you must be strong enough to resist or else you'll be forced to act against your own will. You are actively choosing every step of the way when you use substances. You are choosing according to the ideas, beliefs, and thoughts contained and actively entertained by you *within your own autonomous mind*. Focusing on whether can resist temptation and powerful triggers and say no is a fool's errand. You can't resist nonexistent forces.

This is not about strength or weakness. It is about choices. You are the person who makes the choices about what behaviors you will carry out. It takes no strength to make different choices. You will make the choices that look most attractive to you (PDP) according to your own judgment, your own perspective, and what you choose to think. If you choose to think you'd be better off and happier not saying yes to that drink offer, then you will not say yes to that drink offer. It is that simple. It may feel awkward because you've built a habit and preference for drinking in those situations in the past. Nevertheless, you absolutely have the power of choice in that moment.

To make this momentary choice into a new and lasting preference that guides future choices, you'll have to find greater happiness in it, take note of it, and essentially learn from it. As you do that, saying no to the drink offer in future social situations will feel like the more natural choice to you, with no ambivalence or apprehension involved, it will be as uneventful as turning down the offer of a piece of gum. This change has to start somewhere; it can start *with your choosing to think and act differently in that situation than you have in the past*. This is the reason we must highlight free will and mental autonomy as essential human attributes for solving problems of personal behavior.

Another popular question that comes up when we talk about making new substance use choices is "But isn't addiction genetic?" Let's break this down and see what's really going on when people raise the genetics argument. They're saying that they have no more control over their choice to use substances than they do over the color of their eyes. So, at the very least, they don't believe they have free will regarding substance use specifically; at the most extreme, they may not believe in free will at all, instead, chalking up all human behavior to genetically determined preferences and abilities.

More than 90% of people with substance use problems get over those problems, most without any formal help and in a shorter amount of time than any other "mental disorder." Would it make sense to attribute problematic substance use to such an unchangeable factor as a gene when in fact so many people do change? Do you honestly think those people change by telling themselves they have a gene that forces them to use substances? Research tells us their change comes from "cognitive appraisal"—that is, by voluntarily thinking their options through differently than they have in the past (Sobell et al., 2001). It's hard to do this while you're focused on imaginary obstacles, such as theorized "addiction genes." So again, this is the reason we highlight free will and mental autonomy so you can get on with finding your way to new choices that make you happier.

There are several ways people become convinced that they are not free to make different choices. A few examples of the beliefs people express that go against free will and mental autonomy are as follows:

1. I can't help but use substances when I'm down. (depressed, sad, unhappy)

2. I get irresistible urges and cravings to use substances.

3. I think I have a chemical imbalance that makes me use substances.

4. I can stay sober in a rehab, but when I go home, I'm surrounded by powerful triggers that send me back to drugs/alcohol.

5. If I have too many drinks, my judgment goes, and I buy cocaine.

6. I need to have a drink/drug when I get angry.

7. I don't have enough support to stay sober.

8. I ended up relapsing before because I couldn't get into an aftercare program.

9. Too many of my friends drink/drug. There's no way I can stay sober.

10. Some people can't control their substance use because they live in drug-filled neighborhoods.

11. It runs in my family.

12. Once I have a single drink, I lose control and can't stop.

Each of those beliefs overlooks the fact that you always have free will and mental autonomy. So, although you may agree with the concept of free will in theory and on the surface, do you agree with it in practice? Do you understand the full meaning of it? Do you understand the implications of determinism, the alternative to free will?

Free will is understood as the power to choose. When you have a choice, it means that you have more than one option of what to do, that things don't have to be only one way, and there are multiple possibilities. That you have free will means that you are the chooser among those possibilities. But we need to go a little deeper because people are constantly barraged with the message that those possibilities don't exist.

Many in our culture think the scientific answer is that every previous event people have encountered determines their exact behavior at any given moment. In this theory (determinism), it's assumed that, in the same way the Grand Canyon was carved out of the land by flowing water over millions of years, your personality started out with a genetic endowment of some sort and then was simply carved by the various events you've faced in your life. And like the rocky ground that had no choice in becoming the Grand Canyon—it had no power to fend off the water, move out of its path, or choose not to be worn away by it—you couldn't choose to react any other way to the circumstances into which you were born. The determinist position says that people are as helpless as a lifeless rock in both who they become and whether they change who they are. The Grand Canyon can't choose to become flat ground again.

There are significant problems with this position. First, it is entirely *antiscientific*. Even some of the ancient philosophers understood this.

> The consequence, if all the things that come to be follow on some causes that have been laid down beforehand and are definite and exist beforehand, is that men deliberate in vain about the things that they have to do. And if deliberating were in vain, man would have the power of deliberation in vain.
>
> —Alexander of Aphrodisias, On Fate, circa 200 CE

Things that are done "in vain" have no consequence. It means they're nothing more than a show. Alexander is asking whether nature would really give us an ongoing internal experience—that of deliberating (i.e., consciously thinking things through)—as nothing more than a powerless illusion that affects nothing. Clearly, he's unconvinced that is the case. Think about it. Does nature make things that have no consequence? The solidity of rock has consequence. It makes water take thousands or even millions of years to bore through it, whereas the softness of earth allows water to erode it in a fraction of the time. The heat released from fire melts, destroys, or otherwise changes the form of the things around it. The molecular structure of metal allows electricity to pass through it, whereas the molecular makeup of wood or rubber does not. Every feature of everything in nature has some effect on something, and yet human's feature of consciousness is supposed to be an illusion that doesn't affect our existence one iota. It's absurd, yet 1,800 years after Alexander first argued against such nonsense, we're still facing it (today, they call it epiphenomenalism, the theory that conscious experience happens but that it has no effect and is just the result of predetermined brain activity).

This is as good an argument for free will as there is. We all, as human beings, internally experience ourselves choosing. Why should we believe that our conscious experience is an illusion? If we can't trust our sense of this, then we can't trust any piece of knowledge ever discovered by mankind because all of it would be suspect. All information would be sent to us by deterministic forces, which means our belief or disbelief in any piece of information would have been forced upon us rather than having been arrived at through any rational process of thought. So you have a choice: either believe in determinism or believe in free will. But determinism goes against your conscious experience of choosing, and it can't even be logically asserted, since it destroys the possibility of exercising logic.

Let's look at this from a different angle and apply it to current recovery ideology. Dr. Nora Volkow is one of the leading experts on addiction in the world. She is the head of the National Institute on Drug Abuse (NIDA) and is leading the charge that addiction is a progressive, incurable brain disease and that it is likely caused by a combination of genetic and environmental factors. Her belief in some form of determinism is self-evident, she has even used scare quotes repeatedly around the term to indicate her skepticism of it's existence. And, while Dr. Volkow uses her own inherent abilities to think, reason and act to posit her ideas and build her career and do the things she finds important to her – her theories on addiction deny those very abilities, by asserting that human behavior can be understood purely by looking at brain states and how they cause people to think, feel, and behave (a sort of "neurodeterminism"). In short, she somehow has the ability to think, reason, and choose, but doesn't grant that to others.

She and her addiction professional colleagues tell the rest of the world how doomed they are. This means, of course, that those in this elite class may be the only ones genetically advanced enough not to be at the mercy of their biology – or maybe they're just biologically superior, which is an ugly line of thought. Based on what she has said, she sees the world as full of weak, lost beings, always in need of being helped by those like her who have been blessed with the ability to problem solve (something determinism says cannot exist). While the view that we are all preprogrammed to hurt ourselves seems plausible when *experts* talk about those in dire need of help, the fallacy becomes obvious when you realize the experts themselves do not seem to be vulnerable to it. In other words, their theory does not apply to them. They need it both ways for their arguments to stand up.

This presents a huge problem for the determinists. Folks like Dr. Volkow use thoughts and attention and acts of the mind to discuss and write about the existence of the brain, but then they deny the key faculty they used to create, organize, and write down their thoughts. Their position implies that self-created, chosen thoughts don't exist, but that very discussion requires self-created thought!

This may seem like a far-out philosophical discussion, but it deserves some thought because most recovery ideology denies free will or at least says that "addicts/alcoholics" lack it regarding substance use. It's logically untenable to think substance users don't possess free will at all, and it'd be quite a trick for them to lose it regarding only one specific activity. And, if they could lose grip of the steering wheel regarding substance use, who or what takes over at that point? That is, if substance users are "out of control," who is *in control* and causing them to carry out all the activities necessary to continue using substances? Recovery ideology never even attempts to explain this except by appealing to some sort of demonic possession by "the addiction" or the substances.

Don't let the recovery *experts'* vague and illogical theories sway you. You know that you are choosing. *The Freedom Model* is about reclaiming your power of choice, and little progress can be made without a solid belief in free will. It is a human attribute you'll have to remember to counter the recovery ideology that's been the source of so much of your self-doubt.

Equally important is the attribute of mental autonomy. For example, recovery ideology peddles the illusion that others can stop us from using substances. Many who attend AA meetings will be prodded into getting "a sponsor." The sponsor is to be called upon whenever the person gets the urge to drink or drug. The implication is that sponsors have some actual control in this scenario to stop their "sponsees" from drinking, when in fact the drinkers are the ones choosing. The drinkers are also the people making the decision to participate in this charade. In all reality, the drinkers, and only the drinkers, can make themselves stop drinking. The fact that sponsor is present while this decision is made by the individual is merely happenstance. If the sponsees decide to drink or drug again, it's said that this happened because they failed to call their sponsors. This explanation is one step removed from the truth, which is that they didn't call their sponsors *because they decided to drink/drug*. Autonomy exists as a rule, no matter what illusions the individual decides to focus on. In the end, autonomy presents the fact that all free choice exists *within the individual and nowhere else* (regardless of whether a sponsor, therapist, psychiatrist, family member, or friend is present and involved).

Mental autonomy also means that, while the environment and circumstances certainly provide people with information, influences, and events to which they will react, their minds are still theirs to freely operate as they choose. A minor example of this can be found in childhood when you are forced to be in a schoolroom. If you want to think about playing ball after school or look out the window and daydream, you are fully free to do that, and students often choose to focus on such things rather than the lessons being presented. So, regardless of a lecturing teacher, books, visual aids, and discussions back and forth between the teacher and students surround you, you can still sit in that room and not learn a thing.

A major example of autonomy can be found with prisoners of all sorts. There are those political prisoners who are tortured and commanded to renounce their views but simply won't do it, and they stay imprisoned. Then there are those who renounce their views out loud *while retaining them internally*. They say what they must to escape and then begin working to undermine their political opponents again.

In the concentration camps of World War II, the psychologist Viktor Frankl (2006), himself a prisoner on death's door, noted that, despite the wretched conditions, many prisoners chose to be happy. They decided to not be swayed by circumstance. It's hard for us to imagine such a choice, but they made it. When all was said and done, Frankl's key insight and contribution to psychology based on his observations of human behavior in the death camps was this:

> Everything can be taken from a man but one thing: the last of human freedoms—to choose one's attitude in any given set of circumstances, to choose one's own way. (p. 66)

This has greater significance to your path than you might currently realize. Countless ideas you've been taught about addiction and recovery attribute your choices to circumstances, environment, and the people around you. Yet, if you are truly mentally autonomous, that is, you are the chooser of your own thoughts and no one else can think for you or force you to think anything, then most recovery ideology is useless and distracting you from what will lead to change: your choice to think things through differently.

Here, the philosopher Leonard Peikoff (Peikoff & Berliner, 2012) gives a good demonstration of the autonomy of the mind:

Why can't a mind be compelled to accept a conclusion? That takes us back to what the mind is. It's one thing only: a cognitive faculty, a faculty for grasping knowledge, a faculty for perceiving reality … it has to do this by a complex process of thought, evidence, coming to conclusions, and so on. It has to observe facts, judge, connect, and the result is either knowledge, or at least an honestly held conclusion, even if it's an error. But if a mind avowedly defies facts that are within its awareness—if it says, in effect, "Forget reality, the truth is irrelevant"—the faculty literally cannot function; it would stop dead. There's no way for the person within the confines of his own mind to proceed. The crucial point is that we are not saying it's bad to force a mind, because to say it's "bad" would imply that you can do it but it's wicked. The fact is, you cannot do it, not in the sense of forcing it to come to an opposite conclusion to the evidence it itself sees. To try to force a mind to accept such a conclusion against its own judgment is like saying, "Accept what you know is not true." It's like saying, "Try to believe that red is green, or that two and two is five." And you can't make a man believe such a thing, George Orwell to the contrary. You can drive him crazy, but you can't make him believe it. If somebody says, "Your money or your life," you can give him the money—the gun will make you give him the money—but it won't make you believe that it's his money, and it cannot make you believe that, not the mere act of the gun being held. So what then does the forcer accomplish? He cannot force you to think a certain way. What is it that he does accomplish? He forces you to act a certain way. What way? Against your judgment. He doesn't change your mind (this is the essence of the situation)—he makes it irrelevant. It is removed from life. To the extent of force being initiated against you, your mind has nothing to say about your action. Since force cannot make you think differently, all it can do is rupture the tie between thought and action. Force makes thought inoperative, inapplicable, pointless. (p. 126)

Again, recognizing this feature of humanity is crucial to applying *The Freedom Model*. Will you embrace your autonomy, or will you continue to wait for someone or some set of circumstances to force you to dislike reckless substance use?

How many counselors, sponsors, and therapists will you see? How many group counseling sessions, support meetings, and aftercare sessions will you attend? How long will you keep yourself in a sober-living community trying to shield yourself from use? How many loved ones and recovery coaches will you ask to "hold you accountable" or to limit access to your finances, or to exert other forms of physical control or shaming over you? How much Suboxone or naltrexone or Antabuse will you take in a fruitless attempt to force yourself from continuing to prefer heroin or booze? *How much of this will you continue to do while hoping and praying for the impossible: that these people, circumstances, and substitution drugs will somehow get into your mind and force you to think differently about substances?* It can't be done because of mental autonomy. If you still prefer use, you'll choose that. If you don't, you won't. So *that* is the mental decision to be made: Is it going to be heavy use, adjusted use, or abstinence? Changing your thoughts is *your* task and yours alone. Your mind is the one thing that you, and only you, have the most control over in this world. And through that control of your mind, you also control your behavior, including your behavior regarding substances.

Once you understand these three human attributes—the PDP, free will, and mental autonomy—you will begin to see through all the misinformation yourself and finally start forging a real change to be happier in your substance use habits. Your happiness is in your own hands. It always has been. You just need to recognize this to open a world of rapid, proactive, personal change to yourself.

SHEDDING THE ADDICT/ALCOHOLIC SELF-IMAGE

Your preference for substance use is supported by a bundle of beliefs, habits of thought, and learned connections. The good news is that you can change all this. You can be just like those students (described in chapter 10) who learned that their human nature allows them to grow and change their abilities, or you can be like those who believe their traits are set in stone and then go on to be discouraged and to stagnate in place without growth or change.

Know that you have the power to choose new thoughts and to make new choices and to have these new thoughts and choices add up to new preferences. Chief among the thoughts to be changed is the belief that you're "addicted," that is, that you are using substances *involuntarily*. This belief can be broken down into the dozens of popular mainstream myths about addiction and addicts, such as a few outlined in this chapter—that you can't say no or that your genes have doomed you to a life of heavy substance use. By putting effort into seriously rethinking these beliefs and replacing them with the truth, you will grow and change your knowledge (and consequently, your brain), making yourself feel free to make new choices about substance use.

Then there are all those learned connections that you can challenge and rethink. Do you really need to drink or drug when stressed or depressed? If you've believed this, you may have developed a habit of responding to such emotions by drinking or drugging instantly, with little thought in the moment. You can challenge these beliefs, and when these emotions come up in the future, you are fully capable of thinking through whether you want to react to them by using substances again. You have free will, and with new information on your side, you can choose to obliterate these habits.

The same goes for all the thoughts and choices you've made about substance use over the years that have grown into the strong preference you have today. You can challenge and change those underlying beliefs and grow a new preference. You have the free will that you can exercise now just as you did in creating the preferences in the first place. And because of mental autonomy, your preference can be changed *only* by your own mental effort of choosing new thoughts. But this isn't bad news; it's the best news you could get. It means you have full freedom and the ability to change.

REFERENCES

Frankl, V. (2006). *Man's search for meaning*. Boston, MA: Beacon Press.

Peikoff, L., & Berliner, M. S. (2012). Understanding objectivism: a guide to learning Ayn Rand's philosophy. New York: New American Library.

Sobell, L. C., Klingemann, H. K., Toneatto, T., Sobell, M. B., Agrawal, S., & Leo, G. I. (2001). Alcohol and drug abusers' perceived reasons for self-change in Canada and Switzerland: Computer-assisted content analysis. *Substance Use & Misuse, 36*(11), 1467–1500.

CHAPTER 12:

LEAVING THE CAGE OF RECOVERY

The Freedom Model makes intuitive sense to so many people, yet they remain chained to the idea that they'll have to keep working on "recovery." In chapter 11, we discussed the fact that there are no external processes to force you to change and that, in fact, these processes are a distraction. Let us say it again: there are no plans of recovery needed; there are just choices to be made. It boils down to convincing yourself that you can be happier cutting down or quitting substance use. Once you become convinced, there is nothing else to do other than live out your new preferences. Sadly, even with all this new information and knowledge, you may still be clinging to recovery like Victoria is:

> I agree with everything you guys are saying here, and I've already stopped using. It's awesome. Astounding really, considering how bad I was this past year with the pills. But now I need a plan to maintain my recovery, or I'm afraid I'll end up doing the same things again. I need goals, support, coping methods, tools.
>
> —Victoria, a 34-year-old who struggled with opiates

Our goal in this chapter is to show you why you may still cling to some recovery ideology and how you can completely let it go. Victoria's request assumes there is some special set of behaviors or tools that will save her from consuming pills in the future. Of course, we could respond with the obvious, "Don't ingest pills," but that response, although certainly logical, wouldn't adequately address the core of her issue.

You see, Victoria is not confused about stopping use. She has already proven to herself that she has the capability to do just that. She isn't a person who wants to be "sick forever." She isn't confused about whether the pills have power. She fully understands that she is in control and has always been the one responsible for her use. She understands the myths of the recovery society, and she quit her drug habit quite easily once she knew the truth about her inherent power and the truth behind substances having no inherent power over her. She gets it.

Victoria however is very confused about the future and what the future holds for her now that she has quit. She doesn't realize that what she is asking for (in her quote above) has nothing to do with drugs, or use, or addiction, or any of the above. It's just that she is so used to identifying her life by the constraints of substance use that she is now unknowingly keeping recovery alive in her future (thus she is also unknowingly keeping addiction alive as well). It's not that she wants to use at all; it's just that she finds it hard to fully internalize what to do next without the influence of some addiction concepts being involved. These personalized addiction concepts are a mental habit for her. She is standing there, a free woman, but is unsure of herself in her new free state, so she tends to habitually bring some addiction/recovery ideals back into play.

When Victoria came to our retreat, we provided her the truth about the addiction myths. She accepted the logic and research, and it made real sense to her. She then set herself free. Without a disease, without the concepts of powerlessness or hopelessness, or "addictive substances," there was nothing left to fight.

But now that there is nothing for her to fight, she feels emotionally unsure of herself. This fight with addiction defined her for years, and now it's gone. She is free of that and is not used to this new sensation of freedom. Consequently, she now feels the need to seek out "tools to remain sober." Frankly, she is afraid that she will somehow fail at this new life she has found. This is new ground to her, a new experience. But the question is, does she really need to focus her life on a plan of recovery? Will she fall apart without constant work to fight addiction?

LIVING LIKE A CAGED LION

Victoria is like a lion that has been caged its whole life. When the cage door is finally left open for the cat to roam free, it takes days, sometimes weeks for the lion to leave the cage. And, when it finally leaves the confines of its previous "home," it usually stays close by the enclosure for a period because every part of his new and expanded environment causes the big cat a certain level of anxiousness, fear, and uncertainty. This is where Victoria is. If she were a believer in the disease theory, or in "addictive substances," or in anything else of that propaganda, she would still be lying in the cage with the door shut tight. But the truth has opened that door. Like the lion that left its enclosure, Victoria is exploring her new world but is unsure how to navigate it. In this respect, humans aren't all that different from the big cat.

Victoria is not asking to go to support meetings, or therapy, or outpatient clinics; she's not even asking for "tools." She knows deep down that her request does not make sense. She intuitively knows that most other people don't live connected to therapy or support networks or the like, and now thanks to *The Freedom Model*, she knows it's a lie that former addicts need to be obsessed with recovery. She also knows to a certain level that all those tools and techniques of recovery are part of still being "in the cage." She has outgrown all that. What she really wants to know is how to navigate a new lifestyle that is defined by limitless potential and possibilities, and she is unsure of how to ask that question. This lifestyle is so new to her and utterly unlimited in its potential that she doesn't even understand how to ask the right questions, so she simply says "But now I need a recovery plan, or I will end up doing the same thing again."

So what do lions do after they distance themselves from their enclosure for good? Well, research has shown that these large felines come to grips with their new landscape quickly once they commit to leaving the enclosure. They rely on instinct, and with little cognitive ability to complicate matters, they adjust to their expanded world very adequately. In a matter of months, they hunt, mate, and cohabitate as if they had done it their entire lives, and they do it with little to no coaching. They, like humans, allow their internal drives to motivate their lives. We are not that much different from lions in this respect.

When Victoria stated her need for tools to help her remain sober, she had to be reminded that she, like the lion, has something that empowers her to leave the cage. Her tools already exist inside of her. They are the three human attributes: free will, autonomy, and the PDP. In a free state of mind, Victoria simply needs to plan her future on her own terms. *The Freedom Model* is recognition of what we all possess inside already and the application of these abilities to personal problems. The tools she was seeking were inside her all along! We, like the lion, already have the necessary drive to get far away from the cage of the recovery society. People already can choose how to build their lives; they already are autonomous individuals with individual tastes and likes and dislikes; they already are flexible in their preferences. They are driven to be free because that is their nature. So, while Victoria is asking for a plan of action and tools, what she is really saying is this:

> I have not been free of the recovery society chains for very long. I am unpracticed at being free. I am not used to having so much time to think and act because, in my not too distant past, I was completely absorbed in a drug culture. That culture demanded so much of me that I was forced to react and adapt. Like the cat in the cage, I did not have to proactively think. I just needed to survive and exist and concentrate on the distraction of the fight against addiction. So now, although I feel that I need a plan, support, and tools, what I really need to do is live and move on! And, because I have not lived outside the cage, I am unaware of how to do that effectively.

So that brings us to a new topic: What does it mean to live free, and how does one go about that?

LIVING FREE

Obviously, Victoria has vestiges of recovery ideology still holding her back. If she didn't, she would leave her cage far behind immediately as so many people do. There would be no need for a "plan of recovery." So what is it that is holding her back? She obviously has abandoned the disease and powerlessness rhetoric, so why the need to hold on to other parts of recovery's empty promises? Why stay so close to the cage that imprisoned her for so many years?

Victoria will struggle to find full freedom if she continues to fear the future. When people from the recovery society free themselves from the cage, they can choose to stagnate just outside the cage in a form of an emotional and mental purgatory. For example, they want someone to tell them how to behave and tell them what to do, but they also see freedom's benefits. They are not sure whether they are ready or willing to let go of the comfort provided by their old prison. That mental state is a partial imprisonment. That partial imprisonment is recovery. Recovery is the half state between the cage of addiction and the fruited plains of freedom. It is sitting outside the cage and staring back and forth between the horizon and the cage. They're still stuck because the allure of the cage is the promise of not having to take on the risks and responsibilities that are necessary when they leave it behind for good.

So what do people in this predicament do? Naturally, like Victoria, they ask for tools, coping techniques, plans of recovery, healthy goals, and support networks; they look for something outside of them to rely on and guide them. They ask for external means of change. In general, they want someone or something to tell them what to do next. When you live with a heavy substance use habit, most choices are severely limited and are made for you by the limiting circumstances of that narrow lifestyle. Having a singular focus like drug and alcohol use to organize your life around is simple, even if it is painful. The simplicity can be one of "addiction's" most attractive attributes. Because the drinking and drug-taking lifestyle is so well worn and known to the individual, it takes no thought or creativity to continue down that road. But once the door is opened, once the substance user sees the ruse of the recovery society, that door to freedom cracks open. The lock is broken. Then, it's just a choice of whether they will walk out that door and build a new life.

Essentially, leaving the cage means accepting some level of the unknown, the new and the risky. It means knowing there will be ups and downs in life, that you will make good and bad decisions, that you will succeed and fail, and that all of it will be on you. You won't have addiction to lean on for your discomfort with responsibility nor will you have the burden of recovery to lean on. The cage of recovery keeps that addiction alive. It's a limitation on your possibilities, and it keeps you from making your own decisions. It keeps you from the expansive passion- and joy-based decisions that could take you far beyond your current troubled state. Instead, it keeps you in the realm of "safe" decisions decided by others who infantilize you and mentally hobble you. If you want to get *unstuck* and truly set yourself free, then go all the way and leave the cage of recovery fully behind.

Life is a series of choices, nothing more, nothing less. We make choices based on our internal drive to be happy and based on our beliefs and knowledge of how to provide ourselves that happiness. Victoria's first choice is a simple one: Is she going to move past recovery's trappings (which continue to tie her to her addicted past), or is she going to live free? If she chooses freedom, she will need to let go of the idea that solutions to life's challenges rest somewhere outside of her and realize that the only tools she needs to continue to be happy and free are the ones inside her. Once that realization sinks in, she will know that both addiction and recovery are unnecessary options that can easily be rejected completely and that life can now be both exciting and unlimited.

CHAPTER 13:

SUCCESS

"How do you quit a job?" Nobody asks such a question because the answer is incredibly simple. You tell your boss "I quit," and then you don't return there to work. *The real issue is whether you want to quit that job or keep working there.* Do you see a better alternative? Do you think it's worth leaving that job? Do you think you'll be happier if you do? The answers to such questions determine whether you'll want to quit, and then the actual nuts and bolts of quitting are simple; you just say "I quit" and then go on your merry way. You don't need to resist going back to that job every day.

"How do I quit drinking?" is the same sort of question. It is fully a matter of figuring out what you want. When you know what that is, you just do it. It doesn't take any strength or willpower to not do what you know you don't want to do. It doesn't take any special techniques or steps. There's no effort needed to maintain not drinking or drugging (or moderating those activities), just as there is no effort needed to not work at the job you quit. The effort is simply in figuring out what you really want and then naturally moving in that new direction.

Unfortunately, people don't realize how simple this truly is because recovery ideology and its proponents have confused the issue so much with their misinformation. They've led people into believing they're not free to make their own choices about substance use. They make you think it's highly complicated, that it's an ongoing process, that some sort of treatment is needed, and that it requires a lifelong struggle. In short, they've taught you that you are not free to change by the normal powers of choice that you apply to other problems. Such beliefs are the only thing that stands in the way of anyone making a change in his or her level of substance use.

Our society doesn't seem to have the patience or tolerance to let people be, to let them make these decisions for themselves. It often tries to coerce people into changing their substance use habits. The legal system is used for this purpose by threatening jail time and other sanctions. Families try to do this by means of "tough love." The treatment system tries to coerce you into agreeing to abstinence by equating heavy substance use with a disease, so that you'll blindly obey the doctors' orders. And, from every corner, shame is heaped on you. You're told that your preferred mode of substance use is dysfunctional, disordered, diseased, and *bad*. Your substance use is negatively judged, and you're socially sanctioned for it in any number of ways. Then, you're *assigned* the goal of abstinence from all substance use and adoption of the recovery lifestyle. With this goal, comes a standard of "success"; if you don't adopt and fulfill complete abstinence and "recovery" as your goal, you're declared a failure. If you choose moderation, you're a failure. Even if you abstain fully or moderate to socially acceptable levels but do so without also adopting the recovery lifestyle, you're considered a failure. This is a no-win situation where success becomes nothing more than compliance with the demands of others. To the substance user caught in this coercive game, the idea of success loses its positive personal meaning.

Put all this coercion and the addiction myths together, and you end up with a whole lot of people who do not feel free to make their own choices about substance use. Many try to quit out of shame and coercion and then wonder why "the quit" doesn't last. It doesn't last because "the quit" didn't come from a sense of freely pursuing the happiest option; it came from feeling cornered into quitting. This is the source of most reversed attempts to quit or adjust substance use: people don't feel free to make their own choices. They make these failed attempts based on doing what others think they should do or what they've been scared into doing, not on what they wholeheartedly believe will make them happiest.

The results are that, while abstaining, they are unhappy, and when returning to substance use, they are also unhappy. This becomes a vicious cycle that can chew up people's lives for decades and spit them out feeling doomed to perpetual failure. We were stuck in this cycle ourselves and didn't get out of it until we realized we were free to do so. We have now helped thousands of people take themselves out of this cycle over the years by showing them that they are free too. Thus, here is our definition of success in *The Freedom Model*:

SUCCESS IS KNOWING THAT YOU ARE FREE AND HAPPILY CHOOSING WHAT YOU SEE AS BEST FOR YOU

In *The Freedom Model*, our goal (that of *The Freedom Model* authors and our seminar and retreat presenters) is to show you that you are completely free to choose to change your use of substances in whatever way you see fit. If you feel this freedom after considering the ideas and information we've presented, then we will count that as a successful outcome regardless of what choices you make regarding substance use.

There is no judgment on our part. Our goal is not to persuade you to abstain from substance use or to moderate your substance use. Everyone is different. We cannot say what level of substance use will make anyone happiest. That will differ from person to person and only the people themselves can know that. We don't judge substance use as being bad or immoral. We have no agenda against it whatsoever.

We've used the terms "problematic," "heavy," and "moderate/adjusted" to acknowledge various levels or patterns of substance use throughout this book, but you should notice that we haven't defined what levels or frequencies of substance use fit those descriptions. We haven't even laid out criteria for what problems and other costs qualify people's use of substances as "problematic." These are all subjective terms, the definitions of which will vary according to everyone's personal judgment. What counts as "heavy drinking" to one may be "moderate drinking" to another. What's "problematic" to one may not be to another. This is for everyone to gauge based on his or her unique goals, hopes, life circumstances, experiences, and tastes. Long story short, even if you proceed to use substances in a way that we would consider problematic in *our own* lives, we can't say whether it's problematic *for you*. If you see your level of substance use as worth it and feel free in your choice to do it, then that's all that matters to us. If you see it as not worth it yet still feel free to change it, then we consider that a win too. A returned sense of freedom is our measure of success because when you see a change as worthwhile, you will freely change it.

We truly do not advocate any path regarding substance use. Some cynical readers may assume this position is a clever way to justify the fact that some may continue to choose heavy substance use after learning *The Freedom Model*. However, we know from much follow-up research (carried out by us personally, as well as independent firms) that most of our course graduates have achieved stable, long-term abstinence. If this were our criterion of success, *The Freedom Model* would win in spades when compared to any help based on recovery ideology. We also know of countless outcomes where our graduates have reduced their level of substance use as well. This means the rate of change is higher than our 62% long-term abstinence rate indicates. We know our ideas and information have proven helpful; what's more, they've proven helpful with many of the most tragic and hopeless cases who have attended treatment programs for years with no success. These people were finally able to make a positive change with *The Freedom Model* when nothing else had worked.

We understand some will learn *The Freedom Model* and continue to choose heavy substance use. We have seen this throughout our history. Certainly, we can't force those people to choose differently; we can't make their decisions for them nor can we force them to believe they will be happier using less or abstaining altogether. And most important, we know that we can't know better than they do what will make them happy. We are at peace with the fact that we can't force anyone to abstain from substance use. We discovered the best way that we can help is by showing people they are free.

Because of the difficulty of discerning tone from text, some may think our nonjudgment and definition of success are a passive-aggressive tactic. To some, it reads as if we're saying, "Go ahead and get high all you want; you might die, but hey, that's no skin off our backs." Make no mistake—we hold no such attitude. As researchers who have lived through issues similar to those of our readers, we empathize and know firsthand the pain involved in the hobbled beliefs recovery ideology wields. And, of course, we surely don't want anyone to face an untimely death, but we also hold the deep conviction that acting by one's own judgment and pursuing one's own vision of happiness is the most direct path to a fulfilling life. We also know that each person's autonomy allows him the privilege of doing exactly what he wants to do and that we have absolutely no control over his wishes or lifestyle. Please know that there is no hidden backdoor agenda; we're fully cognizant of our role, which is to present information to you. If that seems to you uncaring or passive-aggressive in any way, you are misreading our motives and the way in which we are trying to help you. In the final analysis, we know you are fully capable of changing and experiencing true freedom. We also know that, if you weren't trying to do what you think you "should do" according to norms, shame, and coercion, then you'd be that much closer to finding out what will make you happiest and truly what *you* want to do.

We also wouldn't want others to tell us how to live and what we should or shouldn't want; therefore, we won't do that to you. And again, we certainly can't judge what a worthwhile life is for anyone other than ourselves. Take for example the soldier who eagerly goes into battle, knowing death is likely. If he does die, who is to say he should've done differently or that his life was a waste? If he felt the risk of death was worth it, then it was worth it *to him*. The same goes for the extreme skier who knows the perils she faces yet says "I wouldn't be happy if I gave up this sport. If I die, so be it; I will have died doing what makes me happy." Or what about the rebellious rock star with a big drug habit? Some of them have died young. Is anyone to say whether their drug use was "worth it" other than they themselves? We think not. They may have thought that living big and dying young was better than living conservatively to a ripe old age. They are right—*for themselves*—because each person defines her own pursuit of happiness.

What's more, heavy substance use doesn't preclude success in other areas of life. Many of those recklessly partying rock stars have lived to ripe old ages and had many amazing accomplishments along the way. Who is anyone to say they "should" have lived their lives differently? How do you define what should make others happy? Saying somebody shouldn't use drugs for happiness is like saying somebody shouldn't collect comic books, shouldn't be a vegan, shouldn't "waste his time" watching football, shouldn't love the person she loves. These are all matters of personal taste and preference.

"But what about all the costs?" many will ask. You can look at this compared to other activities and their costs. Many athletes endure all sorts of injuries and long-term medical conditions as a cost of engaging in the sport that makes them happy. This doesn't have to be an extreme sport either; running or playing tennis can result in chronic health conditions that haunt these athletes for the rest of their lives.

But if it's what they love to do and they think it's worth continuing while understanding that further pain will result, then they are, *by their own actions*, stating that it's worth it to them. That is their right. And it is your right to decide what price you're willing to pay for your happiness.

WHAT IF YOU APPROACHED THE DECISION WITHOUT SHAME?

Let's consider a man who has considerable back and neck problems that the current state of medicine cannot cure. However, by taking high doses of opioid painkillers every day, he can quell the pain enough to enable him to function and find some semblance of happiness. Of course, the constant stream of painkillers is expensive. Taking them as prescribed creates physical dependency that will result in withdrawal symptoms if, for some reason, he stops taking them, and they cause constipation and other side effects he'd rather not have. Nevertheless, taking a steady stream of strong painkillers is the best thing he has found to serve his personal needs.

Should this man be ashamed of his drug use? Most people would say no. They would agree that he should do exactly what he needs to do for his own quality of life. Should this man quit these drugs? Well, if he judges the cost and side effects as worth it, then no. It would be a non sequitur, and anyone who says he should quit or there's something wrong with his opiate use would be sticking his nose where it does not belong. He's the one who judges whether the side effects he suffers are worth it to him. This isn't anyone else's business. Immorality, badness, blame, and shame should not and would not enter this scenario. In fact, most people would recognize that it's good and moral of him to take the actions necessary to secure his own comfort and enable him to function happily.

Would you be willing to approach your own substance use with the same lack of negative judgment that you'd give this man? Would you grant yourself the same moral permission to fulfill your own needs that you'd give the chronic pain sufferer? Isn't happiness as much a need as pain relief? Think of it; with no hope of happiness, people give up their efforts at life, and many even kill themselves. The ability to work toward happiness is an issue of survival. Would you allow yourself the possibility that working toward your own happiness is not only a normal, natural quest of humanity but also a highly moral one?

Our chronic pain sufferer will easily discontinue painkiller use the moment he's genuinely convinced that there's a better solution available to him. If he quits their use, it's not because he's randomly trying to quit painkillers for matters of morality and shame; it's because he's driven by the PDP to take what he sees as the best means to happiness. Even though, in a sense, he's "dependent" on those painkillers, he doesn't view that as a matter of "addiction." He views it as a matter of doing what he needs to do to serve his own needs. Therefore, switching to another means of pain relief is easy when he finds it and also why he's *open* to finding other solutions.

If you can allow yourself to discard the shame and simply make this about figuring out what makes you happiest—just like the chronic pain sufferer—then you can move forward in peace and joy. If you can let it be a matter of pursuing happiness and solutions to problems rather than a matter of overcoming badness, immorality, or "regaining self-control," then you can proceed in a totally different way. That is, you can gauge how much happiness you are getting out of your current level of substance use and explore the level of happiness that you may get out of some adjustment to your substance use. You can compare and then pursue the option that makes you happiest. You can do this confidently, knowing that you're doing what you must to live your best life. Please give yourself the same permission that you'd give the pain sufferer. You both have real and valid needs.

IT'S YOUR CHOICE TO MAKE, AND HERE'S WHY IT MATTERS

Our qualitative research with course graduates who consider themselves successful and happy repeatedly turns up the same theme: they realized they were free to choose. They tell us the most important thing they learned was that they had a choice. Everyone else had been telling them they were imprisoned by the disease of addiction, but from our course, they finally learned they had been free all along.

Another crucial element with these grads is that they openly pursued happiness. In follow-up interviews, they tell us about how they're happily living their lives and pursuing new goals. They also tell us they have come to see that quitting or shifting to a less problematic pattern of substance use *is* a happier option for them and they enjoy it more than their old pattern of substance use. This is in sharp contrast to those who cycle painfully through periods of problematic substance use and see themselves as failures. The self-described failures see a reduction in use as painful and a loss. They see themselves as pushed around by circumstances. They see themselves as not free and unable to choose differently. They focus on the negative consequences and are bewildered at why the negative consequences haven't scared them into quitting yet. They see themselves as helpless and not free, and they are committed to using fear and shame to motivate themselves to quit. It is truly sad to see them struggle.

As I (Steven) write this now, I've been holding classes with an older man who's been through several rehabs throughout his life. He came to us as a last resort to try something new. Each week, he shows up to class and expresses disbelief that his doctor's threats of cirrhosis haven't caused him to stop drinking. For decades, he has been trying the same strategy of focusing on reasons not to drink, and yet he has continued to drink. He continues to drink now even though he needs surgery and his doctors won't approve it until he stops drinking for a while. He presently feels like a failure. He painfully tries to resist drinking every day and then cracks. I am trying to show him that he can see quitting as a positive, a win or a gain, and that he can find happiness in quitting. He seems to ignore this point and then responds by talking once again about all he stands to lose if he keeps drinking. I obviously have no idea how this will turn out, but I fear that if he keeps focusing only on what he stands to lose, rather than what he stands to gain, he will continue in the same cycle that has been so upsetting to him for decades now.

I remember a few extended periods of abstinence I maintained because I was on probation and afraid of going to jail. During those periods, I saw nothing positive about quitting heroin. I saw it as misery. As a result, it always ended with an explosion of use right back into the same heavy pattern that got me into trouble in the first place. I repeatedly felt like a failure. My quits were made from a place of feeling like I "have to quit," so they didn't last. My final quit was done for the express purpose of discovering whether I could be happier without heroin. This "worked" for me; it has lasted 15 years now. I make no effort to maintain it, and I don't resist using heroin because I found that being heroin free was my happier option. I initially felt like a success in a matter of several weeks, and I still feel that way. The feeling wasn't and isn't based on how long I quit but rather on knowing it's my choice and that not using heroin makes me happy.

Surveying the self-described failures and successes, our mission has become clear: we continually seek to develop the most effective means of communicating to our guests that they are free to change and free to choose and that their actions will be directed by what they view as their happiest options. If you act on fear, shame, and shoulds, or thoughts such as *I can't* or *I have to*, then you are not fully embracing and making this choice in an open, direct pursuit of happiness. With this approach, you will likely hate what you feel obligated to do, and you will either reverse course or remain unsatisfied.

So the reason it's important for you to fully embrace that this is your choice and that it's about your happiness is that this is what will lead to your feeling successful. This is what will allow you to effectively change rather than painfully white knuckling doing something you don't like.

When you've operated under the belief that you are not free—*that you are addicted*—then your substance use has taken on a different meaning that makes you feel even more stuck. A night of heavy drinking that you regret becomes evidence of relapse, addiction, and cause for hopelessness. But when you view it as freely chosen, it becomes a lesson to slow down next time, and you then adjust accordingly. Knowing you're free to change, you adjust your substance use in the direction that makes you happiest.

It's important for you to understand that we aren't afraid that some of you will choose heavy substance use upon finishing *The Freedom Model* course. If you know it's your choice and that you are free to make your own choices, then you will find your way to what works best for you. We only fear for those who don't come to understand that they are free.

You are free to approach this however you want, but we'd like to highlight the key freedoms you have that apply directly to any choices you make about substance use.

YOU ARE FREE TO RETHINK THE BENEFITS OF CONTINUED SUBSTANCE USE

You hold certain opinions about substance use, which you can change. You have freedom of mind to think differently. Maybe you've thought you need drugs and alcohol to deal with emotional problems. We want to remind you that you are free to believe they don't help much with that and that you can deal with your emotional problems just fine without substance use. Maybe you've thought you need to use substances to socialize or be yourself; you are free to change this belief too. Maybe you've thought that using substances is the best or only way to really have fun; you are free to change this belief as well. Most people discover over time on their own that they no longer need substances for what they once thought they did.

The benefits of using substances are highly subjective. They depend in large part on what you think and believe. Once you understand that you have freedom in the form of mental autonomy and free will, you can explore the options of heavy and moderate substance use differently. Maybe there's little else left for you to gain from further heavy or moderate use. If you come to see it that way, you will be less attracted to it. Will you give yourself the opportunity to find your happiest option? One way to ensure this is to exercise your freedom of mind to critically think through the benefits of further use.

YOU ARE FREE TO RETHINK THE BENEFITS OF REDUCING OR QUITTING SUBSTANCE USE

You may have thought that life without heavy intoxication would be miserable or intolerable. You are free to challenge that belief and to see life with less substance use as a happier option rather than a miserable loss. There are potential gains for everyone in quitting or moderating if you look for them.

In saying this, we need to be clear that we are not talking about avoiding costs. Avoiding costs is, of course, part of the equation when deciding to change your substance use. But that is a negative, and in the long run, your actions are motivated by positives. The PDP says you will be motivated toward what you see as your happiest option.

Quitting substances can free up time and energy to find more exciting things to do, more peace, a greater sense of freedom, a return to health, and so on. In some ways, these are the reverse sides of the costs, but they are real gains; they are benefits. Will you choose to consider them as you decide whether to abstain, moderate, or use heavily? Will you give yourself a chance to find your happiest option, or will you stay focused on costs rather than benefits? You are free to choose how you think about this.

YOU ARE FREE TO SHIFT YOUR FOCUS FROM COSTS TO BENEFITS

In every area of life, people make their decisions primarily focused on benefits. They don't seek to incur more costs or hope for more disasters to scare them in a new direction. Going back to the example at the beginning of this chapter, if you're unsatisfied with your job, you don't hope for it to get worse to motivate you to quit. What most people do when they recognize that a job or career is unsatisfying is look for a better job or career. The dissatisfaction motivates them to look for better options, but if they don't look or don't find any, they usually stay right where they are. When people think they've got a better job in sight, that is when they quit. Yet, when it comes to this issue of unsatisfying patterns of substance use, many people look for more negatives, more consequences, and more pain to motivate them to quit. It's commonplace for people to tell us things such as "I wish I would get arrested because that would make me quit" or "I wish my doctor would tell me I have to quit; that would make it easier" or "The problem is I don't have enough negative consequences; I'm a functioning alcoholic." These comments are in line with the recovery ideology of a substance user needing to "hit bottom."

It would be quite strange indeed to think things such as *I wish my boss would threaten me more, I wish my coworkers were more annoying*, or *I wish they would give me more work than I can handle because that would make it easier to quit my job*. Most people's natural inclination is to simply look for a better job, a promotion, or a transfer to another department where they think they'd be happier.

A substance use habit is a normal life choice. It can be approached in the same way that people approach other life changes. If you are dissatisfied, you can look for a way of living that satisfies you more, that has the potential to make you happier. You are free to approach it this way, or you are free to continue to think of it as something that you need to fear and are forced out of doing. This shift in approach is your choice to make.

MOVING FORWARD

You get to decide how you proceed now. Will you feel cornered and shamed into quitting, or will you finally reject that thinking and look for your happiest path forward? This isn't a matter of semantics nor a small detail or a minor reframing. This is a dramatically different approach than what recovery ideology advises people to do. It works because all people are driven to pursue the options they see as providing the most happiness.

Our primary motive in life is not to simply avoid costs. If that were the case, then humanity wouldn't keep on improving technology and quality of life. We would all be hunter-gatherers or subsistence farmers like our ancestors. Or perhaps we would not even act to eat and survive—we would just starve and die—that being the least costly option. The longer you live, the more you work, the more effort you expend, and the more you pay for things. Yet rolling over to avoid costs isn't the norm. The norm is that people push forward; they try to increase their happiness, life expectancy, and comfort—even though this entails increased efforts and increased costs. All people are oriented to constantly pursue greater happiness, and they will readily take on great costs in doing so.

You are free to choose to change. You are free to launch a pursuit of this change out of fear and avoidance of costs or to launch this pursuit with greater benefits at the forefront of your mind. You are also free not to change. We've sought to demonstrate all of this to you in this first foundational half of *The Freedom Model* text. If you understand these three attributes, the PDP, free will, and autonomy, then you recognize you already have what it takes to change, to shed the addict self-image, and to see through most of the myths that have made you feel powerless to change.

We understand that you have been fed a mountain of misinformation about substance use and addiction through various means. Choosing to continue to believe this misinformation is choosing to stay imprisoned. New thoughts, new information, and new beliefs are the foundation for new decisions. The next half of *The Freedom Model* will help you to apply what you've learned. In it, you will (1) reclaim your freedom and (2) make a deliberate benefits-to-benefits analysis of your various substance use options to find a path that brings you the most happiness and thus, a path that you are truly motivated to pursue.

You don't have to suffer, and you don't have to struggle "in recovery" any longer. You can permanently put your substance use problems behind you with *The Freedom Model*.

Our goal, for you to feel free regarding substance use, will hopefully be fulfilled by the end of this course. *At that point, we will ask you whether you're ready to make the choice to never be an addict or alcoholic again for the rest of your life.* We need to be clear; we won't be asking you to make a lifelong decision about your future level of substance use. The matter of how much substances you plan to use will be completely irrelevant to this question. You could use drugs every day for the rest of your life and not be an addict. The question instead is about how you will choose to see yourself going forward and how you will subsequently feel. It will be about your self-image.

We've been showing you that nobody is enslaved to substance use. Nobody is ingesting substances against their will. Nobody is "out of control" of their drinking or drugging. It is only their belief in the addictive power of substances, the powerlessness caused by an imaginary disease, and other recovery mythology that makes people feel out of control and enslaved to substances. In short, to be an addict or alcoholic is to take on a negative, learned self-image. You don't have to identify in this limiting way, let people push you into this social role, or wear this label any longer. It is your choice to make. If you choose to let go of this identity permanently, you will never again feel addicted. All you need to do is see through the limiting beliefs of the recovery ideology and grasp onto a more empowering self-image. Then, you will feel your true freedom of choice.

CHAPTER 14:
RECLAIMING YOUR FREEDOM AND HAPPINESS

As we've discussed prior to this point, there is no "plan of action" to "battle" addiction because there is no objective state of addiction to be battled. This is a crucial point that you must understand because the myth of the *battle with addiction* is repeated constantly in various ways within the recovery society and likely has been in your life as well. All views of addiction are just a matter of the mind and how you view your habits. We realize many of you feel as if you cannot stop using substances. It is a frustrating and depressing feeling that we have felt ourselves. But we must remind you that it is just a *feeling* that is a result of your thoughts, beliefs, and perspectives of your options, *not a biological reality*. You have the power to change this feeling. *As soon as you fully realize you are free regarding substance use, it will be both easy and satisfying to make whatever changes to your habits you see fit to make.* Fully reclaiming your sense of freedom means understanding you are free in these two ways:

1. *You are free from addiction.* You know there is no such thing as addiction compelling you to desire and use substances and that your substance usage has *never been* "out of control." For better or worse, your use of substances is what you've preferred, and changing it is a matter of changing your preferences. We have covered this in detail throughout the text.

2. *You are free to change your desires and preferences.* You know that your desire for substances is a function of the benefits you've seen in your level of substance use compared to the benefits you've seen in some other level of substance use (either some form of decreased substance use or full abstinence). In other words, desire comes from the PDP. You know that you can reevaluate the relative benefits of these options and that this will alter your preference for substance use.

YOU ARE WHAT YOU THINK

If you think you contain some flaw that makes it impossible for you to easily, happily, and permanently discontinue problematic patterns of substance use, then you will feel and behave that way. That is, if you think you are an "addict," that is exactly the life you will live—either by continuing problematic use while feeling that you aren't in control of it as an "active addict" or by struggling to resist cravings and feeling fragile, vulnerable to relapse, and deprived while not using substances as a "recovering addict." There is no such thing as a "real addict/alcoholic"; there are only people who choose to see themselves this way, thereby mentally hobbling themselves. It's important to understand that this self-image hobbles them in both "active addiction" and "recovery."

If you have any shred of this self-image, you can choose to shed it. We've provided the information you need to do so. It is now a choice you can make on the grounds of being fully informed of the facts. You can think differently about yourself, and as soon as you do, you will feel freer, happier, and capable of easily changing.

Now, you can reevaluate your preferences and desires for substance use. You are what you think in this realm too. That is, if you think of yourself as having no available route to feeling good other than heavy substance use, then you will remain a person who feels an overwhelming desire for heavy substance use. If you think of yourself as a person who needs substance use as a solution to various problems, then you will feel a need for substances when facing those problems. If you think that substance use is essential for having fun, relieving boredom, or being social and that life without it is a living hell that deprives you of all these things, then you will feel deprived and miserable when you go without substances.

Likewise, if you think that life can be happier and more rewarding without substance use, then you will feel no desire for it, and in fact, you will be happy to not use substances. If you reach the conclusion that there are no more benefits whatsoever to be gained from further substance use, then you will be happy to quit. This extreme perspective shift will make quitting feel completely effortless.

These are two extreme ways substance use may be viewed (as a necessity or as having no value whatsoever to you), and of course, there are many possible shades between these views. There are numerous unique perspectives on substance use that will lead you to various preferences for it and thus, various sorts of desires. You may view it as something that potentially enhances your enjoyment at a party but doesn't have anything to offer you at other times, so you will feel a mild desire for it at parties but not at any other times. You will be able to take it or leave it in those situations. Or you may feel it has little to offer most of the time but that it is *necessary* to facilitate fun at a party, so you will feel little to no desire for it most of the time but an extreme need for it while at a party. You may see it as necessary for dealing with stress, so you will desire it when stressed. You may see it as producing more stress and, thus, have it be the last thing you'd ever want when stressed. However it shakes out, the way you choose to think of your various substance use options determines the feelings you'll have about them and the actions you'll take.

IDENTICAL THOUGHTS = IDENTICAL FEELINGS AND BEHAVIORS

We hope you'll take the idea that "you are what you think" to heart. It encapsulates what we've learned about how the PDP, free will, and mental autonomy work together to allow people to steer their personal feelings and behaviors. You have a motivation to pursue happiness (the PDP), only your own thoughts will determine where you see the happiest path, and nobody can do your thinking for you (mental autonomy); thus, by what you choose to think, you will choose what to do (free will).

"You are what you think" thus explains the trajectory of your substance use habits prior to now, and it also offers the key to changing that trajectory. What it boils down to is changing your thoughts. Quite simply, if you continue to think/believe the same things, you will end up feeling, wanting, and doing the same things. If you make the proactive choice to think different thoughts, then you will feel, want, and do different things. We can't stress this enough: *Different choices require different thoughts.*

The thoughts to be changed depend on the problem you are tackling. If the problem is that you feel addicted and wish you didn't feel this way, then you must identify those thoughts and change them (the addict/alcoholic self-image). Cease seeing yourself as an addict, and you will stop feeling addicted. New thoughts = new results.

If you feel a level of desire for substance use that you wish you didn't feel, you must identify the thoughts that create that desire. Then you must look for new thoughts that will change that desire. The PDP is particularly helpful to remember here, as it tells you that your desire is a product of what you view as your happiest options. Logically then, you will have to look at your thoughts regarding the benefits and happiness potential of heavy substance use as well as the benefits and happiness potential of moderate substance use or abstinence. If you keep the same basic thoughts regarding these options, you will feel the same desires and probably continue the same behavior. If you institute new thinking regarding the benefits of these various options, you will feel and act differently regarding substance use. Again, and we can't stress this enough, *Different choices require different thoughts.*

You are what you think. It really is that simple, but don't forget the "you" in that phrase. That is, don't overlook the importance of mental autonomy to personal change. Nobody else can do your thinking for you. No one can force you to believe or think anything. An overlooked part of this fact, especially regarding substance use, is that *trying to follow the convictions of others isn't the same as building your own conviction.* This can be hard to understand, but here's where it applies with substance use habits. You can't rely on counselors, sponsors, psychiatrists, or therapists to tell you that your life will be better or happier by quitting drugs and alcohol and then expect their recommendation to result in substantial lasting changes to the way you feel and behave regarding substances. They can't get into your head and think for you. Nobody can. Because the human mind is an autonomous fortress, it is impossible to replace your judgment with theirs:

> No conviction makes so lasting an impression on the mind as that which it works out for itself.
>
> —Frédéric Bastiat, French economist

Everyone's mind is an individually functioning entity. Looking to others to tell you what you *should* do or *should* want and committing to following their thoughts on the matter is not equivalent to arriving at those conclusions within your own mind by consciously thinking things through with new reasoning and information to reach the same conclusion. The difference here is like copying the answers on a math test or doing the work to reach the correct answers yourself. For you to feel differently, to be motivated to act differently, you need to think differently *within your own mind.*

Because of mental autonomy, strategies based on other people "holding you accountable" or "supporting your recovery" are doomed to fail because they rely only on other people making judgments of the appropriateness of your behaviors in their minds and then, accordingly, heaping shame, disappointment, praise, or pep talks on you as external motivators.

The question is then, where will a change in *your mind* come from? All external forms of motivation are inferior to an internal change of mind. To the degree that external motivators seem to have any effect, the effect usually disappears when you aren't staring that external motivator directly in the face. Furthermore, external motivators make you feel artificially constrained and deprived, leading to dissatisfaction with whatever reduction of substance use you make in response to them.

Lasting personal change really is an inside job. Only you can do it. What we can offer to help are new ideas and information that you might choose to consider and use in your own thinking. However, it's entirely up to you to choose to think differently. Are you ready to do that? If so, here's a perfect place to start.

CHOOSE A NEW SELF-IMAGE

The self-image of the addict/alcoholic is built on falsehoods. It's reasonable to see yourself this way when you've trusted the addiction experts in good faith. But now that you know the truth (that their vision of heavy substance use is incorrect), the only reason to hold onto this self-image is as an excuse. It doesn't help people to change their substance use habits. It makes those who believe it feel powerless and stuck, and for the small percentage who happen to change despite believing this awful thing about themselves, it robs them of the joy, pride, and confidence they could feel because of improving their lives. More often, it just provides an excuse for maintaining the status quo.

Most important to *The Freedom Model*, the addict/alcoholic self-image blocks the way to preference change. So, if you want to apply *The Freedom Model* to your life, you have to pick a side. Here are the two basic self-image options in a nutshell:

1. *Addict/alcoholic self-image:* I lose control of my substance use. I am stuck with cravings that I am too weak to deal with and may cause me to relapse at times. Life will be a constant struggle for me, and I will have to stay vigilant and seek constant support to battle addiction or "underlying causes of addiction" to maintain recovery for the rest of my life.

2. *Free self-image:* I am now and always have been in full control of my choices to use substances. I make choices about substance use for the same reason that I make all other choices in life—because I am pursuing happiness—and by my own judgment, the choices I have made regarding substance use are the ones that I have seen as necessary for happiness. This applies whether I choose to use a little, a lot, or not at all. I will continue to freely make whatever choices I see as best for me, a perspective that I am free to change at any moment by seeking out new ideas and information.

If you choose the addict/alcoholic self-image, then you aren't applying *The Freedom Model* to your problems. This doesn't mean you can't or won't change your substance use. You might change, but you'll be putting unnecessary obstacles in your own path, making any potential change harder than it needs to be.

Here, it is important that you understand that *The Freedom Model is both a description of human behavior and a way of thinking that facilitates personal change.* So the principles hold regardless of whether you believe them. That is, *anyone* who makes a lasting change to a personal habit/preference has found greater happiness in the change.

> Goals, preferences and priorities articulated either inwardly or outwardly need not be consistent with the choices actually made when confronted with the options presented by the real world. A man may claim or believe that keeping the lawn mowed is more important than watching television but, if he is found spending hours in front of the TV screen, day in and day out for weeks on end, while weeds and tall grass take over the lawn, then the preferences revealed by his behavior are a more accurate indicator of that individual's priorities than either his expressed words or even whatever beliefs he may have about himself. (Sowell, 2010, Kindle location 3114–3117)

So, even if someone believes she is battling a powerful addiction and expresses a hatred of sobriety yet she maintains abstinence, the proof is in the pudding—*she does prefer abstinence.* Her PDP says abstinence is better than substance use. Why pair it with a sense of deprivation and fragility?

Many readers do not thoroughly understand the point of chapter 2—You Have To Want It To Work—so it needs to be clearly stated now. *Everyone who changes his substance use does so by his own power of choice* because, at the time that he changes it, he sees the change as a happier option. This holds whether he uses substitution drugs, support meetings, or ongoing therapy. No matter to what he attributes his change, he is maintaining the change because he sees it as his happiest available option. Therefore, we are saying that *The Freedom Model is descriptive* because it explains these changes. Regardless of whether people understand it, they are making their own choices by their own free will and thoughts in their autonomous minds, which direct them to the change that is the happier option. Their true preference is revealed by their behavior.

The various methods of "recovery from the disease of addiction" unnecessarily pair negativity with personal change. If quitting or cutting back is your happier option and your choice, why not just recognize it as such without all the self-doubt and feelings of deprivation? Why be a martyr? Why see it as a sacrifice? Why continue putting in unnecessary effort and feeling chained to recovery activities of "battling addiction" when one of the main reasons for making a change is to stop feeling enslaved? After all, if you stick with the change, that means you prefer it. A minority of people make their changes in substance use with these methods *despite* pairing their change with all this negativity. Unfortunately, there are many more who reverse course because they believe struggle and pain are a necessary part of "recovery," so they eventually end up hating their changes and going back to problematic substance use.

The Freedom Model as a philosophy to facilitate personal change cuts to the chase and *avoids all that negativity*. So, for you to proactively implement it as a solution, you must embrace it as the truth. In a nutshell, this means

1. shedding the addict/alcoholic self-image,

2. taking on the self-image of a free and flexible person,

3. directly reassessing your preferences to find your happiest option, and

4. then moving on with your life—free from any further charade of battling the bogeyman of addiction.

Do you want an excuse and unnecessary struggle added to your life, or do you want to move on? This is your choice. Which self-image do you want? If you choose the free self-image, you are implementing *The Freedom Model* as a solution and can implement direct preference change. If you aren't convinced after reading through the text, then you are welcome to examine all the supporting research, think things through again, and test out the ideas. New decisions require new thinking.

DIRECT PREFERENCE CHANGE

Your current preferences were built incrementally by learning various ideas about substances, self, and addiction. There were two ways of learning that were involved: getting ideas and information from the environment/culture, and through your personal experience. Then, your experience and ideas comingled over time to form a strong preference. Changing your preferences will work the same way; they will be a unity of new thinking and new experiences. As you work new ideas and information into your thinking and make choices based on them, these ideas will then be tested through experience and form new preferences. This is important to understand because it can explain past "failures" at quitting/moderating and help you be patient as you explore your new options.

Past "failures" at quitting/moderating can be discouraging. If you tried in the past to change your substance use by sheer willpower paired with the same old thoughts, it's not a surprise that your changes didn't last. For example, if you chose to abstain while you continued to believe that drugs are necessary for having a good time, then that belief ensures you won't have a good time while abstinent. The quit attempt is then nothing but misery, boredom, and deprivation. Eventually, you give up your quit and go back to heavy substance use because you still prefer it. The beliefs you paired with this attempt obstructed you from making any positive discovery and preference change.

The same goes for moderation attempts. If for example you tried to stop at two drinks while maintaining the same belief that life is unbearable unless you polish off a full bottle of wine to forget your problems, then you will feel deprived of your stress medicine as soon as you finish the second drink. Again, no preference change, and you're likely to go back to drinking a full bottle of wine in a sitting. The same beliefs blocked any discovery and led you back to the same old behaviors.

The tragedy of all of this is that you come out of these experiences believing you're incapable of change. But you're not incapable at all. These attempts simply lacked new thoughts and beliefs. In the example of our drug user who believes he can't have any fun unless he's intoxicated, there are two distinct belief sets he could've used in his quit attempts that would have been far superior than sticking with the same old beliefs. First, he could have questioned the pleasurable effects of drugs, thought back to when he had fun without drugs, and rethought the potential fun he could have in a sober state of mind, convincing himself that he could have equal or more fun without substances. Then, going out for a night of fun without drug use, he could test and prove this new belief to himself even further with experience. This gives him the best chance of forging a new preference. If he couldn't convince himself beforehand, he could at least be open to the possibility and then test it. He could simply remind himself that plenty of people have fun without drugs and that maybe he can too if he tries. Then, he opens himself up to this discovery when he goes out to have a fun night without drugs. He may begin to prove it to himself and begin to develop a new preference. But if he tests the experience and holds on to the same old belief that he can't have fun without drugs, then he is sure not to have fun to "prove" to himself that life without drugs is misery.

"You are what you think" also means that you will find what you're looking for. In the above case, that means if you still believe you can't have fun without drug use, you'll find misery and deprivation. Granted, you may stumble onto some discoveries by accident, but why not set the stage for positive discovery with new thoughts and on open mind? There are simple reasons that most people attempting "recovery" don't do this. First, change is approached as fighting a mysterious entity called addiction rather than changing a personal preference. Then, if coercion is in play, the focus is on getting others off your back rather than exploring happier options. And finally, if the reduction of costs/harms/consequences is your focus, then you will be distracted from maximizing your potential benefits in life. Bring new thoughts to your efforts to change, and you will facilitate real preference change. Keep the same old thoughts and beliefs, and you can expect the same old results.

The other reason you need to know that preference change is accomplished through a unity of new thoughts and experience is that this can help you be patient on your way to preference change. It can calm down the panic that causes so many people to give up. You built your current preferences by pairing various beliefs about substances and self with many choices and experiences over time. For example, if you were exposed to the idea that alcohol helps relieve stress, then you eventually turned to it when you were stressed, experienced stress relief, and through that experience, began to see it increasingly as a solution.

Pharmacologically, alcohol doesn't relieve stress for anyone; we'll explain this fully in chapters 17 and 18. Nevertheless, this belief repeatedly paired with drinking and the belief that you're unable to deal with stress led to the growth of a strong connection between stress and alcohol in your mind. If you did this, then as a result you now feel an intense need for alcohol at the slightest negative emotion. You prefer to drink in response to stress. Changing that preference will take an open mind. You will have to dare to question such things as whether alcohol really relieves stress and whether you're so fragile that you even need a stress-relieving drug. We will present you with the facts, but you still may not be fully convinced. That's fine so long as you're open to thinking differently and then testing this possibility by facing your moments of stress without alcohol. As you get through these moments, you will begin to discover that you don't need alcohol to deal with stress. Or perhaps you have an open mind to this information, you remember it, and then you do drink when stressed. You may ponder whether the alcohol is relieving anything as you drink it and discover that it isn't. You will change your preference if you pair new thoughts with the experience.

This process of severing the connection between stress and alcohol may be instantaneous if you find the new information extremely persuasive and think back on past experiences. But if it's not instantaneous, you can take comfort in the fact that it could be incremental, like most preference change. Many of our students knew that even if they struggled a bit, they could change with effort and the struggle was a normal part of growth rather than a sign of inability (remember the discussion of mindsets in chapter 10; it applies here). You can learn not to feel like you need alcohol for stress if you're open to it. Life is a constant process of incremental preference change, and our preferences for substance use are no exception. If you're open to questioning, exploring, and learning, you can and will make new discoveries and changes.

The key to all this is to be open-minded and aim directly at exploring your options rather than hoping that your desires will magically disappear. If you seek out new information and try new thoughts and ideas and combine them with new experiences, you cannot lose. You will discover either happier options or that the same old options truly are your happiest. But if you know that you gave yourself the chance to fully explore these options, then you can move forward happily, whether or not your preferences change. If you quit or moderate happily, and reduce costs while increasing happiness, then that's a win. If you discover that heavy substance use is truly what you want, then you can stop regretting the high price you pay for it and simply accept it as the cost of happiness.

The only real loss here is whether you approach change with the same old thoughts leaving no room for discovery. If you do that again, you'll never know what you might be missing. Reclaiming your freedom and happiness means becoming open to all options, thus giving yourself the best chance at finding the one that brings you the greatest amount of happiness.

With that said, there is a common way that people still fail to give themselves this opportunity. That is by being overly focused on the consequences of substance use and feeling obligated to quit. We will obliterate these obstacles in the next chapter.

For now, remember these key points:

1. *You are what you think.*

2. Identical thoughts beget identical feelings and behaviors.

3. Different thoughts beget different feelings and behaviors.

4. *You can choose to never be an addict again*, no matter what you choose in the way of substance use because it is nothing more than a self-image.

To apply *The Freedom Model* as a solution, you'll need to choose a free and flexible self-image over the addict/alcoholic self-image.

REFERENCES

Sowell, T. (2010). *Intellectuals and society.* New York, NY: Basic Books.

CHAPTER 15:

MOTIVATORS VS. DETERRENTS

The Positive Drive Principle is all about your motivation. It drives you down the path where you see the most happiness. If you come to see greater happiness in a new path, the PDP will propel you in a new direction. This shift will be achieved by focusing on benefits.

Unfortunately, because of the negativity surrounding substance use and decades of misinformed recovery ideology, many people attempt to change their substance use with fear of consequences and various negative strategies. They fail because they don't address the motivation behind the process of personal change. You can try to deter yourself from certain behaviors with all your will, but your natural drive to pursue happiness eventually wins out. Eventually, you move toward whatever you believe you need for happiness. Every failed attempt at changing a substance use habit is based on deterrence. Every successful attempt is based on motivation. This chapter will expose the deterrence-based strategies as ineffective so that you can ditch them and focus on motivation.

YOU DON'T "HAVE TO" QUIT

When people seek help for substance use problems, they're usually full of fear and shame and feel cornered into quitting. Many want to get right to it, swearing off drugs and alcohol forever and then seeking to learn "how to resist the cravings." In earlier chapters, we extensively discussed addiction theory to present you with a clear understanding of the problem. We know by now that many readers are chomping at the bit, and we can see their impatience building. In our courses, some eventually say to their presenter, oftentimes in a loud and insistent tone, "Yeah, yeah, yeah, I agree addiction isn't a disease—NOW TELL ME HOW TO QUIT!" There is a sense of panic inherent in this, and panic is not an ingredient for making positive decisions.

Then, while the presenter is explaining that loss of control is a myth, the topic of moderation naturally comes up. This topic often brings another explosion of "I can't moderate; *I can't talk or think about it. I JUST HAVE TO QUIT.* I can't drink in moderation! I can't ever drink again! Abstinence is the only option that will work for me!" Rushing into quitting and refusing to see it as a choice is a major problem. We recommend that if you are thinking these things, then slow down. How will you reach a conclusion about where greater happiness lies for you when you're consumed by fear and panic and you're using them to jump to the hasty conclusion that you must quit?

The fact is that you don't *have to* quit. You really and truly can drink or drug again. You can do it heavily or moderately or you can abstain. That's reality. People enter treatment programs every day proclaiming that they *have to quit* and swear off substances forever; then they complete their treatment, walk out the door, and resume problematic use again. So discussing it as if there is no choice is completely ineffective. There is a choice; it is your choice. So it's important to acknowledge that truth and openly consider all options as potential possibilities rather than jumping into abstinence with little or no thought.

COERCION AND ULTIMATUMS

We hear the following statements all the time:

"My ex-husband is trying to get full custody of the kids. If I drink again, he'll win. I have to quit."

"My parents are making me quit smoking pot. They'll stop paying for college and take away my car if I keep smoking. I have to quit."

"My doctor says I'm on the verge of getting cirrhosis. I have to quit drinking."

"I can't believe the people I end up with, and the places I find myself in. It's disgusting. I'm a cocaine addict. This isn't how a man of my background should be living. I have to quit."

"Heroin will kill me if I don't quit. I've lost three close friends already. I have to quit."

All these folks say they "have to quit," yet it simply isn't true. Certainly, this truth is obvious, that there is always a choice, but it must be consciously considered. The 19-year-old college student doesn't *have to quit* smoking pot. He *can* keep doing it, that is, if he finds it more valuable than a free ride through college. If he does quit, it will be his choice because he thinks that having college and a car paid for by his parents will make him happier than smoking pot.

The divorced mother *can* keep drinking, although a cost of that may be losing custody of her children. Certainly, there have been many people in these exact situations who have continued using substances and been willing to pay the price. This isn't a small point; many people pay extremely high costs to keep using, and they are fully aware of them. This isn't some rare, obscure thing that happens once in a blue moon; it's commonplace. So to act as if you must stop without considering all the options is not necessary. The only reason you jump to the abstinence route and bypass even the idea of reducing your level of consumption is because recovery ideology has scared you straight to abstinence with its doomsday rhetoric.

You truly don't have to quit. It is *your choice* to quit. You are free to quit or to continue using. Own it. If you're quitting because of a health reason, you can feel as if you have to quit and be miserable about it, or you can proudly think *I'm quitting drinking/drugging to improve my health and have a happier, longer life.* Did you just get that? The idea was converted from a negative to a positive statement, one that concentrates on the benefits of change. Nobody *is* actually forced to quit because of a health problem; in fact many don't. The price is high, but some people choose to pay it.

When you think you *must* do something, you're not owning it. You are obscuring the fact that it truly is *your* choice. You are choosing it with a sense of coercion, obligation, or duty, and framed in this way, the choice to quit is a way for you to absolve yourself of responsibility for the outcome when you choose to get drunk or high again. Not only that, but quitting out of duty, obligation, or coercion is highly unmotivated and, thus, quite dissatisfying and frustrating and can even be painful because it doesn't feel as if it's your choice. You will eventually feel deprived and then crave what it is you desired from the beginning—to use heavily. It doesn't feel like it's what you want because it isn't. The missing element when you choose in this way is recognition of benefits—happiness in the various options open to you: heavy use, moderate use, or abstinence. If you feel powerless and pushed around in your quit attempt, then where is the happiness in that? If you see no happiness in quitting, what will keep you motivated to stay stopped?

SHAME AND SHOULDS

While many people feel cornered into quitting by others, that isn't the case for everyone. Sometimes nobody is breathing down your neck to quit. There are no ultimatums, no probation officers, and no nagging spouses. There is just you and your own thoughts nagging at you. You tell yourself things such as:

> "I shouldn't be using cocaine at my age."

> "I should be successful by now. I shouldn't be wasting my time partying."

> "I can't keep smoking. I'll get emphysema. I have to stop."

> "I shouldn't have a drink at lunch when the kids are almost out of school. I am a bad father."

> "I can't keep getting high like this. What would people think of me if they found out?"

The problem with this thinking is the same as with the ultimatums. Positive motivation is noticeably absent. You *can* keep smoking, getting high, or drinking. You don't *have* to stop. Furthermore, the *shoulds* you're entertaining are empty. They contain no positive reason for why change would be good and attractive. Again, this is important; without a positive motivation, the changes you make will only be temporary. Greater happiness provides positive motivation in the new direction and is the fuel that keeps the changes you're making moving forward. Without that positive motivation, the fuel of said change will run out to a return to the benefits of your old habit. Without any positive reason for a change in use, the change is avoidance based—avoid disease, avoid shame, avoid stigma, avoid a negative self-image. When you direct these kinds of statements at yourself, they are an attempt at self-deterrence.

> If we do something stimulated solely by the urge to avoid shame, we will generally end up detesting it. (Rosenberg, 2015, Kindle location 2555)

Is it any wonder that your previous attempts at quitting or reducing your substance use with this kind of negative start ended in failure? You know full well that you can keep on doing the very things you're trying to *demand, shame,* and *should* yourself out of doing. So you stop for a while, hating it and feeling deprived the whole time, and that deprivation becomes so unbearable that you go back to your habit. Why do you go back? It's no mystery; you go back because you think it'll feel good or satisfy a need. You think you've been missing out. You never really found moderation or quitting as being more attractive. If you've been powering your quit attempts with deterrents and avoidance-based strategies—*shame, should, I can't*—then your mental state upon quitting is exactly like that of the 19-year-old who's been told he has to quit smoking pot. You really don't want to make this choice, but you feel cornered into making it. There is some motivation, but it's minimal and paired with an equal or greater sense of loss.

There is no joy in feeling cornered, coerced, shamed, or obligated to do something. If there is no joy, there is no lasting motivation. So jumping the gun on deciding to quit forever is the wrong way to go about this. Knowing you are free to make whatever choice you see fit and then carefully reassessing your options is the way to proceed with happiness, confidence, and resolve.

HOLDING ONTO POWERLESSNESS

Quitting out of fear is not effective either, and that's exactly what the black-and-white notion of either abstinence or disastrous substance use engenders. Did you recoil when we told you that "loss of control" is a myth and moderation is possible? Was your reaction *I can't think about moderation. I just have to quit?* If you stick to this thinking, then you may yet make another joyless failed attempt to quit.

The myth of loss of control (that is, the 12-step allergy model of addiction, e.g., "one drink equals a drunk") is a myth used to maintain fear of substance use and make people feel cornered into abstinence. If you have spent any time at all in 12-step meetings or treatment, you've heard a plethora of slogans and horror stories meant to scare you into maintaining complete abstinence. Research has shown that those who attend 12-step treatment and meetings have higher rates of dangerous binge usage than those who are not taught they will lose control.

We aren't discussing moderation to promote it (this is important—we aren't advocating any path regarding substance use). We discuss moderation because we're honest about the full range of options, it's a path of substance use many people will choose regardless of our mentioning it, you are no different than the average person in your ability to moderate, we don't judge substance use as bad, and considering the full range of options allows you to choose more freely than does feeling cornered into a choice. To say that you *can moderate* isn't to say that you *should moderate.* You will choose whatever you find most attractive. Openly assessing your options is better than choosing one in which you're not invested. Many readers will find great happiness in adjusting their level of use, and we're happy for those who do. *The Freedom Model* is about freely pursuing what makes *you* happy—not what others think you *should* do.

There can also be wonderful positive reasons for choosing abstinence. Abstinence simplifies change; helps you feel emotionally independent and powerful; eliminates all substance-based risks; and frees up your mental resources and time to devote to new goals, rebuilding your life, and exploring activities that may be far more exciting than substance use. When you become abstinent because you "have to," then you're not looking for positive reasons to quit. You're not looking for joy. You might recognize benefits along the way by accident, but you might also continue to be miserably focused on what you think you're losing by being abstinent and live with a sense of deprivation. We know where that road leads—right back to the same old pattern of substance use that costs you so much. Then use becomes the lesser of two evils, which still makes it more attractive than abstinence.

If you're thinking in this way, your insistence on clinging to the idea that you "can't" adjust your level of use illustrates a dangerous strategic error. You're attempting to scare yourself into abstinence yet again, to deter yourself. You're trying to remove choice from the equation or at least severely limit it to a choice between disastrous use and trouble-free abstinence. You see yourself as choosing between a *happy disaster* and a *miserable calm*. Holding this perspective means the happy disaster always wins. It's the "devil you know" or put another way, the better of two dissatisfying options.

STARTING OFF ON THE RIGHT FOOT

As you think about and eventually decide what your future substance use will be, remember that all the following statements reflect painful obligation:

1. I have to
2. I must
3. I should
4. I can't

These words don't need to remain a part of your thinking regarding your future substance use. If you've been telling yourself any of these things, for example, that you "have to quit," then you can decide to recognize that this just isn't true and stop repeating these false mantras. It'll be worth it for you to recognize and own your choices. Thinking *I have to quit* is not the same as thinking *I want to quit*. If you choose to quit or adjust your level of use, this would be the first and most crucial fork in the road. One road is unnecessarily painful, and the other can be joyful or at least better with positive reasons for change.

Making a self-determined and successful adjustment in your substance use habit can be a happy and highly motivating experiment. It can be a process of discovery. Will you be open to discovering what makes you happiest, whether that be adjusting use or abstaining, rather than feeling like a deprived martyr? It's your choice. You can approach it from whatever angle you like with whatever level of use you'd like.

CATEGORICAL THINKING: GOOD AND BAD SUBSTANCES

Substances are neither categorically bad nor good so thinking of them in this way is inaccurate and creates problems. Each decade has its demons, and opiates are today's *evil killers*, which are said to addict people and drive them to overdose. Yet, for thousands of years, they have served as miracle drugs to treat many ailments when medical technology hadn't yet delivered anything better. In the days when people literally died from coughing, the opiates offered cough suppression that enabled many to survive while their immune systems fought off deadly diseases, or at least opiates made their deaths less painful. Alcohol, in certain frequencies and quantities, can lead to cirrhosis and other deadly conditions, yet in smaller quantities and frequencies, it can be good for the heart. Ibuprofen can wreak havoc on the liver but can also reduce pain and swelling from several ailments. Water is necessary for human survival, but in overabundance, it can end life. None of these substances are fully good or fully bad.

When people view the substances that make them high as categorically good, their desire for them becomes overblown, and they end up wanting them in every situation, at every time. They may use them at times and in situations where their usage may not serve them well. On the reverse side, when you think of any substance as categorically bad, issues are raised as well. This often comes up when you try to swear off substances forever. You know they have served you well in some ways at certain times. Therefore, you are lying to yourself when you try to portray substances as categorically bad and ignore the reasons you wanted them at certain times. This tactic clearly doesn't work when anti-drug crusaders use scare tactics to demonize drugs to children, and in fact, this misinformation causes other problems. As children grow up and find out drugs aren't as awful as they've been told they are, they tend to throw the baby out with the bathwater, assuming everything they've been told about drugs is a lie. Likewise, playing the anti-drug crusader with yourself and portraying substances as categorically bad, while in your heart you know otherwise, is just as problematic.

Honest, accurate, and realistic analysis is what's needed for the best results. You may decide to never use a substance again, but you don't need to panic and tell yourself lies to make this decision. You may honestly discover that a specific substance now has very little to offer you, that the thrills have gotten boring. This view would lead to a more comfortable and easier decision to stop using that substance, leaving you excited to discover what else life has in store. The panicked view that relies on fear of substances to try to force you to quit may leave you feeling deprived, anxious, and depressed. So remember this—substances aren't inherently good or bad; they are good and bad to the degree that they are useful to you. They are relatively good and relatively bad, that is, in comparison to other options and other uses of your resources.

CATEGORICAL THINKING: PRIORITIES

We often hear blanket statements such as "I put alcohol ahead of my family" or "I'm putting drugs before my life." Yet these statements never seem to be categorically true. These beliefs tend to form because, in some situations, when faced with an either/or choice, people choose the substance. An example is a woman's husband tells her Saturday morning "You'd better not drink today; you need to put the kids first," and then she drinks and goes at it hard all day long. What's overlooked is that she worked hard earning money for the care and well-being of her family all week long. Six out of seven days, she had been putting them first, and then, on one of those days, she decides she wants to drink to be happy. These blanket statements don't do any good; they simply make people feel bad. There's much more give and take, nuance, incremental trade-offs, and prioritization than people recognize when they're panicked and trying to make a strong decision to quit substances. It's not just a black-and-white decision.

We can see this even with the most extreme substance users, such as the homeless heroin user. If he did put heroin use ahead of everything else in his life, then he would willfully prepare an extra-large dose for injection to purposely overdose and die. But he doesn't. He carefully prepares his doses with at least some caution so he can continue to exist. He puts some effort into finding a place to safely sleep for the night. He gets some food along the way to nourish himself enough to keep going.

We could look at any number of cases and find that they all include a more mixed and nuanced set of priorities that fluctuates at various times and in various situations. So to say that you've put drugs above everything else when your actual behavior demonstrates otherwise is inaccurate and overly negative thinking. You are what you think, and such distorted thinking won't lead to the clarity you need for more fruitful decisions. We understand the tendency to do this when it comes time to try to make a change, but it isn't helpful.

We will be discussing the costs of substance use, and we realize it may be tempting for you during this discussion to think of your past in categorical terms. You may try to get down on yourself to tip the scales toward quitting and beat yourself up about how you always put your substance use ahead of other things, but it's rarely that simple. Has thinking this way led you to a permanent change in the past? That's obviously not the case if you're reading this now. It takes new thoughts to get new results, so try cutting yourself some slack and being more realistic with your analysis.

What's more likely is that you've made incremental trade-offs with your substance use. Sometimes, these trade-offs gradually lead to a situation where substance use has become fully prioritized over everything else. An example is a college student who postpones schoolwork now and goes out partying. She may start to see her grades suffer, yet she still puts some work into attending classes but not enough into studying to get the grades she wants. It's a mixed bag. It may lead to a situation where everything seems lost so she completely gives up on her studies, but rarely does the situation happen because she made the blanket decision to abandon school for drugs. Life is more often made of momentary decisions and situational trade-offs that can have cumulative effects.

Whether you've reached a point where substance use seems to be your full priority or where your priorities are mixed and continuously fluctuating, no good comes from pretending that the decisions were categorical. Rarely does anyone decide that he has no use nor care for his family and he always chooses drugs over them. Please don't unnecessarily shame yourself. It won't help you to achieve the clarity of thinking that allows you to discover what choices have the most benefits and will bring you the most happiness.

Now, we're going to address some issues regarding the costs of substance use and ask you to remember that you've been willing to pay these costs incrementally according to your views in the moments when you've made your choices. Your preferences were built incrementally rather than categorically, and in most cases, they apply in nuanced ways. While it may be tempting to say "I've put drug use before my freedom," if this were really true, you wouldn't wait a second after leaving a crack house to smoke your crack. You'd whip out a pipe and start smoking right there on the street, where cops are constantly patrolling. Of course, you don't do that because you really do give your freedom priority; you wait until you can find a place that is safe for you smoke it. So please resist the temptation to portray yourself as having made categorical decisions to prioritize one thing over all others every time because that's inaccurate.

EVERYTHING HAS A PRICE

There's a proverb that goes "God said take whatever you want, just pay for it." It means that everything comes at a price. There is no choice in life without cost. With drugs and alcohol, most of these costs are well known and easily predictable. For example, as you're taking your seventh or eighth drink on a night out, you know you're going to be hung over and have a hard time functioning at work in the morning. When you spend your entire paycheck on cocaine, you know you're going to have trouble paying rent on the first of the month.

Regarding recovery, these plainly understood costs become more ominous. Definitions of addiction usually include a phrase such as "drug seeking and use, despite harmful consequences."

"Consequences" is a technically correct term to use here, but it comes with a *connotation* that can muddle your thinking. The word makes it seem as if these costs were unforeseen or the result of a complex process. Consequences seem distant and beyond your direct control. But in fact, most of the "harmful consequences" of substance use are known to substance users at the very moment they choose to use substances. Those who do not approve of your substance use often recite the consequences to you to try to motivate you to change as if you were unaware of them. Then, this becomes your personal mantra, and it's not helpful.

Consider this: Every day, I like to go to a fancy coffee shop and get a large iced red-eye with half and half. What if I described my preference in this way: "I'm losing $5.75 a day because of coffee, but I keep using coffee despite these negative consequences."

That's a weird statement, isn't it? Such verbiage obscures what's really going on and makes me a victim of coffee. I know the coffee costs $5.75, but I'm willing to pay that price for it because I really like it. Here's what's important: there is no actual loss because I see the trade-off as worth it at the time. But in my statement, it sounds like I'm stuck in some puzzling, vicious cycle. It mentally distances me from the choice I am knowingly making and conveniently leaves out that I am willingly paying this price.

Here's another statement: "I keep using cocaine even though the consequences are that I can't pay my rent at the end of the month. I am out of control." This language also obscures what's going on. It makes not having money for rent seem like a chance happening, an unfortunate, unpredictable result, when in fact, it was clear as day while you spent your paychecks on cocaine that you wouldn't have enough money at the end of the month to pay your rent. The truth is you were willing to pay the price of dealing with a shit storm at the end of the month so you could get high in that moment. Own it. Though you haven't wanted these little disasters, they have been the price you've been *willing to pay* because you really preferred cocaine that much.

If you want to make something seem accidental, call it a loss: "I lost my _____ because of drinking." Is that really accurate? When the outcome of a choice is so easily predictable, it's not a loss. It's a price you were willing to pay. In short, losses are, for the most part, *unexpected*. In contrast, the *costs* of our choices are usually known and agreed to at the moment we carry out the choice.

Prices and *costs* are terms that describe what's going on much more clearly than negative consequences or losses. If you have experienced some costs that weren't so easily predictable, then go ahead and call those "negative consequences"; there certainly are exceptions. But in the spirit of fully owning your substance use and recognizing the freedom you hold over your choices, you might want to start thinking of the results of your substance use as the *price* you have been willing to pay for the benefits you've seen in substance use.

One of the most popular arguments used to support the false concept of addiction goes like this:

> Who would choose to keep drinking even when they could lose their marriage, license to drive, job, and health because of it? Nobody would freely choose to lose all this. They must not be in control of themselves. It must be an addiction, a mental illness.

At first glance, this logic makes sense, but that's only because it ignores the benefits that the drinker sees in alcohol. In short, it highlights costs only, and from this perspective, heavy drinking appears irrational. But we've reviewed many of the benefits people see in substance use. For a drinker who finds great pleasure in alcohol, believes it genuinely relieves his stress, and sees life without it as unbearable, he chooses to drink in pursuit of its benefits even though it becomes costly. This is what drives the desire and the behavior. Is the choice to drink heavily any different than the choice to drop $100,000 on the car of your dreams?

This logic also makes the error of categorical thinking. A marriage is never lost over one night of drinking, although ultimatums may be given and eventually come to pass. More realistically, this individual chose drinking in ways that damaged the marriage incrementally, according to what he believed he needed to be happy at the time rather than as a blanket decision to give up the marriage in favor of drinking. People also incrementally give up their marriages because of work or exhaustion or any other number of reasons by losing interest sexually or ignoring their partner's wishes to have date nights and quality time or to plan vacations together. People usually know these choices are taking a toll, and at the time, they're willing to pay that price because they see it as the best available option. They're living out their own preferences, which sometimes cumulatively add up to bigger prices. No addiction need be imagined explaining this; life is messy.

Recovery crusaders ignore the preferences of those they call "addicts" and replace them with their own preferences. They ignore the immediate needs and desires of individuals and focus only on long-term outcomes. They also believe the substance user to be mentally incompetent. The *costs* thus become "negative consequences" that should be causing the substance user to stop what she's doing but somehow isn't. Recently, author Maia Szalavitz, espousing the pet theory that addiction is a neurological learning disorder, expressed this logic when she was asked to justify her view:

> Addiction is defined as compulsive behavior despite negative consequences. Negative consequences is synonymous with punishment. It basically means you're failing to learn from punishment. So that is a problem with learning. [Note: she means it's a problem with learning on a neurological level.] (Young, 2017)

What she calls "punishment" and "negative consequences" the substance user simply sees as the price of substance use at the time he makes his choices. It's not that he's neurologically unable to learn to stop making this choice; it's that he sees the relative benefits of the choice as worth the price at the time. If you want to critically examine your preferences and discover whether you have better options available to you, you can't afford to fall into the trap of ignoring that you genuinely thought/think the cost of your substance use has been worth paying.

The assumption is that heavy substance users are unaware of what their substance use is costing them at the time they do it but, as the consequences come full circle, the substance user should be deterred from making the same choice again. This is like assuming people don't know the price of things they purchase with a credit card until the bill comes the next month and then calling the bill a "negative consequence" of credit card use. This would distort the reality of the situation, which is that, when you buy something with a credit card, you know what it costs, and you're planning to pay for it later.

Assuming that heavy substance users are somehow unaware of long-range consequences, recovery ideology says they need to be made aware of the "negative consequences" through confrontation of denial. And then they need to be conditioned through constant recovery efforts to always stay hyperaware of these consequences so that, the next time they think of using substances, the consequences will finally deter them. The "addicts" who act upon this advice mentally recite all the "negative consequences" next time they want to use substances in an effort at self-deterrence. This often doesn't work, and they go ahead and do it anyway. This usually leaves them confused and filled with shame.

The fact is that, since these negative consequences are costs that substance users have been willing to pay all along, reciting them doesn't change the fact that they're still willing to pay this price for what they believe they need to be happy. The balance of the PDP is still tilted toward the same decision. As we said in the "You Are What You Think" section of chapter 14: *Quite simply, if you continue to think/believe the same things, you will end up feeling, wanting, and doing the same things.*

Harping on costs that you're already willing to pay isn't new thinking. It's the same old thinking although, now that you're focusing on it more, you will feel worse about your choices. This isn't an improvement.

Some self-acceptance and acknowledgment of reality is in order here. You are doing your best to achieve a happy existence in a world of scarcity, the human condition being one where, as Justice Oliver Wendell Holmes is attributed as saying: "None of us can have as much as we want of all the things we want."

So, *like every other person who has ever lived and ever will live, you make trade-offs.* You know you can't have everything you want so you try to get what you think serves your needs best within the constraints of your life. Those who portray substance use as categorically unworthy of the costs involved ignore this reality.

Let's go back to our example of the marriage that dissolves slowly over time because one of the partners doesn't see the date nights, quality time, and vacations as being his happiest options in the moment. Is this marriage meant to be? Let's say that he focuses only on the long-term good of maintaining the marriage. So he does the date nights, quality time, and vacations—all while disliking them but for the sole purpose of saving his marriage. Yet he lives feeling deprived and unhappy so that one day in the future he will still be married. This marriage isn't making him happy, so he may be the one that eventually dissolves it. But more likely, he'll gradually pull away from engaging in all that "quality" time. The thing that will save the marriage is finding quality time that both he and his spouse enjoy and they both see as their happier option in the moment. Whatever it consists of, it will work in the moment, be enthusiastically chosen, and keep the marriage intact.

Focusing only on some imagined/fetishized good in the future is a strategy that ignores the reality of human life, which is that our optimal decisions are a union of both future desired states and immediate satisfaction. If a marriage eventually ended because there was no way for both parties to find satisfying moments together, then either one or both spouses preferred to end the marriage. We can't have everything we want. The human condition is one of constraints and scarcity. It makes no more sense to sell out your present moment for the future than it does to sell out your future for the present moment. This means that finding your happiest options is a nuanced process and that it can't easily be boiled down to categorically good and bad choices.

So we say this: there is no cost-free choice in life. I (Steven) choose to live in New York City. This means paying a higher rent for less space and accepting that owning a car and making trips outside the city are cost prohibitive to me. But the benefits to me are easy public transportation (I love not having to drive) and proximity to diverse cultural events and activities that I enjoy. It means I get to socialize with a wider variety of people and do more new things than I would like to do in the country or suburbs. The smaller range of convenient mobility and smaller living space are trade-offs I happily make for the privilege of living in a more densely populated area with more social, career, and cultural options. I would absolutely love to hop in a car and go snowboarding at the first sight of snow every winter (a favorite activity from the first half of my life and that I still enjoy), but it takes more planning than that because I choose to live in a city without owning a car. It's a trade-off that I'm willing to make. It's not a "negative consequence" of living in a city. The same goes for carrying heavy bags of groceries home from the store; I'd love to transport them door to door in my own car, but lugging around heavy bags of groceries is one of *the prices I pay* to live in a city. There are myriad benefits available to those who choose to live in less densely populated areas that I couldn't describe. I forgo those options/benefits in favor of those I prefer in city living. They are a cost of my choice because I can't have as much of everything that I want.

Choosing a career comes at the cost of other careers you could have chosen, or it can trade off spare time for money or money for passion. Some who go into the arts or activism know they can't make a ton of money in their field, but that's a trade-off or price they pay for the satisfaction of following that passion.

An entrepreneur may take on far more hours than an hourly worker, be on call constantly, and often bring her work home. This is the price she pays for her passion and for the potentially higher income she may acquire. It's the trade-off she makes for the benefit she finds in being her own boss. On the reverse side, someone may choose lower-paying hourly work for the benefit of not having to worry about work when he clocks out.

Becoming a parent can often come at the cost of personal hobbies and pursuits but is done for the joys of parenting. Athletes accept potential injuries as the cost of their preferred sport. Those who choose to be in the public eye, such as politicians and celebrities, accept public scrutiny and a lack of privacy as the cost of having influence and admiration. We could go on and on with examples, but the point is this: life is full of trade-offs, and everything has a price. A heavy substance use habit can be seen in the exact same way.

Risk of arrest or health problems may be a price you are willing to pay to use substances. We could say this about any of the easily predictable costs. You can always change your opinions on whether these trade-offs are worth it. Many quit positions in the public eye so they can have privacy. Many move from the city to the country to have more space and freedom of mobility. Many entrepreneurs give up a business and get a salaried job to have more time for themselves and their families. Many people find compromises between contradictory pursuits, but everyone pays a price—*makes trade-offs*—for whatever it is she chooses to do; it's unavoidable.

Acceptance and realization of costs is a great first step to happily finding your best options. Costs don't have to be baffling; they are just a fact of life. You aren't crazy or diseased because you've been willing to pay a high price for something. It may have been worth it to you at one point. If it's still worth it, then you can happily continue without shame and disappointment in the knowledge that it's a cost you're willing to pay. If it's no longer worth it, then you can happily move on to whatever way of living you find to be more rewarding. In the realm of substance use, this means owning that both your past usage and any further usage or quitting is and always has been your choice to make.

Making new choices means transforming your thinking about substance use and alternative uses of your time, resources, and energy. It's not just a matter of recognizing that substance use is costly—it's also a matter of weighing out the benefits of your various options to figure out what level of use is worth what it costs in matters of time, money, energy, and other scarce resources. So it's important not to make categorical judgments about substances being good or bad or rush into making priorities categorically preferred when life actually contains much more gray area than that. We don't want to add fear and panic to this decision-making process. We simply want you to be tuned into the issues that help you gauge the maximal amount of happiness that you can get out of substance use. Sometimes, that may mean some level of use will still be preferred, and sometimes that means discontinuing use altogether since it has outlived its happiness potential to you.

Deterrence-based strategies can bring you only so far. Allow yourself to let them go and make any potential changes to your substance use be based on positive motivation.

[Note: This chapter was heavily influenced by the writings of Thomas Sowell in his many books on economics and history. Specifically, we are utilizing his discussions on categorical thinking and trade-offs and applying his theories to our topic of life changes regarding substance use.]

REFERENCES

Rosenberg, M. (2015). *Nonviolent communication* (3rd ed.). Encinitas, CA: PuddleDancer Press.

Young, B. (2017, April 12). Drug addiction more like learning disorder than disease, says best-selling author. Retrieved from http://www.chicagotribune.com/lifestyles/health/ct-shame-drug-users-says-best-selling-author-20170412-story.html

CHAPTER 16:

FORGING A LASTING PREFERENCE CHANGE

When you stop approaching your substance use as a matter of "battling addiction," you're left with the fact that you have a strong desire to use substances. Throughout *The Freedom Model*, we've called this your *preference* for substance use. You can change a preference, and you can stop wanting to use substances to the same degree that you have in the past. It starts and ends with changing the way you think about your options.

WHAT IS A PREFERENCE?

> The Oxford Dictionary defines "preference" as "the fact of liking or wanting one thing more than another."

The first thing to know about preferences is that to prefer anything is to think it's a better option than some other options you have. *A preference isn't based on what you think about something in isolation; it's based on how you think it stacks up in comparison to other things.* This point cannot be stressed enough: you will not change a preference by looking at one option in isolation. You must include a comparison to other options. In the realm of substance use, this means that simply looking at the costs and benefits of a drug is not enough to make you not prefer it. We prefer some things over other things.

To make this point clearer, let's look at an example of owning a motorcycle. Let's say you are getting bored with your current motorcycle; you've had it for years, and it's been needing repairs lately. But you love that old machine; many memories of trips through the mountains were made on it, and you had some really good times. So you spend a day making a list of the costs versus the benefits of owning that bike. Still unsure of whether to sell it, days drag on as you compare the list. As time passes, you realize it's been a difficult decision about whether to keep the motorcycle. A week later, you go for a ride on the old machine and pass by a motorcycle dealership. You see the new models that came out that year. Suddenly, your bike looks and feels really dated in comparison. The many benefits of the newer bikes catch your fancy, and you drive home knowing you'll go back to the dealership to make the trade. What happened?

You preferred the benefits of the new bike to the benefits of the old one. This point is crucial: once you saw that new paint and chrome, the cost of owning the old machine wasn't a factor in your choosing to get the new bike. Think about that. The cost involved with owning "old reliable" was forgotten in the presence of new chrome and unscratched paint. What motivated the change was the bright new motorcycle sitting next to the old one; the choice was suddenly easy to make. What was once your dream bike 15 years ago, with all its bells and whistles, has become a comparably faded relic when sitting next to the new one. Simply stated, costs *and* benefits of *a single option* do not motivate us to change as effectively as when we add in the benefits of a comparable option. Here is why: a benefits-to-benefits analysis works because it uses a person's basis for motivation, the PDP, in the decision-making process. When change is motivated by a pursuit of happiness and comparing the benefits of various options, progress and change are the natural outcomes. In contrast, just comparing the costs versus the benefits of only one option will lead to indecision and staying with the old, known option.

The idea of comparing the benefits of various options should not be confused with replacing substance use habits with something like a hobby, working out, or meetings. This replacement theory will be covered in detail later in this chapter, but it needs to be said now so you don't go down that dead-end path. Replacing a substance use habit with anything else is ineffective because of the motive behind such replacements.

In the motorcycle analogy, the man chose the new bike for its benefits, not to distract himself from the old bike. In contrast in the replacement scenario, your intention is not primarily to seek the benefits of going to meetings or working out but rather *to distract yourself from doing what you like to do*, which is to use substances heavily. Whenever people try to distract themselves from something, such as heavy substance use, they still prefer it and will eventually go back to it. *Going back to it shows they still prefer it.* So as you move forward, it is important as a starting point to be honest with yourself about how much you prefer substance use before seeking alternative, beneficial options. Replacements will fail if you still prefer to use heavily, whereas being motivated to seek the benefits of a new option and moving on from an old option naturally works. This distinction is not small! It's important to understand so you don't kid yourself into trying to replace substance use with a temporary distraction in which you're not truly invested.

To prefer is to like one thing more than another. Of course, what you prefer can change from moment to moment depending on any number of factors. When it comes to relatively unimportant things, such as which brand of soda you prefer, you may easily and uneventfully go against your preference, with no pain or disappointment, and choose another brand because the one you prefer isn't immediately available. But then there are the more meaningful preferences, such as where you'd like to live, with whom you want to spend your time, or what career you want. You have built these preferences with serious conviction over long periods of time, and building them has involved many personal reasons and beliefs and has often included a plethora of experiences and much trial and error.

If you were displaced against your will from the hometown you prefer and had lived in for 20 years because of a natural disaster or financial troubles, you would be upset and have a difficult time adjusting and might be planning how to immediately move back. It's also possible that you'd learn to prefer your new home, but more likely, you wouldn't be able to just snap your fingers and make that happen on demand. Such preferences can be deeply ingrained. Like the old motorcycle, the preference for heavy substance use patterns is much the same. It's a deeply ingrained preference that you've learned and developed with time and experience. Most people don't instantly change it with a snap of the fingers, but it absolutely can be changed.

When we discuss the preference for substance use here, it's important to know that we're not talking about a momentary whim of liking substance use but rather a strong belief that substance use is an essential activity for maintaining happiness. The next thing to know about preferences is that if you are seriously considering an option, you see benefit in it. If you didn't see any benefit in it, then you wouldn't consider it at all. So not only is a preference based on a comparison; it is a comparison of options that are all seen as having benefits. This is important. If you see no benefits in an option, it never makes it into your comparison. For example, when someone is deciding what to do with extra money, they may consider spending it on a vacation, investing it in the stock market, or putting it into a savings account. Each of these options has some distinct benefit whether immediate pleasure, potential financial gain, or a sense of security; you will prefer the option you see as bringing you the most happiness. One option that would never make the list is setting the money on fire because most people see no benefit and thus no happiness in this act.

As absurd and pointless as it would be to burn a bunch of cash, this example hopefully makes the point that people are driven by the *benefits* they see in things. The Positive Drive Principle dictates that an essential component of any chosen option is perceived benefits. People don't refrain from burning cash, because it has high costs. More accurately, it never enters their minds as a serious option because they don't see an ounce of benefit in it.

The dominance of benefits in decision making should be clear by now. Motivation comes from perceived benefits. Nevertheless, those who struggle with problematic substance use tend to focus primarily on costs to motivate them to change. What's more, they don't consider the benefits of alternatives. Whether you realize it, this has likely been what you have been doing as you've tried to change. Really think about it. Has this strategy ever worked for you in a lasting way? If not, then a new way of thinking is in order—a focus on the benefits of multiple option. Please understand, we're not saying that costs don't matter or that they don't figure into the decision to change. However, they're not the prime motivator, so it's time that you shift your attention toward the benefits of your options.

Try to remember, staring at the costs of use will almost always make the high you get from a substance look more appealing, not less appealing. The PDP works on relative happiness values, not on costs. If a high from cocaine is fun to you, staring at a foreclosure notice that has been served to you because of your pricey habit is not going to make getting high on cocaine less appealing. *It might for a moment*—and then you will find yourself going to get coke again. This time the high you will get from the cocaine, when compared to the feelings associated with looking at the foreclosure notice, is a much better option. And it isn't even a close race; cocaine will always win until you develop a new option that you prefer. So again, costs are very temporary motivators, and without a new option to compare to the cocaine high, the old standby of cocaine will remain your go-to option. Knowing this and knowing the temporary effect costs have on decision making, doesn't it make more sense to shift your gaze to new and more beneficial options so you have different options from which to choose?

We've now established two keys to preference change:

1. Focus on benefits.
2. Focus on the benefits of *more than one option.*

While this is simple, it's still easy to miss the point because of how you've learned to analyze the world around you. As you move forward, if you find yourself thinking solely of the costs and benefits of using substances, then you've missed the point. You are looking at only one option. You're the guy mulling over his precious old motorcycle who's not happy with it anymore but afraid to let it go. You cannot come to prefer another option until you allow yourself to look at another option.

MULTIPLE OPTIONS

Once you understand this, you need to find some new options to include in your comparison. This is very important. People often overcomplicate it by coming up with alternative coping mechanisms, hobbies, or goals as other options, thinking they need to replace their habit with something very lofty or complicated. But this matter is far simpler than that. The first option is your current troubling level of substance use, which we'll call "heavy substance use." The most immediate other options you can compare to this are:

1. Adjusted substance use (what most call "moderation")
2. Abstinence

These options are so simple that they're often completely overlooked. Your immediate reaction to our mentioning them here may be to think to yourself *Of course, I'd be happier if I could just quit; of course, I'd be happier to moderate. Yet, if you truly believed that, then you would've quit or moderated already and happily sustained it.* The fact that you haven't done so shows that you aren't really convinced that these are happier options. In this case, your actions speak louder than your words.

Some of the confusion may lie in the fact that when you say that you'd be happier moderating, what you mean is that you'd like an option that reduces the costs of heavy substance use while also retaining the benefits of that level of use. This realization is just a starting point; it's now important to look at your opinion of the benefits involved in *both* options: heavy substance use and moderate substance use. It may not be clearly defined. Until now you have seen heavy substance use as having more benefits than moderate substance use and worth the high costs involved. This is likely true regarding to the option of abstinence as well. You can't expect to initiate and sustain either of these options when your overall view is that heavy substance use is your happiest option.

So although these options are simple and straightforward, there's more to unpack and reconsider than meets the eye. If you want to change your preference to moderate use or abstinence and thus actually change your behavior and sustain one of those options, then you will need to find a way to see one of them as your happier option. That is, you will have to like one of those options more than you like heavy substance use; that is what it means to prefer it.

There will be more to consider in "adjusted substance use" since it's not just some predetermined amount or frequency of substance use but rather an option that could include a wide range of potential adjustments. We elaborate on this in a later chapter, but for now, remember that these are the basic options for you to consider:

1. Heavy substance use
2. Adjusted substance use (what most call "moderation")
3. Abstinence

Have you ever really thought about the benefits in those other options, or did you just think about the costs of heavy substance use? Are you willing to critically explore the potential benefits of all these options? To do this, it helps to set aside the costs of heavy substance use. That's the critical distraction here. You already know the costs; you've already shown you're willing to pay them, so why concentrate on them. You know these costs have a low or temporary deterrence quality. There's little to nothing left to discover by thinking about the costs of heavy substance use. So do yourself a favor now, and take a couple of minutes to think through what we've said and then see whether you agree with this simple statement: *There are enough costs in heavy substance use that it's worth exploring whether moderation or abstinence would be a more beneficial and happier option for me.*

If you can do that, then you can get on with discovering your happier options rather than beating yourself up over the costs of one of those options. Don't let yourself get distracted from this task by guilt and shame and dwelling on the costs. Motivate yourself by moving toward happiness rather than away from costs. For most, this is a huge transition in their thinking. There are a few more pitfalls we need to discuss so we can help you clear the way to happier options.

THE PROBLEM WITH REPLACEMENT

Here is a common trend that can end in serious frustration. Many people try to find alternative activities to pit against substance use, things to take up their time and distract them from their desire for substance use. They often think they must come up with something spectacular to replace heavy substance use. While these strategies seem intuitively correct, they unnecessarily complicate the process of change and distract you from the real issue, which is centered in substances and your potential levels of their use.

One popular replacement activity is going to the gym. Many people get some mileage out of this, and it seems to work. But what happens when you're sick, too tired, or just don't have time for the gym? You're left without an activity to deal with the abstinence that you've been forced to choose but don't prefer. Eventually, if you never preferred abstinence as being more attractive to you than heavy substance use, then you will feel what the recovery culture calls a "craving." You may wonder why you're *craving* now, after you've been replacing alcohol with the gym for several weeks. Shouldn't you be over the hump? Shouldn't the fact that you're working out produce the energy and good feelings needed to replace the desire for substances? The truth is, the *hump* has very little to do with reality; it's just an arbitrary milestone you set that is a distraction from the reality that you still prefer substances. When you find that the gym, the new workout regimen, or your new focus on nutrition isn't cutting it and you find you prefer using substances over those distractions, it's a good time to learn a simpler formula to solve the problem. Now is the time to refocus on the three basic substance use options:

1. Heavy substance use
2. Adjusted substance use (what most call "moderation")
3. Abstinence

If you have not taken the time to truly reconsider those options, your preference will likely remain the same, and your desire will nag at you. Of course, it is possible that, in those few weeks of going to the gym, you could also be rethinking these options and discovering you no longer prefer heavy substance use. But why not just start out on the right foot and begin rethinking your options immediately instead of counting on luck and hoping your preference changes by chance. Why not make preference change the focus of your option analysis?

Life isn't a set of binary choices between going to the gym and getting drunk. So it doesn't make sense to replace drinking with such an activity. What happens when you go to a party? Will you start doing push-ups the moment you find yourself wanting a drink? What makes more sense is to find out whether you can be happier without alcohol or with less of it so you can exist happily in any situation, not just in a replacement activity.

Here's another issue to consider with such replacements: while you are refusing to generate a benefits list for the moderation and abstinence options, you're also leaving your opinion of the benefits of heavy substance use fully intact. What you might discover if you critically examine your preference for heavy substance use is that it no longer is as beneficial as it once was to you. As you proceed, we're going to offer critical thinking on the benefits of emotional relief, lowered inhibitions, and pleasure/euphoria.

With courage, critical thinking, and experiential learning through proactively testing your options, you may discover that heavy substance use is boring and you do not need it for any sort of relief. You might discover more relief, more excitement, more happiness in the moderation or abstinence options. But if you jump right into replacement, you're sidestepping these issues. It would be like the motorcyclist telling himself he needs to go to the gym to forget his dissatisfaction with the motorcycle he once enjoyed so much. That would be weird, right? That's because it ignores the issue completely, that being his issue with his current ride. In the same respect, why hope that preference change will magically or accidentally happen by replacing it with random and unrelated distractions when you can proactively do something to address the issue head on by looking at moderation and abstinence options directly?

To really understand this, you need to acknowledge the depth of a strong preference for heavy substance use. It isn't just a meaningless hobby to be replaced with another meaningless hobby. Those who have trouble quitting and go through personal turmoil over it really believe they *need* it for happiness. If you already had a "take it or leave it" view for heavy substance use, then you would've easily replaced it already and would not be troubled by ongoing desire. If that's not you, then you need to tackle it head on, discover why you've seen heavy substance use as so essential to happiness and moderation or abstinence as intolerable options. Those views won't change by just replacing substance use with going to the gym.

The same goes for replacing heavy substance use with "alternative coping methods." These replacements keep you from addressing the preference directly and add another issue to the mix, further complicating it. If you're using heavy substance use as a "coping method," that is, as a solution to your problems, you would be better off examining the benefits of it and finding out whether it truly solves any of those problems. Critical thinking shows that it doesn't solve problems, and if you discovered and became convinced of this, you would never feel the desire to use it as a "coping method" again. However, by sidestepping this issue and thinking you need an alternative coping method, you keep it alive in your mind as a potential coping method. You give it credit that it doesn't deserve by putting it on an almost equal plane with effective coping methods.

Again, what happens when you don't want to use those coping methods or when they don't seem to work? Some problems are going to leave you with some amount of frustration and emotional pain. In these cases, you will likely find yourself itching to use substances heavily again as a coping method. Yet, if you had addressed the issue head on and explored the benefits of the three options, you might've found that, even with various life problems going on, you get more happiness from moderation or abstinence and don't solve any problems with heavy use. That change in perception would do away with heavy substance use as a potential coping method for good and improve your overall level of happiness. Are you willing to give it a chance, or will you sidestep the issue with replacement?

The gym is great. Effective coping methods are great. We hope you achieve your various goals, aspirations, good health, productive relationships, and all the other joys of life. We encourage you to do everything that you want to do and pursue your own vision of happiness. But to address the issue of a strong preference for heavy substance use head on, the most direct way is to critically and directly explore the benefits of the three options, not replace your current option to use with unrelated temporary distractions. Heavy substance use problems are seldom so narrowly limited to an extra hour of the day that can be replaced with a trip to the gym or rare moments of stress that simply require a coping method. The preference is usually wider ranging than that. Reassessing the three options allows you to address the full depth of the preference. What's more, when you've eliminated your preference for a troubling degree of substance use, you become much more effective at chasing and achieving all those other life improvements you want.

Remember, there is a lot to be discovered in directly exploring the three options:

1. Heavy substance use
2. Adjusted substance use (what most call "moderation")
3. Abstinence

DON'T MAKE YOUR CHANGE
UNNECESSARILY CONDITIONAL

A related way that people miss out on a full and direct preference change is by tying reckless substance use to life circumstances. These are the "learned connections" that we discussed in chapter 6. Here are some common learned connections:

1. I'll moderate my drinking when my relationship gets better.
2. I'll quit cocaine when I get a new job that is less stressful.
3. I'll give up the painkillers when I get over my depression.

You've got it in reverse.

Heavy drinking usually takes a toll on a relationship. The roller coaster of cocaine use could make it harder to find another job. Continuing to believe you need painkillers to deal with depression will make you feel even more powerless and depressed.

When you make your potential effort to change conditional on these things, you're guaranteeing you won't ever make the change. The same is true for any of the things that recovery ideology calls the "underlying causes of addiction." The underlying causes of addiction theory is one of the most damaging classes of learned connections that is common today. We covered this theory in detail in chapter 6, but it's worth briefly revisiting the concept here. When people consider other life issues and problems as causes of substance use, they are promoting two myths. First, they are reinforcing that substance use is caused by something other than their own desires and wants. Second, it means that they must avoid these "causes" to keep from uncontrollably using. This is a serious error in thinking in that there is no such thing as a stress-free life or a trauma-free life or a depression-free life. So, if these learned connections are true for you, then you are doomed from the beginning. Of course, this is not the case. Hence, the reason we call these connections "learned." You've learned from recovery ideology that you are caused to use by these circumstances, and in that belief, it becomes a very real condition for you. You are what you think.

By living your life within the artificial constraints of these learned connections, you essentially stop living, out of the fear that you might encounter stressors that are too great or depression that might set off your uncontrolled use. You're mentally shifting the locus of control to external circumstances when in fact your autonomous mind is where the power really resides. It is a choice to connect normal life challenges to "uncontrollable" substance use. The same principle that mucks up replacement operates with learned connections too. That is, maybe the stars will eventually align just so, and then you'll stop the heavy substance use; but the stars may also move back out of alignment. You might lose that job, enter another period of depression, or hit rocky ground again in your relationship. Because you've made substance use conditional and connected to these normal life challenges, you'll go back to heavy use.

It doesn't have to be this way. We don't know what your happiest option is; only you can know that for sure. Perhaps it's to use tons of cocaine when work is tough, but maybe it isn't. Exploring the three options head on is a more direct path to discovery. If you try it first, you might find that you can be happier with moderation or abstinence no matter what your job situation, what level of depression you have, what kind of trauma exists in your life, or what your other life circumstances are. Will you give yourself the best chance of finding your happiest option? If so, disconnect these learned connections now, and deal with substance use as a single issue. What will it be: heavy use, adjusted use, or abstinence?

UNHAPPINESS ISN'T A CAUSE OF HEAVY SUBSTANCE USE

With all our talk about heavy substance use being driven by the pursuit of happiness, there is a common misconception people have about *The Freedom Model*. They think that we're saying depression or unhappiness causes heavy substance use. This is the most common learned connection. The next logical misconception is that the solution to heavy substance use is to get over unhappiness or depression first and then sobriety will follow. Let's be clear and firm about this: we do not believe nor mean to teach that heavy substance use is caused by unhappiness or relieved by happiness.

You can be genuinely unhappy or depressed and not feel the slightest need or desire for heavy substance use. In fact, 80% of people with mood disorders do not have substance use problems, and the minority who have both substance use problems and mood disorders, such as depression or bipolar, have no special difficulty getting over their substance use problems. Their rates of "recovery" are just as high as those who don't have these problems (Lopez-Quintero et al., 2011). Take a moment to let that sink in because it's contrary to our cultural belief.

No matter what your current level of happiness is—whether you're depressed or living in constant bliss—you will prefer heavy substance use if you see it as your best path to happiness, and you will not prefer it if you don't see it as your best path to happiness.

The solution to your substance use problems is not to get happier first but to simply cease to believe that heavy substance use is your best available option for acquiring happiness. Again, trying to resolve unhappiness first is indirect and keeps heavy troubling use alive as a potential option for when unhappiness hits again. That learned connection is dangerous to keep fixed. Carefully exploring the three options with a focus on benefits is the most direct path to developing a lasting preference change that could eradicate any further attraction to troubling heavy substance use patterns. Furthermore, when you no longer feel dependent on heavy substance use and stop paying all its costs, you regain so many resources that can now be devoted to building your happiest life possible.

THE PREFERENCE RUT

A preference for heavy substance use is usually built slowly over time, as you find you prefer substance use in stronger ways, in more and more circumstances, and in greater portions of your life. Then, as you start to pay the heavy costs, it goes one of two ways: either you begin looking for adjustments that result in more happiness or you lament the fact that it costs so much as you keep doing it the same way and beating yourself up over it. If you've kept the costly pattern going for a long time, along with anger and shame over the costs, then you're in quite a rut. You've probably forgotten what it's like to live without hating your choices, what it's like to enjoy a moderate level of substance use that leaves you with no regrets; or what it's like not to feel a nagging *need* for substance use.

There most likely was a time in life when you had plenty of fun and excitement without costly levels of substance use. You probably dealt with many life problems before without attaching them to heavy substance use. There was probably a time when you didn't have such a singular focus on one repetitious activity. But during the time you've been in the rut, bored with the repetition, tired from the nagging sense of need and dependence, hating the price you're paying for something that's lost its luster, you've forgotten that you really can have a happy and exciting life without this costly option. Are you ready to explore and rediscover your potential for greater happiness? The rut is "safe" in some sense because it's predictable. But the longer and deeper you've been in the rut, the more you stand to gain and discover by peeking out of it and getting a fresh look at all three options.

Are you willing to start in a direct manner, by exploring the three options? Are you willing to believe in the possibility that adjusted use or abstinence holds more benefits than you previously thought it did? Are you willing to see those options being more than just devoid of the costs and benefits of heavy substance use? Are you willing to question the benefits of heavy substance use?

Perhaps you've already started this process. You might be thinking there's real freedom to be gained in the other options. You might already be experiencing a taste of greater happiness by imagining life without a sense of need for heavy substance use or by entertaining the thought of permanently changing your preference rather than riding the fence. Have the courage to jump over to the other side to see what it has to offer; you can always go back if you don't like it.

Remember, the choice is yours and yours alone and new choices come from new thinking. You'll find the following chapters offer more ways to shake up your preference.

REFERENCE

Lopez-Quintero, C., Hasin, D. S., de los Cobos, J. P., Pines, A., Wang, S., Grant, B. F., & Blanco, C. (2011). Probability and predictors of remission from lifetime nicotine, alcohol, cannabis, or cocaine dependence: Results from the National Epidemiologic Survey on Alcohol and Related Conditions. *Addiction (Abingdon, England), 106*(3), 657–669. https://doi.org/10.1111/j.1360-0443.2010.03194.x

CHAPTER 17:
QUESTIONING DRUG EFFECTS

People take for granted that drugs and alcohol have a set of miraculous effects, negative and positive, harmful and helpful. Some of these effects are the inevitable outcome of a substance's pharmacological action. However, some of these effects are either nonexistent or the product of *nondrug factors*. Since your view of substances motivates your decisions to use them, it's worth sorting through these various effects to understand which ones really come from the drugs and which ones don't. A changed view on the powers and effects of substances will lead to a change in the motivation to use them.

In this chapter, we challenge some of the most deeply held views on the powers of substances. But before we do this, it's important to note that we are not saying substances have no effects at all—they most certainly do. Whenever we have this discussion, some people get annoyed and say "So you're saying drugs don't affect a person?!" Let us be clear; of course, they do. What we're saying is that they don't affect people in the ways that are commonly believed and discussed.

Substances can physically stimulate or sedate our bodies, including altering heart rate, blood pressure, breathing, temperature, digestion, and neurotransmission. These things happen without question, and we needn't get into the finer details of all these effects. We acknowledge that these effects occur as a matter of pharmacology and that they play a part in the total experience of using substances. Succinctly, here is what we mean when we say that substances don't carry certain powers—substances do not change the *content* of your thoughts. Under this umbrella, we will show you that substances change very little about you but your *beliefs* about what they do is what makes the experience with substances seem so powerful and life altering.

There are effects that substances are said to have that are sensational and warrant careful critical thinking. For example, substances are said to have the power to addict people, provide pleasures that outweigh any nonsubstance activity ("euphoria"), lower inhibitions, cause violence and aggression, or relieve emotional distress. These effects are far harder to pin down pharmacologically, and in fact, in most cases, no plausible pharmacological explanation whatsoever is available. Therefore, some of these believed effects may not even be a direct or an indirect result of the chemical action of the substance on the body and brain at all. Other effects involve pharmacology, but not in the straightforward way you've been led to believe in. A nuanced understanding of this is eye-opening.

Throughout the 20th century, many researchers have uncovered the fact that what people believe about substances and the circumstances in which they use them plays a far greater role than pharmacology in what people experience while using substances. To stress the importance of these other factors, some have said that the "drug, set, and setting" should all equally be considered when discussing the effects of intoxication.

1. *Drug* refers to the actual pharmacological effects of a substance.

2. *Set* refers to psychological factors, such as the mindset of the individual taking the substances, including beliefs, expectations, intentions, and more.

3. *Setting* refers to the social, physical, and cultural environment/circumstances in which substances are taken and the information this conveys to the substance user (it is essentially another aspect of mindset).

Sociologists who observe drinking practices have noted that the same amount of the drug alcohol may be taken in a pub or at a wake and seem to have significantly different "effects." At the pub, drinkers may become euphoric, talkative, aggressive, and jovial and engage in behaviors considered inappropriate, such as being overly flirtatious, making sexual advances, or speaking in off-color ways. At the wake, drinkers may become dysphoric and quiet and reserved, talk in hushed and sensitive tones, weep, and become more proper and polite. Let's pick this example apart from the drug, set, and setting point of view.

The *drug* effects of a few drinks of alcohol are a rise in pulse rate and blood pressure, impaired coordination, and a release of endorphins (which can be perceived as pleasurable). These physical effects brought on by the pharmacological action of the drug will happen equally to the drinker at the pub and the drinker at a wake. Though it's interesting to note that, even though the endorphin action happens to both, the drinker at the wake may not be feeling pleasure.

The *set* effects are those that come from the mindset of the individual, including his thoughts, beliefs, and intentions. Most go to the pub with the intention of having a good time, socializing, and presenting a fun-loving image to others. They believe alcohol facilitates these things, so when the physical effects of the alcohol are felt, they begin to feel more sociable, euphoric, and stimulated. Most go to the wake with the intention of mourning the passing of a loved one, showing their pain and sorrow to others who care and commiserating with them. They believe alcohol facilitates these things, so when they drink, they begin to feel they are more able to express their sadness, to cry and show their negative emotions as well as concern for others who are also mourning.

The *setting* effects are those that people are cued to experience by the environment (both physical and social). The pub may feature loud music or noisy sports games on an array of televisions. This tells the patrons it's acceptable to be loud and boisterous. The wake features somber music at a low volume. This tells the mourners they should remain quiet and reserved. The pub is full of people looking to get away from life's responsibilities for a while and have a good time. This tells people it's acceptable to smile, be jovial, and let go of the worries they have outside the pub. The wake is full of people looking to show their respect, offer a shoulder to cry on, or find support from others. This tells people it's a place for quiet and sensitivity. The pub may feature a pool table, darts or other amusements, or open spaces such as a dance floor. This tells patrons that they can be stimulated and active. The wake may be held in a home, funeral home, or some other type of hall, where the space is filled with tables and seating, active open space is scarce, and there are no forms of entertainment offered. This tells the mourners to be subdued in their behavior. Moreover, the social landscape at the wake is filled with several generations; deference to elders is expected, and care is given to set a good example for the children in attendance. In contrast, the pub may often feature a more limited age group with people closer in age and class as peers, and this has wildly different social dynamics that lead to extremely different behaviors. The presence or absence of relatives in these settings further changes the social expectations and thus the "effects" of drinking in these situations.

These examples of a wake and a pub may resonate with you, or you may be thinking your experience at wakes and pubs is very different. Either way, the point still holds. Wakes can be very different depending on the culture, ethnicity, local customs, or religious orientation of the primary participants involved. The behavior we attribute to alcohol can be extremely different depending on whether it's an Irish pub, a biker bar, a cocktail lounge, a dive bar, a gay bar, an after-hours spot, a sports bar, or a commercial dance club. Each of these *settings* sends different messages to the drinker, and each is often approached with a different mind*set*. These variations prove the point that most of the emotional and behavioral effects that get attributed to alcohol have little to do with the direct pharmacology of the *drug* ethanol. If the pharmacology ruled the behavioral and psychological effects of drugs, then you wouldn't see variation in these effects from place to place, person to person, and even from one day to the next in the same place within the same person. Set and setting wouldn't matter. But they obviously do. You don't need to look through a microscope or at a brain scan to see evidence of this – it is available to the naked eye of anyone who chooses to look.

Because alcohol is used so openly, it lends itself to this analysis easily. Everyone has seen plenty of different outcomes from the use of alcohol. This applies across all intoxicants as well. People approach various drugs with different expectations and intentions, and this plays a massive role in the effects they feel when using. The same applies to settings. For example, today, many people think of LSD as providing an enjoyable experience. Those who use it take it with the intention of enhancing experiences at concerts or dance clubs. Many take it with friends seeking a spiritual experience or while on outdoor activities like a hike. But what if this set and setting were changed? Early research on LSD provides a look at the outcomes when a starkly different set and setting comes into play:

> LSD research of the 1950s was dominated by the idea that the drug could be used to induce and study mental illness. By labeling LSD a psychotomimetic [drug capable of inducing madness] and expecting a certain outcome from experiments, psychiatrists instigated the very responses they expected to find. Presupposing that patients become mentally ill under the effects of LSD, they were creating expectancies which fostered negative experiences and aggravated adverse effects. Other factors of set and setting were also liable to unleash a variety of adverse reactions. Many of the subjects who participated in research were hospitalized psychiatric patients who had little choice about partaking in experiments. Preparation for sessions was poor, often consisting of the casual suggestion that the patient will experience a few hours of madness following the ingestion of the drug, not a soothing notion, to say the least. The possibility of positive experiences or therapeutic benefits was not mentioned, and there was no therapeutic intention involved. Setting was equally bleak. Experiments habitually took place in the formal environment of hospital rooms lit by fluorescent lights. There was often no possibility to recline or get the rest which can be direly needed in some stages of hallucinogenic drug reaction, and patients were often subjected to endless batteries of psychological and physical tests. The social setting was composed of hospital psychiatrists who studied patients impersonally. After the experience, users were left without any peers with whom to share their experiences and without any framework with which to make sense of it. It is no wonder then, that experiences were overwhelmingly negative.
>
> (Hartogsohn, 2017)

When LSD was given in an institutional research setting to a person treated like a lab rat, and with the expectation that it would cause psychosis, the experience was negative rather than positive. Again, take note that none of this is meant to deny that drugs have effects. They do, and LSD happens to be a particularly powerful psychoactive drug that alters brain activity and leads to auditory and visual hallucinations among other effects. However, whether these *drug* effects are perceived as enjoyable is ruled by the *set* and *setting*.

So again, by reviewing these far-ranging examples of the depressant drug (alcohol) and hallucinogenic drug (LSD), you can see that the *drug, set, setting* model explains drug effects well. It demonstrates that drugs aren't all they're cracked up to be and that many of their effects are illusory. From here, it's not hard to apply the model to whatever your favorite drug happens to be. For good measure, let's look at an example from another popular class of drugs—the stimulants.

Columbia University neuroscientist and drug researcher Dr. Carl Hart, PhD, has said that the prescription amphetamines Adderall and Ritalin are nearly identical in chemical composition and effect to the street version of methamphetamine. These different versions of amphetamines work in the brain in slightly different ways, yet all increase cognitive abilities, enhance the ability to concentrate and focus, relieve fatigue, and raise blood pressure and pulse. Moreover, when given in a laboratory to test subjects who are seasoned illegal meth users, they cannot tell the difference between the two (methamphetamine and d-amphetamine [prescription]; Sullum, 2014).

Dr. Hart has been talking publicly about these facts about amphetamines to combat drug hysteria on a societal level. He says that we should see the legal and illegal versions of amphetamines as basically equivalent and notes that we shouldn't fear legal amphetamines more because of this. Until now, the public has been hyped into believing amphetamines are an especially "addictive" drug, yet their legal counterparts (Adderall and Ritalin, among others) are used by people in ways that don't even resemble "addiction." They are often used to good effect, helping some people to have more energy, concentrate better, and become more productive.

There are plenty of methamphetamine users out there who are productive, accomplished people. They use a little bit now and then to give them a boost. There are regular users as well, such as a string of celebrities given meth by a physician the Secret Service dubbed "Dr. Feelgood." His clients included President John F. Kennedy, Nelson Rockefeller, *Twilight Zone* producer/writer Rod Serling, composer Leonard Bernstein, and playwrights and authors, such as Henry Miller, Anais

Nin, and Tennessee Williams. (Getlen, 2013) They are all highly productive legends in their respective fields, seen as making very positive contributions to our culture.

Today, despite the fact that the chemical makeup has not changed, meth is now seen as a drug that turns people into monsters. It's been known to be used by violent biker gang members. Meth users are implicated in all sorts of crimes that are often violent. Dr. Feelgood's amphetamine formula was even taken by the Nazis, and he blames it for turning them into soulless killing machines.

Of course, outside of the laboratory, you may see very different effects in users of these drugs. But since the basic pharmacological effects (*drug*) are the same, this leaves you with differing *sets* and *settings* as the basis for different observed feelings and behaviors among individual users. Do you become a productive genius or a monster when using meth? Do you have fun and party while on it or go to a dark, depressed place? Do you become highly focused or scatterbrained? We can find plenty examples of these contradictory outcomes. None of them are determined by the drug itself, and thus they are not really "drug effects." They might more accurately be called "set and setting effects."

This "drug, set, and setting" relationship has been well known to researchers and academics for several decades. Unfortunately, it hasn't been well known to the public nor to the police, anti-drug crusaders, government officials, and the recovery society, all of whom continue to spread overblown myths about the pharmacological effects of substances, both positive and negative.

For one example of a negative myth about the pharmacological powers of substances, let's consider PCP. If you had watched the popular TV show *Cops* during the 1990s, you would've seen plenty of cases where the cops claimed their violent offenders were high on PCP. The drug has a reputation for turning people into superhuman, violent criminals who can't be stopped from attacking anyone in sight. Yet, when PCP was medically tested on hundreds of people in controlled settings, "not a single case of violence was reported."(Sullum, 2003) So just taking PCP won't turn you violent, yet it has this reputation. What's more likely is that some very violent people happened to take PCP (set), or being a street drug primarily available in high crime areas, these settings may promote violence so use of the drug gets associated with violence (setting). I (Steven) remember believing some of these myths about PCP and violence, yet then I thought back on my time as an avid user of the drug. I used it in party settings with many people hundreds of times, and yet none of us ever became violent in the process.

For an example of a positive myth about the power of a drug, consider the reputation that alcohol has for relieving stress, anxiety, and anger. The recovery society unknowingly promotes this myth with the claim that "alcoholics drink to self-medicate their underlying issues of stress, anxiety, etc.," thereby endowing it with the power to pharmacologically take away negative emotions. They say that anger is a trigger for drinking, purportedly because it has the power to relieve anger or to help people cope with anger. And granted, there is no shortage of people saying things such as "I was so angry that I just needed to have a drink to calm down." Now, consider the fact that alcohol use is also associated with 40% of violent crimes (Wilcox, 2015). Anger is an emotion essential to the motivation of violence. How is it that alcohol could calm you of your stress and anxiety and take your anger away yet stimulate and agitate people as well, in some cases to the point of violence? Of course, this is a contradiction, so alcohol couldn't pharmacologically do both these things. Yet it continues to have the reputation of both causing anger and relieving it.

The truth is that alcohol neither relieves nor causes anger. *Set* and *setting* are the factors involved that determine the effects. That is, people's thoughts and beliefs about what alcohol does to them and what's warranted in various situations rule their emotions and behaviors while drinking. Pharmacologically, alcohol sedates, slows down neurotransmission, and causes disorientation and loss of equilibrium. It may cause you to slur your words, but it doesn't cause you to utter words that challenge someone to a fistfight. It may cause you to lose your balance and be unable to walk a straight line, but it doesn't cause you to walk up to a man and take a swing at him.

Please don't forget this example of the contradictory powers attributed to alcohol; it's particularly poignant to the lesson of this chapter. You have full freedom of what you do and feel emotionally when using substances. These are the results of what you think and believe, not the results of the pharmacological effects of substances.

YOU CAN'T NEED WHAT DOESN'T HELP YOU

To *need* is to "require (something) because it is essential or very important." The recovery society and treatment professionals portray substance users as *needing* the pharmacological effects of substances to relieve emotional distress and inhibitions. Part of how they do this is by forwarding theories that say substance users have either a preexisting chemical imbalance or that substances have changed their brains to the point where the only thing that can make them feel good is more substances. They repeat claims about the emotional powers of substances—that they soothe anger and help with trauma and relieve depression and anxiety and other emotional issues. They push the theory that those who've suffered trauma have had their brains permanently changed in a way that leaves them with levels of stress, which can be "self-medicated" with substances. And finally, they claim that without "alternative coping methods," the "addict" will be forced back to using substances. This all implies that substances can pharmacologically relieve emotional pain and thus can be "needed" for such purposes if nothing else is available.

We are presenting the view that substances don't serve these purposes and thus can't be "needed" to serve them. Just as you can't need a cupcake to treat a tumor, you can't need alcohol to take away your anxiety. It's possible for someone to believe she needs a cupcake to treat a tumor. Her perception of a need and desperate want of a cupcake wouldn't be any less real because it's motivated by a falsehood, but if she learned that cupcakes don't cure tumors, then she would stop wanting it for that reason. She might still desire a cupcake for the taste and nourishment, but such a level of desire is far lower than what she felt when she believed she "needed" it.

PLACEBO EFFECT AND ACTIVE PLACEBOS

To further illuminate the subject, we'll discuss the phenomenon of placebo effects. In medical research, placebos have traditionally been pills that have no active ingredients. Some are made of sugar, which is why they're often referred to as "sugar pills." There are also placebo injections (usually saline is used) and placebo procedures where patients were cut and sewn back up, as if they had been given a meaningful medical procedure (one of these cases was a knee surgery, and those who got the placebo surgery had better long-term outcomes than those who got the real surgery!). The role of the placebo in research is to find out whether a given treatment is effective or some other forces are at play, causing patients to feel better. Those other forces could be things such as patients' own immune systems, perceptions of symptoms, the limited natural course of a disease, or the expectancy of recovery and changes they make to their lifestyles because of expected improvement.

Many prescription drug trials split their test subjects into a group who receives the medication with active ingredients and a group who receives a placebo pill with no active ingredients. Logic holds that if those who receive the real medication experience more improvement in signs and symptoms, then the drug has a positive effect, and if they don't do better than the placebo group, then the drug doesn't work. This practice has taught researchers more than whether prescription drugs work—it has taught them that expectancy is a powerful force. It has taught them that expecting to get well can make people get well for many conditions.

Not surprising, the area where placebos have the biggest effect is in psychiatric medicine. Many antidepressant trials have shown that placebos work almost as well as the real drugs at relieving depression. Interestingly, in both those who receive the real drug and those who receive the placebo, *those who experience more side effects are more likely to recover from depression.* This encouraged the researchers to try testing the antidepressants against something called an *active placebo*, which is "a real drug that produces side effects, but that should not have any therapeutic benefits for the condition being treated."

To understand the active placebo, you must first consider what it's like to be involved in a prescription drug trial. You're depressed; you sign up for this new drug trial in the hopes that this will be the miracle drug that finally relieves your condition. You sit down with the doctor to sign consent forms and get a rundown of what to expect. He tells you that you may get an inert placebo or you may get the real drug. He then tells you that you might be getting some bad side effects, such as dry mouth or drowsiness. Then you get your bottle of pills, not knowing whether they're the real thing or not. But if after taking them for a week or two, you don't necessarily feel better yet and you also haven't had any dry mouth or drowsiness, you begin to think you're not on the real drug. Disappointment sets in, and you start to believe you won't get any better because you're on the placebo. This is called "breaking blind" because you were supposed to be blinded to whether you were on the real drug, but you figured it out anyway.

The other side of this is that if you do start to experience dry mouth and drowsiness, you think *Yay, I'm on the real drug; I'm gonna get over my depression!* In this case, you've also broken blind. As you can imagine, this causes an obstacle for researchers trying to figure out whether the drugs are truly effective because breaking blind modifies expectations and it becomes impossible to tell whether the patients' depression was relieved by their expectations or by the pharmacological effects of the drug. So, with some of these antidepressants, as we said, researchers decided to use an active placebo, which is a drug that has none of the active antidepressant ingredients but contains some ingredients that will produce side effects, such as dry mouth and drowsiness. This heightened the placebo effect so that, in 78% of antidepressant trials where active placebo was used, there was no clinically significant difference in outcomes between those taking the drug and those taking the placebo (Kirsch, 2010, p. 20).

The lesson here is this: many of the psychological/emotional effects you think you get from drugs aren't directly caused by the pharmacological action of the drug. In this case, the patients developed expectancy that the pill they were taking would improve their mood. They connected it with side effects, fleshing out the expectancy a little more to "if I get dry mouth and drowsiness, I am on the real drug, it has taken effect, and my mood will improve." Then, when they experience those side effects, they take them as a cue to become optimistic, and this improves their mood.

This *active placebo effect* has been present in all the examples we reviewed in the beginning of the chapter. You expect alcohol to relieve your anger, you know that when you start to feel tipsy or warm the alcohol is taking effect on your body, and then bingo, you allow yourself to let go of your anger. It is you and your mind relieving your anger, not alcohol.

Researchers Norman Zinberg (1984) and Andrew Weil (1998) were among the first to run a controlled study on the effects of marijuana in people who had no experience with the drug and had never seen anyone else do it and thus had very few if any expectations of its effects. They did this at Harvard in the late 1960s. Weil came out of it with this conclusion:

> To my mind, the best term for marijuana is active place-bo—that is, a substance whose apparent effects on the mind are actually placebo effects in response to minimal physiological action.

He went on to say that "all drugs that seem to give highs" are also active placebos. Note that this isn't a denial that the drugs people take have pharmacological effects that agitate their bodies and brains in some way. But it is a more nuanced understanding of how people seem to get psychological effects from using these drugs. And since the expectancies of what a drug will do vary from person to person, place to place, and time to time, this makes sense of the illogically contradictory effects attributed to drugs. Those effects aren't really coming from the drugs; they're coming from a combination of the drug, set, and setting, and the active placebo model ties it all together.

For example, look at the following chart. It describes the multitude of effects attributed to many substances. Most of these effects would apply to almost every substance. Certainly, almost everything on the chart has been attributed to alcohol. Notice that it's set up to show some of the directly contradictory effects side by side. This is to highlight the absurdity of the notion that the same drug could pharmacologically cause both states.

THE PERCEIVED EFFECTS "CAUSED" BY IDENTICAL SUBSTANCES

Peacefulness and lovingness	Hostility and violence
Relaxation	Stimulation
Creativity and an active focused mind	Clearing your mind, forgetting, haziness
Sociability, more outgoing	Withdrawn, in your own world
More sensitive and easily aroused	Emotionally numbed and deadened
Causes anger	Cures anger, calms ("takes the edge off")
Concentration and focus	Impulsivity, poor judgment, distraction, and impairment
Agreeable, friendly, and affable	Belligerent, improper, and impolite
Bold and courageous	Timid, nervous, and impaired

THE GLARING CONTRADICTIONS

This chart contains mostly perceived benefits, but a few costs appear here as well. For example, it's widely believed that alcohol can make people become angry, violent, and aggressive—the term "firewater" sums up these "powers" of alcohol. Yet it's also believed that alcohol can cure anger, causing people to relax, calm down, and even become kinder and more loving. These supposed positive psychological effects of alcohol are so popular that people have come to refer to drinking in some cases as "self-medicating" or a "coping mechanism."

Alcohol's status as anger medicine presents a psychological benefit, and its status as a cause of anger presents us with a psychological cost. What you must recognize if you want a realistic, truthful understanding of substances is that a single substance couldn't simultaneously have contradictory powers and effects. Alcohol can't both cause and cure anger. Such a claim should be instantly recognized as nonsense. Yet most people live their entire lives believing all these contradictory claims about substances. That is because our culture is obsessed with pharmacology; very few people know about the drug, set, setting understanding of substance effects, and even fewer know about the active placebo effect. Instead, they prattle on about "powerful drugs." When confronted with these contradictions, many will say "Well, they affect different people in different ways," and by that they mean that each person's genetics and brain are different, so that is why there are different effects. But this doesn't explain the fact that you can see different effects in the same person on a different day or in a different setting. I have an uncle who is notoriously a mean bastard when he gets drunk. The stories from around town are legendary. Yet he spent most Thanksgivings and Christmases at my home and sat there drinking whiskey most of the day. He was fun and funny. I never once saw him get mean or nasty in our home. He didn't want to get mean or nasty in our home. The truth is, the whiskey never made him nasty and vicious—that was just how he wanted and chose to be in some situations.

Marijuana can't make you more creative, populating your mind with ideas *and* clear your mind so that you can relax and forget the world. These are opposite powers. Cocaine can't make you an uninhibited party animal *and* a focused individual ready to get all your work done. Let's not forget about paranoia, which is also attributed to cocaine and methamphetamines – you can't be paranoid and uninhibited at the same time. Alcohol can't make you relaxed, calm, and detached from your surroundings *and* get you riled up to dance and party.

All these examples represent opposite psychological powers that the exact same chemicals supposedly exert upon your brain. A quick review of these claims as we have just done shows how utterly absurd they are. Yet most people still believe in all these powers. Why?

It's a simple logical error that they make and the product of learned falsehoods. It's an error we can only assume has been happening for as long as these substances have been used. Basically, people confuse causation with correlation. Because substance use is paired with an intention to relax, when people experience relaxation, they attribute it to the supposed chemical powers of the substance. Then, when an intention to get wild and party is paired with substance use, people do the same thing; they attribute the stimulation they experience to the same substance they believed had the power to relax them yesterday. Again, when you put these two powers side by side—stimulation versus relaxation—you can understand that they're exact opposites and thus can't be caused by the same substance. Yet that never occurs to most people, and they continue to attribute these contradictory powers to substances. Despite the impossibility, they continue to feel these effects.

The placebo effect is an amazing thing. You can tell a person that a completely inert pill will relieve his pain and then it happens. This is because people have a great fascination with and faith in the power of chemicals, and with good reason, because chemicals can do many amazing things. But oftentimes, people give substances credit for things that the substances are not doing.

If you chose to go fishing for a day to relax and forget your stressful thoughts, you would see that for exactly what it is: proactively changing your thoughts (and thus feelings) by focusing on something else. You wouldn't think that there's a special chemical in fishing rods that relieves stress. Yet, if you choose to get drunk to relieve stress, you don't see it in the same way. You don't understand that you're doing the same thing as with the fishing; you're shifting your focus away from stress and choosing to focus on the activity of drinking alcohol. Instead, you give credit for any stress relief you feel to an imagined special power of alcohol. And so has the rest of humanity, for ages, because of our fascination with the powers of chemicals.

It's easy to make this error. Substances have several strong physical effects; they impair the senses of sight, touch, hearing, and even equilibrium; they slow reaction times; and they provide physical sensations that people call a high, buzz, or drunk. Since substances can provide such overwhelming physical experiences, people then tend to attribute anything they do mentally at that same time to effects of the substances. There's an active placebo effect here, and it's working in both directions with substance use. First, society misleads you into getting various placebo effects from substances, and then you mislead yourself by misattributing even more powers to substances. Either way, you connect the physical effects of substances, the way they perturb your brain and body, with psychological/emotional things that you experience and thus end up believing in this wild laundry list of effects that we've been discussing. Most of what you think about drug effects are socially learned and constructed, just like the addict self-image you learned about in chapters 8 and 9. There are various ways people learn these myths.

It just so happens that in young adulthood, when people are going out to do a bunch of new, scary things they've never done before, that is also the time when they have the freedom to do the most experimenting with drugs and alcohol. So, if they've been awkward about finding a romantic or sexual partner, they may choose to finally do so now that they've moved to a college campus where they're free from the baggage of having known everyone since kindergarten. They also happen to look for a partner while at a drug- and alcohol-fueled party and succeed in finding a mate. They could attribute it to their mindset about the new surroundings and new peers, or they could attribute it to the substances they ingested. Many will attribute it to the substances. *I need to get drunk to meet girls* may be the thought. They have just created a reverse placebo effect and created the perception of a need for alcohol to socialize. They gave alcohol credit for something the alcohol didn't do. They gave it credit for something they set out to do and were doing when they happened to be drinking alcohol at the same time. It's a causation versus correlation error in reasoning by which we giver substances credit for things they don't really do.

Most people don't share this next belief, but it's a good example of the same error in action. Get any group of heavy substance users together in a candid discussion, and might find one or two who say they drive better while drunk or high than they do while sober. How could they believe this when the impairment to the senses caused by drugs and alcohol is so obvious? It's simple. On some occasion (perhaps more than one), they drove while drunk or high and were downright paranoid about being pulled over by the police. So they ignored all distractions and drove extremely carefully, precisely following every rule of the road. Then they left this experience with the belief that intoxication causes them to drive better. But they're mistaken. Their desire to avoid interactions with the police is what really made them drive more carefully. The physiological effects of alcohol still slowed their reaction times and likely affected their vision and balance. If any unforeseen circumstances arose on the road, they would've been less able to deal with them than if they had been sober.

Maybe someone pulls her first all-nighter at college or work finishing an important project at the last minute while high on some drug. She amazes herself with the results, turning in some great work, on time. Again, if this happens while she's coming of age—while simultaneously having more responsibility and more freedom to use substances—she may attribute her success to the substance she used. By doing this she's ignoring the passion and desire she has to rise to the occasion in this new chapter of her life. The substance had little, if any, direct contributions to her success and may have even hindered her in some fashion. It is far more likely that her strong desire to complete the work and achieve success was what caused her success.

People are so enamored with biology and the power of chemicals that, whenever they're involved in any experience, they give substances all the credit for things that they did themselves, by their own powers, for their own reasons. Do you have the courage to take this new perspective and knowledge and apply it to your list of reasons for heavy substance use? Maybe your list of reasons will shrink once you critically examine it. Maybe you don't "need" substances the way you once thought you did. The next three chapters will cover three categories of perceived benefits of substances:

1. Emotional relief (of stress, anxiety, depression, anger)

2. Lowered inhibitions (powers to make you more social, sexual, free speaking, courageous)

3. Pleasure

Once you know you don't "need" substances for any of these things because they don't truly do these things, they become something you can easily take or leave. As you allow yourself to imagine being just as happy or happi*er* with less or no substance use, your PDP shifts, and change is a joyful experience rather than a loss. With your free will and autonomous mind, you can use the following chapters to critically rethink your options and find your happiest one; your free will and autonomy could also be used to uphold the illusion that your favorite drug is a magical all-purpose elixir. It's up to you.

REFERENCES

Getlen, L. (2013, April 21). The Kennedy meth. Retrieved from http://nypost.com/2013/04/21/the-kennedy-meth/

Hartogsohn, I. (2017). Constructing drug effects: A history of set and setting. *Drug Science, Policy and Law, 3.* https://doi.org/10.1177/2050324516683325

Kirsch, Irving (2010, January 26). The emperor's new drugs: Exploding the antidepressant myth (pp. 19–20). [Kindle ed.]. New York, NY: Perseus Books Group.

Sullum, J. (2003, January 3). Killer drugs. Retrieved from http://reason.com/archives/2003/01/03/killer-drugs

Sullum, J. (2014, February 20). Hyperbole hurts: The surprising truth about methamphetamine. Retrieved from https://www.forbes.com/sites/jacobsullum/2014/02/20/hyperbole-hurts-the-surprising-truth-about-methamphetamine/#578dabb229f1

Weil, A. (1998). *The natural mind: A new way of looking at drugs and the higher consciousness* (rev. ed.). Boston, MA: Mariner Books.

Wilcox, S. (2015, June 27). Alcohol, drugs and crime. Retrieved from https://www.ncadd.org/about-addiction/alcohol-drugs-and-crime

Zinberg, N. (1984). *Drug, set and setting: The basis for controlled intoxicant use.* New Haven, CT: Yale University.

CHAPTER 18:
THE ILLUSION OF EMOTIONAL RELIEF

The idea that drugs, such as alcohol, marijuana, and heroin, provide relief from emotional pain might be one of the most dangerous myths ever. Many self-described addicts and alcoholics truly believe they need substances to relieve their emotional pain, such as stress, anxiety, depression, anger, and trauma. This belief results in increased desire and a firm belief that there is no chance of ever quitting or moderating their use of substances. And it's all for naught since the drugs *never relieve the emotional pain, not even temporarily*, and may even become the source of increased stress and upset as their use takes a toll on your life.

> Alcohol and drugs never relieve emotional pain, not even temporarily.

If you think that substances help you with emotional pain in any way, it's imperative that you read this chapter and learn that this effect is fully an illusion. It's a placebo effect. While it is true that people report that *drinking* relieves their emotional pain, the drug *alcohol* itself does not pharmacologically relieve emotional pain. This is an important distinction. Drinking is an activity approached with certain expectations and intentions—a mindset. When drinking, many people give themselves permission to forget their troubles, and their friends and family may give them a pass while drinking as well. This is all to say that drinking involves much more than the drug alcohol. *The ritual of drinking may relieve stress while alcohol itself does not relieve stress.*

Substances don't help you with emotional pain. They don't emotionally numb you. They aren't tools for the "self-medication" of emotional problems. A glass of gin is no more effective at taking away emotional pain than a glass of milk. When you understand and internalize this reality, you will stop feeling like you "need" substances for this purpose. That feeling will change as your thoughts change because of the basic way that emotions operate:

> Your emotions result entirely from the way you look at things. It is an obvious neurological fact that before you can experience any event, you must process it with your mind and give it meaning. You must understand what is happening to you before you can feel it. (Burns, 1999, Kindle location 682)

Burns, along with many other cognitive psychologists, as well as philosophers throughout the ages, explain that we interpret and evaluate the events and conditions of our lives and that an *emotion results from our interpretation/evaluation*. If you believe an event signals a favorable outcome, such as meeting some need or desire of yours, you feel happiness. If you interpret an event as a success resulting from your effort and choices, you feel pride. If you interpret an event as leading to an impending harm or loss, you feel stress or anxiety. If you interpret an event as an injustice, you feel anger. If you interpret a negative condition of your life as being one where you have no control to effect a change, you may feel sadness or depression. These are the basics, and there are more for sure, but the principle is simple, *an emotion is an evaluation.*

When Burns says that "You must understand what is happening to you before you can feel it," he is pointing out an easily verifiable principle. Consider the victims of a con, like those who invested their money with the infamous con artist Bernie Madoff. They were all delighted while thinking that they were receiving massive returns on their investments, making easy money. They did not understand that they had invested in a ponzi scheme and were losing everything. If they understood their investment as a gain, they felt positive emotion over it. While feeling happiness, unfortunately for them, they were really victims. Had they understood that they were being victimized, they might've felt intense dread, anger, and maybe even depression. They did feel these things once they learned of Madoff's scam in the media and when they finally understood what had happened to them. They were happy until they gave new meaning to their investment with new knowledge. Our interpretation of events determines our emotions.

The degree of any emotion depends on the degree of goodness or awfulness you see in an event or a condition. The worse you think something is, the worse you will feel. The better you think something is, the better you will feel. One particularly helpful technique of cognitive psychology is to reevaluate the awfulness of an event because people often blow negative events and situations out of proportion, making their negative emotions overblown and particularly troubling. This is how a sad event becomes a depressing event, a minor inconvenience becomes a terrifying stressor, and so on.

Terms like *awfulizing, catastrophizing,* and *magnifying,* have been used to describe the process where people distort the severity of the negatives in their lives. For example, Madoff's victims could have seen their losses as something from which they could never recover, or they could have mentally accepted the losses and believed they could push forward learning from their experience. They could have seen their investment in such a con as a sign that they're born suckers, altogether incapable of making good decisions, or they could have seen it as an isolated bad decision, which was easy to fall for because so many others fell for it too, and believe that they can do better in the future. All these potential thoughts about the incident would lead to different emotional (including motivational) outcomes.

In this cognitive model, we deal with our emotions by changing our evaluations in a few different ways and can become less troubled as a result. Techniques fitting this model can be learned from books, therapy, and folk wisdom and are applied by people to their own problems. What's more, they've been proven more effective than any of the therapies currently available. This shows that all people create and manage their own emotions. *Our emotions don't happen to us.* And even though they involve neurotransmitters, they don't begin by the random release of these neurotransmitters—they happen *by* us—in our minds emanating from the way we think about our life and world, and then our thoughts trigger the release of neurotransmitters in the brain as one component of how they're physically felt.

One of the most common emotions people say they use substances for is stress. The American Psychological Association (APA, n.d.) describes stress as "a feeling of being overwhelmed, worried or run-down" and says that it "includes any uncomfortable emotional experience accompanied by predictable biochemical, physiological and behavioral changes." A National Institute on Alcohol Abuse and Alcoholism (NIAAA) paper on alcohol and stress defines stress in cognitive terms, explaining that it's the "interpretation of an event as signaling harm, loss, or threat" (Sayette, 1999). With these definitions in mind, it's clear that stress encompasses many negative emotions and is a matter of perspective.

Under the cognitive model of emotions, it's clear that changing your interpretation of the event you're stressed about reduces the stress. If you see the event or situation as less indicative of a loss or harm you will feel less stress. If you accept the loss or harm as something that you can manage, you feel less stress. If you challenge your perception fully and find that you can see the event as not threatening at all, you may feel no stress. If you begin to see a silver lining of a gain in the event, you may even feel some happiness and excitement. Your emotions change as you reevaluate an event's meaning and significance to your life.

The amount of time someone spends thinking about an event matters too. You may think some condition of your life promises upcoming harm or loss, but if you put it aside mentally and focus on other things, much of or all the stress will go away until you start thinking about it again. Rumination keeps stress alive and strengthens it, whereas focusing on other things can dampen, decrease, and even facilitate a complete triumph over stress if or when you return to thinking of it you now realize it wasn't as bad as you initially thought.

There are many more possibilities for how your different choices in thought will modify your emotions. This was just a quick overview, but if you want to know more, there are plenty of great books on the subject. It's time for us to get back to discussing substances.

DRUGS AND ALCOHOL CAN'T THINK FOR YOU

Substances don't change the content of your thoughts. They don't suddenly force people to think a bad event is a good event. They don't remove thoughts from your mind and don't provide thoughts to your mind. That is, if you think an event represents a threat of loss or harm, you won't change that evaluation simply by having a drink, popping a Percocet, or puffing a joint. You will feel stress if you continue to focus on thinking the event is significantly threatening. You can continue to think this way even while drunk or high. Many people do. If you need evidence, plant yourself on a stool in your local dive bar, and spend a night talking to the patrons. You will find that some are thinking happy thoughts, some are thinking angry thoughts, some are thinking sad thoughts, and some are even jumping back and forth between all sorts of thoughts, rapidly traversing the entire range of emotions. If you come back the next day, you might see some of the same people drinking the same amount of the same drinks yet thinking opposite thoughts and experiencing opposite feelings than they did the previous night. Many of you reading this will recognize that you've done it yourself. This isn't a new observation, but it's one that people don't often consider while they're romanticizing substances and endowing them with magical emotional relief powers.

Although many people have felt stress relief while using substances (i.e., relaxation), this experience alone isn't sufficient proof that these drugs pharmacologically relieve stress. The issue must be examined more carefully; we'll use alcohol as our example since it's the most popular drug believed to relieve stress. We have all grown up seeing scenes on television and in the movies where someone is nervous or stressed out in some way and needs to take a drink to deal with it. We've seen the scene where a man loses his job or wife and goes to the bar to relieve the terror, worry, and pain over this loss. Many of us grew up having seen our parents pour themselves a drink to relieve the stress of a hard day's work or just to calm them down when they're worked up. We've all heard the phrase "drowning your sorrows in alcohol," which paints the picture of emotional pain as a living being that literally dies when people drink alcohol. The belief that alcohol relieves stress is deeply ingrained in our culture. Many of you reading this have probably used it for stress relief yourselves; the authors certainly have.

Here's the reality: if you search the medical journals and books about alcohol for an explanation of how alcohol relieves stress, you will find nothing conclusive. Certainly, you will find accounts of people drinking with stress as their reason and subjective reports of its relieving stress, but you will find no credible scientific explanation for how it does so or even whether it really does. In fact, the NIAAA - published a review paper on existing research addressing the question of whether alcohol relieves stress and stated that:

> To the surprise of many investigators, the relationship between alcohol and stress was inconsistent. Alcohol consumption reduced stress in some studies, did not affect stress responses in other analyses, and exacerbated stress in still other investigations. (Sayette, 1999)

The results of existing research are inconsistent. While drinking, sometimes people experience stress relief, sometimes they don't, and sometimes they get more stressed. Again, if you spend time observing people drinking, you'll see the same results. This alone should show that alcohol doesn't relieve stress. But when we're romanticizing alcohol as an effective stress reliever, we conveniently forget about all the times it doesn't relieve stress. We also forget about the fact that alcohol has a reputation for making people angry as well (an emotion that falls under the umbrella of … you guessed it—stress!). Being angry is the exact opposite of the cool and calm state of stress relief. Please note this now, and don't forget it: alcohol has a reputation for creating these opposite states—*relaxation* and *stimulation*. That's a contradiction. If a new headache pill hit the market, quickly gaining a reputation for both relieving headaches and making them worse, do you think it'd be on the market very long? Probably not, as most people would realize that this new pill doesn't really relieve headaches; likewise, we should probably conclude that alcohol doesn't really provide stress relief when it also seems to result in the opposite effect.

Beyond showing that there is no reliable stress relief provided by alcohol, the NIAAA review also showed that when/where stress relief is found, there is no agreed upon scientific explanation of whether or how the alcohol pharmacologically relieves stress. Indeed, the researchers said "*the evidence for a direct stress-reducing effect of alcohol remains somewhat controversial*" (Sayette, 1999).

They put forth a few different theories that have been researched, each of which seemed to contradict the other. Where stress relief was found, it depended on such things as distractions being present while drinking. Left without distractions in laboratory settings, drinkers became *more stressed*. There was no real answer on the question of whether alcohol pharmacologically relieves stress, and the paper concluded with "To date, the precise pharmacological mechanisms" behind alcohol's supposed stress-relieving properties "remain unclear." That was in 1999. We contacted the author (perhaps the leading researcher in this subject of stress and alcohol) in 2016 to ask whether much had changed since he wrote that paper and whether he knows of any new notable research on whether alcohol relieves stress; he had nothing specific to offer.

To sum up, the science has shown that alcohol does not reliably relieve stress and there is no proven mechanism by which it pharmacologically does so. A pharmacological mechanism that explains why people experience stress relief while drinking will not be found because the relief is created by other processes. This is a complicated issue to dissect, but people must understand it to get to a place where they know they don't need alcohol and other drugs for stress relief. To do so, they need a clear understanding of stress.

Foremost, stress is an emotional response, resulting from a personal assessment that a given event or condition represents harm or loss. Stress is that sense of dread you feel when, for example, you write a snappy email, hit send, and then worry that it will provoke anger or be misunderstood in a negative way; when you say the wrong thing and worry about what others will think of you; when you have too many appointments and errands to run and fear you won't get them all done; when you screw up at work and think you may be fired; or when you spend too much money and start to realize you won't be able to pay your bills. Then, immediately after you make such an evaluation and feel the negative emotion, it triggers the release of transmitters, such as adrenaline, noradrenaline, and cortisol, all of which cause a multitude of physical symptoms in your body. The APA lists several physical results of stress, including tensing of the muscles, heavy breathing/hyperventilation, increase in heart rate and blood pressure, production of epinephrine and glucose to prepare the body for fight-or-flight situations, and more. Sometimes, some drugs may alter some of these *physical symptoms*. In doing so, they may seem to relieve the *emotional* part of stress, but it's important to know that they actually don't.

Drugs relieve only some of the physical symptoms of stress, and they don't even do this reliably or consistently. For example, alcohol often lowers the heart rate so that it may appear to relieve some symptoms of stress, but it also raises blood pressure, which is a symptom of stress. So, while it may reduce one symptom of stress, it increases another. *But sometimes, it even raises the heart rate* in addition to blood pressure, causing an increase in two of the symptoms of stress at the same time. [*Remember, these are the physical symptoms of stress, downstream from the emotion and the evaluation underlying the emotion.*]

The effects of another reputed stress reliever, marijuana, are just as confusing. It both lowers blood pressure and raises heart rate, again, canceling out one symptom of physical stress while adding another. Researchers from the University of Chicago reported that marijuana often reduces stress at low doses but increases stress at higher doses, even leading to panic attacks. (University of Illinois at Chicago. 2017). But even this dose response isn't predictable or consistent and is often overridden by the expectancies (or lack thereof) of the individual taking the drug.

In early 20th-century America, when marijuana use was rare and deviant and the available marijuana was far less potent than today, admissions to psychiatric hospitals for marijuana-induced psychosis were at their highest level. Drug psychoses, defined by researcher Howard Becker (1967), are "the anxiety reaction of a naive user occasioned by his fear that the temporary symptoms of drug use represent a permanent derangement of his mind." There is no doubt that one feels an intense amount of stress while experiencing psychosis. Becker showed through his research that this negative reaction to the effects of marijuana decreased steadily over the decades into the 1940s though, as marijuana came into wider use and there was enough of a subculture around it educating people of what to expect from it. As people learned to interpret the effects differently, their reactions switched from terror to pleasure and relaxation. Whether it will be a stressful or relaxing experience, then, is highly dependent on expectations. That is, there is no guarantee that marijuana will pharmacologically reduce stress.

One theory on how sedatives and downers relieve stress and anxiety is that they slow down the brain to a point where you can barely think. If you can't think, then you can't think stressful thoughts, right? It makes enough sense, yet it's commonplace to see extremely intoxicated people getting angry, depressed, agitated, sad, and stressed. There may be little cognitive activity happening when someone is extremely intoxicated on alcohol, prescription sedatives, or opiates, yet their brainpower can still be used to think negative thoughts. Drugs may significantly decrease your brain activity, yet they still do not dictate the content of your thoughts. While conscious, people are always thinking.

We've run into plenty of people who experience stress relief from using stimulants, such as cocaine or amphetamines. Ironically, these drugs act in a way that *creates* many of the physical symptoms of stress. They can raise the heart rate and blood pressure and intensify breathing, putting the body into the same fight-or-flight mode triggered by stressful thoughts. What's more, *stimulants* increase brain activity. So, if the theory held that decreasing brain activity somehow erased the ability to think stressful thoughts, then the increased brain activity should result in more stressful thoughts. Yet again, there are plenty of people who say that stimulants relax them. The truth is that whether you're on your last gasp of brain activity on the verge of nodding out on heroin or you've got a surplus of brain activity on cocaine, you are still the chooser of your thoughts. The drugs cannot choose your thoughts for you. You are free to choose stressful thoughts as long as you retain an iota of consciousness, and you will feel the results of your chosen thoughts.

CONSTRUCTING THE ILLUSION

Now that we've provided a fuller understanding of stress, the conclusion should be getting clearer: the emotional stress relief some people feel at some times while using substances is coming from their own minds. However, many people fall prey to an illusion that substances are pharmacologically changing their emotions and the content of their thoughts and then give those drugs all the credit for something they've done themselves. This illusion needs to be understood so you never again fall into the trap of thinking you need substances for stress relief. We're going to pull back the curtain now by demonstrating three ways that people actively take part in the illusion, unknowingly tricking themselves into believing that drugs take away stressful emotions:

- *Distraction*—focusing on intoxication as a means of distracting yourself from stressful thoughts.

- *Bandaging*—relieving some of the *physical symptoms* of stress with a drug and then hoping it will magically take away the thinking that creates the emotions of stress.

- *Getting a reprieve*—using intoxication as an excuse to keep others from pressing you on potentially stressful responsibilities.

Cultural beliefs, learning, the placebo effect, situational factors, and the actual physical effects of substances play a part in each of these traps because they lay the foundation for the illusion that the substance is the active agent of stress relief. But in fact, the emotions of stress (anger, fear, dread, unease, etc.) are only ever relieved by the individual changing his or her thoughts, which is done at will (that is, by choice, with or without a substance).

As you consider some different perspectives, you'll see that, although you may experience stress relief while drinking or drugging, it isn't pharmacologically coming from the drug.

THE POWER OF DISTRACTION

What's really going on most of the time when people use drugs as stress relievers is that they're distracting themselves from their stress-producing thoughts with the activity of ingesting substances and their physical effects. Much like we discussed earlier, the feeling of stress relief often comes before any physical effects are felt. They are deciding to relieve their stress or take a break from it prior to drinking or drugging, so the actual stress relief begins to happen in anticipation of it. Once again, the substances didn't relieve the stress; the individual's thoughts did.

We presented a thought experiment in an earlier chapter, and it's worth revisiting since it neatly explains the situation. Imagine you've had several drinks and you are feeling totally relaxed. You get in your car to drive home, and a cop pulls you over. Are you stressed in this moment? Hell, yeah, you are.

The same goes for if you've smoked some marijuana and you run into someone who you don't want to know that you're high. It could be any drug, really. If it's an illegal drug you've taken and you still have some in your pocket and you run into the police, you may experience enormous anxiety. If you find yourself in these situations, you will most likely find yourself feeling stress.

One of the authors (Steven) shot up a bunch of heroin and felt great. He nodded out on his mother's couch only to be awakened moments later. His pack of hypodermic needles and other paraphernalia had fallen out of his pocket, and she had found it and was screaming at him. The stress, the terror, and the sheer dread at what this event meant to him were tremendous. He quickly ran out of the house, jumped in his car, and disappeared for a week, living in his car and avoiding everyone.

The point is that in each of these situations, even though there's a drug in your bloodstream that is believed to pharmacologically relieve your stress, you will still feel stress when facing a situation that you perceive as threatening. If the drug truly relieved stress pharmacologically, then you shouldn't be able to feel the stress in these moments. Yet we've all been there (if not in these exact scenarios, then in some situation that is principally the same).

The drug isn't relieving your stress, even if you do happen to feel stress relief while using it. What you've done is shifted your attention away from whatever stressful thoughts you were thinking about and onto your feeling of intoxication—in other words, the buzz/high was used as a *distraction* from stressful issues. The examples above illustrate the power of this shift of focus because they're instances of being confronted with a hard-to-ignore, stressful situation, which practically grabs your attention. Stress follows.

It's important to recognize that if you wanted to distract yourself from stressful issues and thinking, you could use anything, for example, a movie, a book, an athletic activity, or a social engagement. People do this all the time; it's called "getting your mind off it." So drugs are not special in that they're often used as a distraction, and they aren't any better than anything else at being an object of distraction. For anything to be sufficiently distracting, it just needs to be liked as a distraction by the individual using it.

Drugs have a special reputation for stress relief, the origins of which we can only hypothesize. It's probably because their effects seem to provide a full-body experience. As a result, drugs have seemed magical throughout the ages to our less technologically evolved ancestors. In our own age, we have become so enamored with the physical sciences that we still hold onto the dream of magical elixirs for psychological issues and have left the magical reputation of drugs unexamined. Regardless of how this reputation began or is sustained, it's not because the drugs possess any pharmacological power to relieve the emotional side of stress.

In our society, we've all grown up believing in the magical reputation of drugs so when we use substances we feel some level of a placebo effect of stress relief. We then give them the credit for stress relief that we are creating ourselves by choosing to shift our attention away from stressful matters. And finally, combining this placebo effect with processes of learning and habit, we often learn to take the effects of substances as an instant cue to let go of stressful thoughts. But be cautious not to twist it around. You are the one who is doing the letting go, not the substances.

You are relieving your own stress by choosing to put your stressful thoughts aside while intoxicated. Don't give drugs the credit for something you are doing. Remember, there is nothing that guarantees people will reliably feel stress relief upon taking drugs. People can just as often be sad, stressed, or upset while drinking; the phenomenon of "crying in your beer" attests to this fact. Everyone chooses what he or she thinks about even while intoxicated. And everyone chooses what he or she believes. Having considered this analysis of substances and stress, you can choose to stop believing they have the magical power to relieve painful emotions.

BANDAGING—A VICIOUS CYCLE

As we discussed above, since emotions are the result of our interpretation of the events and circumstances of our life, they are truly changed only when we change those interpretations. Put more simply, if people think differently, they will feel differently – the principle "you are what you think" applies. Since substances do not provide content to your thoughts or alter the course of your thinking, they simply can't change your emotions. But they can alter some of the physical feelings that are caused by your emotions, such as the increased heart rate and blood pressure, tenseness of muscles, heightened energy for a fight-or-flight response, and changes in breathing.

Although some of the substances have mixed results at relieving these physical symptoms and they can increase some of these symptoms, some are better than others at this task. For example, opiates and some prescription sedatives are better at reducing several of these symptoms than alcohol or marijuana. But let's go a step further and imagine there's an ideal drug that perfectly and reliably reduces all the physical symptoms of stress. This perfect drug still wouldn't touch the source of stress from which these physical symptoms flow: the emotion of stress—the worry, anger, sadness, and fear. These are evaluations of the mind, so they operate on a mental level, not on a physical level. As we have discussed above, you can find plenty of examples of people deeply sedated by substances but still entertaining stressful thoughts and feeling stressful emotions.

With this fully understood, we know that substances will never be a solution for the emotion of stress. They may physically numb you, but they will never emotionally numb you. They will never change your belief that some event poses a grave threat to you. They may only slow your heavy breathing or reduce the rapid heart rate that results as you think of that threat. Know this: the substances never touch the emotions. Therefore, they cannot be a medication for emotions.

Many substance users address the downstream physical symptoms of stress and convince themselves that this is addressing the emotion of stress. As they eventually think of their stressful thoughts again, they feel more stress again and attempt to "drown it" in more substances again. It still isn't solving the problem!

Unfortunately, many substance users keep this cycle up, and as the stressful issues and the stress itself get worse each time they think about these issues, they stubbornly return to more substance use to address the emotion of stress. They do this because they've mistakenly learned to believe that relief of some *physical* symptoms of stress is equivalent to relieving the *emotional* pain of stress. They begin to think that they just need a higher dose to do the trick. This is a vicious cycle that can end tragically. More pills will never touch the source of the issue: your personal perspective of the challenges you face in life. The only way to change those emotions is by changing your perspective.

If you want to relieve the physical symptoms of stress with substances, go ahead; that may be helpful on some level. But don't be fooled into thinking it relieves the emotion of stress. It can't and never will because, again, emotions are the result of your interpretations and evaluations of the events and circumstances of your life.

REPRIEVES

Since stress is an assessment of the events and circumstances of your life, then if those conditions change, you may have less to interpret as stressful, and thus stress may go away. For example, imagine you have kids and a hectic schedule of five different sports games to bring them to over the weekend. This could be an extremely stressful schedule. Now, imagine your spouse says "You've been working too hard lately. Take the weekend off to do whatever you want, and I'll cart the kids around to their games." Boom! Just like that your stress is gone because there's nothing for you to be stressed about. Your partner has given you a reprieve from a stressful responsibility.

The same thing can sometimes be achieved by becoming intoxicated. If you start drinking early Saturday morning, your spouse may realize you're in no shape to cart the kids around, so he tells you (probably angrily) that he'll take care of it. Boom! Just like that your stress of taking care of the kids on Saturday is gone. You've gotten a reprieve.

The effect of this circumstance is that while you may feel some stress about issues between you and your spouse, you feel no stress about taking the kids to those games. You stay home getting drunk, feeling less stress than you would have had you been playing the busy parent all day. There is a net reduction in stress. Alcohol is involved, so you give alcohol the credit. But as in all our previous discussion, it should be clear that the alcohol didn't pharmacologically relieve your stress. Nevertheless, this episode can add to the illusion that alcohol is an effective stress reliever. Now, consider the same effect may happen if you wake up with a nasty head cold. Your spouse, seeing how sick you are, offers to cart the kids around to their activities. Certainly, the head cold isn't a stress reliever, and neither is the alcohol.

Being drunk (much like getting a bad cold) absolves people of some life responsibilities. There are plenty of other circumstances where this may be the case. A temporary state of drunkenness convinces others to give you a reprieve. You may choose to do this more often and increasingly rely on it, thinking you need the active drug in alcoholic drinks to relieve stress. This increases your desire to drink when you feel overwhelmed with life and eventually can lead to your feeling that you're addicted to alcohol.

Taking it a step further in the truly extreme cases, life as an "alcoholic" or "addict" may convince others to give you an even bigger reprieve. Little by little others start taking over your responsibilities and picking up the slack for you, and they stop relying or depending on you in any way. As stressful as life with this horrible identity can be, it may still seem less stressful than a life that involves responsibility to others. In the most extreme cases, going back to our example with the kids, your children's grandparents may take custody of the children, absolving you of all child-rearing duties and their attendant stress.

As your life revolves around a substance, you may believe that your use of this drug has made life less stressful, and indeed *the use of it* has. But the pharmacological properties of the drug are not the active stress reliever in this equation. It's the reprieve that relieved the stress, a social response to your substance use.

The reprieve doesn't just happen interpersonally. Sometimes, we give ourselves a reprieve. If we use a long-acting drug, such as alcohol, we can then tell ourselves *I can't deal with my responsibilities today, so I'll put them out of sight and out of mind until tomorrow.* And indeed, you will feel less stress for today, but again, the alcohol didn't relieve the stress; the reprieve did. This can also be done on a larger scale when you fully give up on civilized life and any responsibilities to simply chase a substance high. People give themselves permission to let everything go. Doing that is less stressful in some ways, but you could also give up on life responsibilities without using substances. However, in our current cultural landscape, being "addicted" is a ready-made reason to give up your stressful life responsibilities.

In some cases, the problematic substance user might even begin attending rehabs to avoid life's stresses. In this situation, rehabs become a bubble in which to avoid life for a bit. We know many people who have cycled in and out of treatment centers with this motivation. Unfortunately, this scenario backfires in a big way. Here's how and why:

Attendance at rehabs reinforces all the myths we've been talking about throughout this book. For example, one of the most common rehab myths that is promoted is that *the substance users must avoid all stressful "triggers" that might set off a relapse when they return home after their treatment has been completed.* This teaching is predicated on the idea that addicts or alcoholics are too weak mentally and emotionally to deal with any stress without a support network in place when they go home. The users are then given an excuse to avoid all of life's inherent challenges in their quest for the utopian stress-free existence. This ideal sounds good the first time people go to rehab, especially for those who are already attracted to absolving their responsibilities in life and putting those responsibilities on others around them. But there's a fly in this ointment. With that teaching, comes a sense of being handicapped and disabled. And, while this might sound attractive at the time, it gets old as those around the users begin to wear out from the users' lack of responsibility, culpability, and ability and begin to complain. These people are annoyed and angered because they are now expected to carry the substance users' workload in life. The problem gets worse the longer this idea is reinforced by multiple treatment stays and further family participation in the ruse. You see, the substance users are told to avoid all stressors and triggers because they are weak *and simultaneously taught at the same rehab that being high relieves stress.* So how do you think this works out in the long run?

The compliant treatment participants try desperately to avoid all stressful triggers that are listed in their rehab exit plans. But, of course, life doesn't work the way the users want it to, and eventually, no matter how hard they try to avoid all stress, the natural stressors of life slap them in the face. That's when they go back to drugs and alcohol *because the same rehab reinforced to them that substances relieve stress.* Do you see the catch-22 here?

Here it is stated another way. Treatment says "You better avoid stress because you are weak. Because you are weak, stress will lead to a relapse. When you relapse because you didn't avoid every stressful trigger, you realize you must stop using at all costs because using will kill you." But you keep using because that same rehab reinforced the idea that substances will relieve the stress that causes the relapse! You then drown in confusion and increased use. This cycle is tragic because all the ideas contained in this circular mess are myths—you're not weak or handicapped, it's impossible to avoid all stress in life (and "triggers"), and substances do not pharmacologically reduce stress.

SIDE ISSUE—BLACKOUTS

Some people who drink alcohol or take benzodiazepines to the point of blackout may think that, at these levels, drugs do remove stressful thoughts. A blackout is a state in which memories are not stored so that you may wake up the next day with no memories of stress (or anger, hostility, sadness, etc.), but that doesn't mean you didn't experience these emotions. You just don't remember them. The truth is that people are conscious while blacked out, they display purposeful behavior, and they exhibit the full range of emotions. In fact, it's essentially impossible to tell that someone is in a blackout at the time because they are simply highly intoxicated.

The only real exception to what we've demonstrated in this chapter so far is drug-induced unconsciousness. When people pass out cold from substance use, they stop thinking stressful thoughts but only because they've stopped all conscious thinking whatsoever. Is extremely heavy substance use such as this a solution for reducing stress? Maybe, but it's extremely costly. Likewise, people might view being left without stressful memories because of a blackout as a benefit, but this can be extremely costly as well because this is the level of intoxication just before total unconsciousness and overdose. Furthermore, many will attest to the fact that wondering the next day what they did during a blackout is an extremely stressful experience.

WHAT APPLIES TO STRESS APPLIES TO OTHER EMOTIONS TOO

Stress is an emotion initially resulting from our interpretation of the events and circumstances of our life. Downstream from that emotion are the physical symptoms of that stress. While substances may temporarily relieve some of those *physical symptoms*, substances can never relieve the *emotion* of stress because they cannot change our assessments of the events of our lives nor do they determine the subject matter of our thoughts. The emotion of stress can only ever be relieved by seeing things as less stressful and more manageable, fixable, and tolerable.

Knowing this, you can conclude that substance use is not even a temporary fix for stress. We can't stress the importance of this enough. Many people are quick to realize that substance use causes more problems that lead to more stress, so they know it isn't a long-term solution. But, if you think it's a short-term solution, you may feel a great want for substances in those immediate moments when you feel stress. Substances aren't a crutch for dealing with stress nor are they a temporary stress reliever. They just plain don't pharmacologically do anything for the emotion of stress. While you may experience emotional stress relief when using substances, that feeling of relief doesn't come from the substances themselves—it is an illusion that they relieve the emotion of stress.

Stress is an umbrella that includes many emotions, such as fear, anger, sadness, and worry. This discussion of the principles regarding stress and substances should be applied to *all* negative emotions:

- Substances don't pharmacologically relieve stress.

- Substances don't pharmacologically relieve anger.

- Substances don't pharmacologically relieve sadness.

- Substances don't pharmacologically relieve worry.

- Substances don't pharmacologically relieve trauma.

- Substances don't pharmacologically relieve *any negative emotions*, not even temporarily.

You may like the physical effects of substances, so you may feel some happiness in using them. We are not contesting that. But enjoying substances is not the same as having them remove your negative emotions about the other conditions of your life. You may receive relief from some of the physical symptoms of negative emotions by using substances. We aren't contesting that either, just pointing out that the physical symptoms are not the same as the emotions. You may genuinely feel emotional stress relief while using. We also aren't contesting that. But it matters that the relief isn't coming from the substances. It's coming from your own mind.

You will be assessing the benefits of substance use at various levels to finally decide whether you want to use them at some level or completely quit using them. As you make your benefits list, you now have the knowledge necessary to realize that relief of negative emotions by substance use is an illusion—it isn't a real benefit of substance use, and know that you know this you can leave emotional relief off your list.

REFERENCES

American Psychological Association. Understanding chronic stress. (n.d.). Retrieved from http://www.apa.org/helpcenter/understanding-chronic-stress.aspx

Becker, H. (1967). History, culture and subjective experience: An exploration of the social bases of drug-induced experiences. *Journal of Health and Social Behavior, 8*(3), 163–176.

Burns, D. (1999). *Feeling good: The new mood therapy.* New York, NY: HarperCollins.

University of Illinois at Chicago. (2017, June 2). Low-dose THC can relieve stress; more does just the opposite. *ScienceDaily.* Retrieved August 17, 2017 from www.sciencedaily.com/releases/2017/06/170602155252.htm

Sayette, M. (1999). Does drinking reduce stress? *Alcohol Research & Health, 23*(4), 250–255.

CHAPTER 19:

LOWERED INHIBITIONS AND THE LICENSE TO MISBEHAVE

You're at a bar with friends having a few drinks, watching your favorite team on the big screen. You see a guy at the bar who has had a few too many turn to the guy next to him and start shouting obscenities. The second guy jumps off the bar stool and takes a swing at him, and a fight breaks out but is quickly subdued by two other patrons and a burly bouncer who escorts the two men outside. Immediately, a young woman comes running from the other side of the bar pleading with the bouncer to go easy on one of the men. She cries, "Don't hurt him; he's just drunk. I will take him home."

There is a widespread belief in our culture that substances lower inhibitions, obliterating some mental barrier so that people become more open and honest about what they think, who they are, and how they feel. In other words, when under the influence, some other self is unleashed by the alcohol. Most people attribute the effects of alcohol and other substances to making them more sociable and outgoing, more forward and daring romantically or sexually, and act more aggressively and offensively. It is as if people repress what they believe are their less socially acceptable moods and behaviors until they use drugs or alcohol. The belief is that substances have a pharmacological key that unlocks all this behavior.

Although it's true that many people feel empowered to behave differently when they use substances (e.g., alcohol as "liquid courage"), *the claim that substances pharmacologically lower inhibitions is untrue and represents an illusion.* The "drug, set, and setting," understanding that was discussed in chapter 17 explains this phenomenon perfectly. We used the comparison earlier in *The Freedom Model* between drinking at a wake versus drinking in a bar to demonstrate this general principle. However, the primary set and setting operative in creating these effects is so broad and subtle within our culture that it's almost invisible. We've literally been immersed in it our entire lives. As such, it's virtually impossible to step outside of it to see its influence. Luckily, mountains of data have been gathered by social scientists all around the world to demonstrate the fact that substances don't truly lower inhibitions. We'll be referring to this and other data throughout the chapter to question this class of substance effects; in so doing, we'll replace the belief in pharmacologically lowered inhibitions with the more accurate concept of a socially/culturally granted "license to misbehave" while intoxicated.

CAN THE SAME SUBSTANCE CREATE OPPOSITE EFFECTS?

On its face, it's illogical to believe that any substance can be responsible for producing effects that directly contradict each other. Nevertheless, the belief in these contradictory effects is completely accepted in our culture. Let's review some of these perceived effects of drugs and alcohol and revisit our table from earlier in the text that puts those effects side by side with their contradictory counterparts. Then, you will be able to see the absurdity of our cultural beliefs about drugs and alcohol:

THE PERCEIVED EFFECTS "CAUSED" BY IDENTICAL SUBSTANCES

Peacefulness and lovingness	Hostility and violence
Relaxation	Stimulation
Creativity and an active, focused mind	Clearing your mind, forgetting, haziness
Sociability, more outgoing	Withdrawn, in your own world
More sensitive and easily aroused	Emotionally numbed
Causes anger	Cures anger, calms ("takes the edge off")
Concentration and focus	Impulsivity, poor judgment, distraction, and impairment
Agreeable, friendly, and affable	Belligerent, improper, and impolite
Bold and courageous	Timid, nervous, and impaired

The list of contradictory effects and powers that substances are believed to have over people is endless. When looked at side by side, you can clearly see that it is completely implausible. But people don't see that because they've been surrounded by others displaying these contradictory effects their entire lives and most people have experienced them personally. What's most puzzling is that the same person can experience these contradictory effects while using the same substance from one day to the next, as a noted drug and alcohol researcher observed decades ago:

> Sometimes alcohol may be a relaxant (the martini after the hard day at the office) and sometimes it may act as a stimulant (the first drink at the party). (Zinberg, 1984, p. 172)

It can't be true that alcohol has the power to both stimulate and relax you. So how is this explained? The truth is that alcohol itself does neither of these things pharmacologically, nor does marijuana, cocaine, heroin, or any other drug. It's time to open your mind to the possibility that these are not pharmacologically induced effects and allow for the possibility that something else is occurring. As you proceed, remember we're not denying that substances have physical effects. We're highlighting the emotional, behavioral, and psychological changes that accompany substance use, which are of a different category than the sensorimotor and other physical impairments caused by substances.

You'll notice that many of the effects we listed involve the way people behave socially while intoxicated. Hostility and aggression are perfect examples. There are many times when people become more argumentative, challenging, disagreeable, and even violent when drinking. Here's a common example. Everyone is having fun at a family gathering when one man who's had several drinks decides to tell off his brother. He goes on a tirade airing a lifetime of resentments and grievances in bold fashion for everyone to hear. There's a little back and forth. Eventually, he shoves his brother, and a fistfight breaks out. Just then, their uncle jumps in the middle and breaks it up. Then their mother says to the brother who was attacked, "Calm down; he doesn't mean it. He's just drunk. *It's just the alcohol talking.*" Both brothers may calm down and make up, or they may go their separate ways and never again discuss the issues raised in the drunken tirade. Typically, this kind of exchange is written off as the product of drunkenness, that is, they blame the alcohol as the sole cause of the behavior. The brother who started the brawl gets a pass and is not held responsible for his behavior. This result, the fact that he knew he would get a pass because of being intoxicated, is *exactly* what incentivized the initiation of the argument while he was drunk.

Another common example is a man and woman have been friends since grade school. He had a crush on her throughout high school and never acted on it. Now, in their early 30s, they're at a mutual friend's party, and both have had several drinks. In a moment alone, he admits his long-standing crush and leans in to kiss her. She backs away, and her response is a friendly but firm "Go home; you've had too much to drink." This incident is pushed aside as the product of drunkenness and never spoken of again, and they can remain friends. This result is *exactly* why the proposition was made while drunk.

The accepted wisdom is that alcohol has somehow chemically caused these behaviors in people. But the fact that those two behaviors, expressing affection or romantic desires and picking a fight, are diametrically opposed should at least call into question the validity of the explanation. Which category of behavior does alcohol produce, expressions of affection or overt hostility? It couldn't realistically produce both because they are opposites.

The more sophisticated answer, we're told, is that alcohol causes these behaviors indirectly by lowering inhibition, thus allowing people to feel freer to express their hidden desires, whatever they may be (an *inhibition* is defined as a "restraint on the direct expression of an instinct"). However, there are just as many examples where people become unsure of themselves, nervous, and withdrawn and display *increased inhibition* while drinking or using drugs. Drug and alcohol experts have struggled to explain all this but have not yet arrived at an agreed upon neurological or pharmacological explanation that ties it all together. The fact is that this type of answer may never arrive because pharmacology and neurology may be the wrong scientific fields to solve this puzzle.

A simple social-psychological explanation has been around for decades and is backed up by extensive research: people usually behave within the boundaries set for them by society, and it just so happens that *our society applies different standards of behavior to intoxicated people than it does to sober people.* Those standards are obviously *lower* for intoxicated people. So we all face lower expectations from others while drinking and especially when we're drunk, and we know this. *We know that we can behave differently and get away with it; it's a "license to misbehave."*

If you take a moment to think, you will come up with behaviors that are more accepted by you, personally, when you know someone is intoxicated than when he or she is sober:

- Off-color jokes
- Cursing, swearing
- Promiscuity
- Public urination
- Spitting
- Smoking
- Aggressive, hostile behavior
- Arguing
- Being overly flirty or sexually aggressive
- Off-color discussions of any kind

The contrasting standards when sober and intoxicated are sometimes hilarious. Just watch the way that many very proper and polite people let the offensive jokes fly when they're drinking. We've all seen situations where the most judgmental people give others a pass on offensive language, topics, and jokes because the others are intoxicated. We see entire groups of polite people who regularly take great care not to be offensive, in the right situation, suddenly and dramatically change when they are intoxicated.

Now, let's be clear. No group of people intentionally hash out a different set of standards that they'll apply to each other when drunk. They don't say, "I think we should give each other leeway to be offensive when we drink," and in fact, the guidelines are often unclear. Nevertheless, the lines are blurred, and they know it. We also needn't assume that people consciously think to themselves before telling their offensive jokes *I have to be so careful about what I say all the time, but now is my chance to tell that offensive joke and get away with it.* Yet that is exactly how they act. It's as if there is an unspoken agreement, or "tradition" might better describe it.

THE ORIGIN OF THE LICENSE TO MISBEHAVE

Where does this unspoken agreement (license to misbehave) come from? Societies have always allowed varied conduct at special times and in special settings, such as ceremonies, rituals, and holidays. Alcohol and other drugs have a reputation for causing behavior change. We've grown up seeing people misbehave while drunk. We've seen them given a pass, and thus, we've seen what is otherwise unacceptable behavior attributed to the powers of substances. And we've accepted that's how it is. Most people believe that alcohol changes behavior and makes people behave in ways they wouldn't when they are sober. They believe it, and like a placebo, they experience this behavior change while drinking or drugging (or at least they feel the freedom to behave differently even if they don't always exercise it). They know intimately that it's acceptable while drinking or drugging to do many things that they wouldn't normally do while sober. The costs of acting differently while intoxicated are lowered, thus changing the incentives and possible outcomes of certain behavior. This effectively has created a *license to misbehave*.

This license is what facilitated our two scenarios above. The man who while drunk confronted his brother chose that time to do so because of the almost guaranteed forgiveness he'd receive if he went too far. Because people attribute such strong words and actions to alcohol (and drugs), he had a license to behave that way with less fallout than there'd have been if he had uttered them while sober. Likewise, the man who professed his love to his longtime friend chose a moment of drunkenness because it was a lower risk situation. The license to misbehave made the potential rejection less embarrassing by blaming it on the alcohol and allowed for culturally acceptable excuses after the fact.

The practice is so popular that we sometimes acknowledge its existence. There was a hit song about it titled "Blame It" by Jamie Foxx and T-Pain. In the verse, he sings to a potential sexual partner and says he knows that she doesn't want to "seem like she's easy." In the chorus, he explains with much repetition, that she can "blame it on the alcohol" if they hook up. Thus, they can hook up without her being considered easy. She can retain her conventional reputation because the alcohol made her do things she wouldn't normally do. Granted, the song may be controversial by current standards, but it's the license to misbehave that he's talking about. And it resonated because it is a genuine practice in our culture.

Still, you may be scratching your head, thinking that the license to misbehave exists because alcohol truly does make you more outgoing, hostile, aggressive, impolite, or more sexual. You may be painfully shy while you are sober and have frequently used alcohol to be more sociable. You may be uptight and reserved sexually and have believed your entire life that you needed opiates and benzos to relax and be more daring sexually. There are as many beliefs about the *powers* of substances as there are people. The fact that various societies, cultures, and other subgroups have issued such *vastly different* licenses to misbehave is what proves that the license is the actual facilitator of these behaviors rather than the pharmacological action of the alcohol.

THE HISTORY OF THE LICENSE TO MISBEHAVE

The license to misbehave has been operative for a long time but was formally discovered and articulated only in the mid-20th century, most notably beginning with the work of Dwight Heath. He was an anthropologist who went to study the Camba, a small tribe of indigenous people who lived in isolation in the jungles of Bolivia. He did not set out to study their drinking, yet when he went back to Yale after studying them, some of his colleagues who worked in the alcohol studies department questioned him about the Camba's use of alcohol. Heath had kept plenty of notes on it, and what he described enthralled the alcohol researchers. The Camba had drinking sessions almost every weekend, beginning Friday and lasting into Monday morning, and on any holiday, through the next day. At these times, they drank almost continuously, and some people would pass out for stretches of time, wake up again, and rejoin the nonstop party to keep on drinking. He said that their drinking was also "so formalized as to be a secular ritual." Read Heath's description of their behavior while they were drinking:

Just as it was unthinkable that anyone would drink in any other context (except that of a funeral) it was also unthinkable that anyone would have negative consequences from drinking. Drunkenness was a quiet affair of simply staring into space or passing out for a while. Aggression, whether verbal, physical, sexual, or other, was virtually unknown among the Camba, drunk or sober. Similarly absent were boisterousness, clowning, maudlin sentimentality, or other exaggerated comportment such as tends to be associated with intoxication in other cultures. No Camba suffered or could even imagine such a thing as a hangover, and people worked at difficult and dangerous tasks (such as harvesting sugarcane) just a few hours after a party ended. Accidents were rare, and the drinking problems that are common elsewhere, such as trouble with the police, absenteeism, guilt, psychological or social discomfort, were meaningless to them. (Heath, 2000, p. 162)

What's more, the alcohol they drank was "raw fuel produced by local sugar refineries and sold as primer for the popular stoves and lanterns that operated on kerosene vapor and silk mantles." When Heath's colleagues tested it, they found that it was *178 proof, or 89% alcohol by volume* (Heath, 2000).

So here we have people drinking massive amounts of alcohol more powerful than any other society makes available, and yet none of the changes in behavior that we normally attribute to alcohol and its powers to lower inhibitions are exhibited. It was this sort of information that sent researchers in the direction of analyzing drinking practices and behaviors in several isolated cultures, tribes, and societies around the world.

The culmination of this extensive research was recorded in detail in the book *Drunken Comportment*, in which sociologists Craig MacAndrew and Robert Edgerton (2003) gathered accounts from researchers all over the world to demonstrate that there is no uniform response to alcohol. They found cultures where people displayed uninhibited sexual behavior when drinking, and cultures where no such disinhibition occurred. They found the same for aggression. They found cultures where aggression and sexuality seemed to be released by alcohol, where one or the other was released by alcohol, and where neither was released by alcohol, and much like the Camba, people's inhibitions didn't seem to be affected one bit by alcohol. They showed examples of six such cultures where no lowered inhibitions were seen. They found examples of cultures where most people become *more inhibited* when drinking. By compiling their extensive data, they showed that alcohol does not lower inhibitions at all.

What they showed is that people behave within a range of limits of what their culture allows to them while intoxicated. They called this phenomenon the "within limits clause"; we're calling it the "license to misbehave" because this term more accurately conveys what's happening with our readers.

If you are still unconvinced, consider these accounts from the Micronesian islands in the early 20th century. Ethnographers observed the people of Ifalik, an isolated Micronesian atoll with a population of about 500. They found that these people experienced no negative changes in behavior upon intoxication. They were peaceful when drunk. Why didn't any of them get angry or violent when drunk? Why didn't they misbehave?

Were they drinking some special gentler form of alcohol than we do? The answer is no. All alcohol made for drinking is essentially the same, with the active ingredient having the same molecular form. Different variations of alcohol are made from different organic substances, but the basic components of alcohol remain the same. In this case, they were making their alcohol from coconuts in the manner that it was made throughout most of Micronesia at the time. But that same coconut alcohol that resulted in passive and peaceful behavior in one area of Micronesia was found to be associated with misbehavior in many other parts of Micronesia, such as the islands of Truk or Butaritari. Several sources cited in *Drunken Comportment* demonstrate this; accounts of wife beating, kicking dogs, and other hostilities were rampant on the other islands when people drank coconut alcohol while no such behavior was seen among anyone in Ifalik.

Were the Ifalik people genetically different than their neighbors? Genetic studies revealed that Micronesians share a common genetic heritage. The various islands were settled by Taiwan Aborigines and East Asians 3,500 years ago, and being geographically isolated, they didn't mingle with other gene pools. So, whether from Ifalik or another Micronesian Island, such as Butaritari (where coconut alcohol has been called a "devilish intoxicant"), all these people come from the same genetic makeup and drink the same alcohol.

So, if the differences in behavior can't be attributed to genes nor to some variant of alcohol, then what is the source of the differences in behavior?

The Ifalik culture looked down on aggression and did not accept aggression even when someone was drunk. Therefore, the Ifalik people didn't have a license to misbehave when they were drunk. As a result, they never became aggressive while they were drinking even though their genetic counterparts on neighboring islands who were drinking the same alcohol engaged in a notable amount of aggression.

On Truk, when males between the ages of 15 and 29 were drinking, they would go down to the center of the village and challenge each other to fights. If they couldn't find another man to fight, they'd hurl rocks at homes trying to get someone to come out and fight them. If that didn't work, they'd eventually take it out on a woman or an animal. Aggressive behavior while intoxicated was a rite of passage that these young men engaged in, but after the age of 29, they were considered to be mature. They changed their behavior around the age of 30 even though they continued to drink. (Marshall, 1978)

Those young men on Truk had a license to misbehave when drunk until the age of 30, whereas their distant relatives on Ifalik had no such license to misbehave. Any claims that implicate genes, neurology, pharmacology, or a specific mixture of alcohol as the causative agent for such drunken behavior do not hold up against these examples.

This is but one example among countless examples of isolated cultures where either no license to misbehave or a very specific license to misbehave exists and the locals behave accordingly. It can be seen again and again. Yet, if you had grown up in Truk at the time of this study and known no other way of living, then you'd believe that alcohol has the effect of unleashing the violent warrior within you. Now, consider the fact that you have grown up in your own culture with its own ideas about the effects of alcohol, which may not be objectively true at all. Our culture surrounds us like water surrounds a fish. If the fish could think and reason, they might never realize they are in water. The fish would never see life on dry land nor even know that such a life is possible. That is how it is for us living in our culture except we can observe, think, and see through our travels to different cultures and our own research that the ideas we take for granted may not exist elsewhere.

Once you step outside your own culture to look at other cultures, you find amazing things. For example, the amount of alcohol consumed per capita in Ireland has traditionally been equal to or lower than that in many other countries throughout Europe. Yet Ireland has rates of alcohol-related behavioral and health problems that far exceed those other countries. Many have made the comparison to Italy, where alcohol problems are far rarer, yet most people drink every day. Behaviorally, the Italians do not show the same aggressiveness as the Irish either. The same is true in China, where stronger alcohol is consumed than in most parts of the world, yet only 2% of arrests involved intoxication. In comparison, in the United States, 45% of arrests involved intoxication (mid-20th century). Researchers have pegged cultural differences as the explanation for this, and it was confirmed by the same relative shortage of alcohol-related crimes among Chinese immigrants in New York City during the same period. They just didn't have the same license to misbehave while intoxicated in Chinese culture that existed in so many other cultures (Marshall, 1979).

The license to misbehave also subdivides within nations and regions along class, age, and religious lines as well. Once you open your mind to this phenomenon, you'll begin to see it among people in your own social groups. Some people in some circumstances seem to have their inhibitions lowered by substances, but in other circumstances, they don't. It's all a matter of simply looking for it. Once you see it, it can't be unseen. Substances don't lower inhibitions; rather, people are held to different standards among different groups, in different times and places.

Set and setting rule this class of "drug effects," and it goes beyond alcohol to almost any drug you can imagine. The behavioral effects of cocaine will be different in a crack house than they are in the backroom at a country club, and they'll be different again in a dance club. The behavioral effects of pot will be different when used in a rec room by high school students than they are when used by adults at a music festival and different yet again when used by patients using pot as a medicine. Levels of inhibition and the behavior substances supposedly produce will differ from person to person and situation to situation. Furthermore, levels of inhibition can change on a dime when one moment you're high with your friends parked in a car and the next moment a cop knocks on the car's window. These simply aren't drug effects. They're set and setting effects and the effect of a perceived license to misbehave, but they are so clearly a conditional license too that it becomes impossible to "blame it on the alcohol" once you fully understand the fallacy.

One of our presenters was discussing this cross-cultural research with a young student currently embroiled in the wild college party scene, and he could see a lightbulb turn on in her head. She identified the license to misbehave quickly, stating "Oh—like it's all right to hit on someone when you're drunk, but it's creepy to hit on someone when you're sober?" Yes, it's exactly like that. And this is where the license must be examined to debunk some of our culture's perceived benefits of alcohol and other drugs.

THE ILLUSORY BENEFITS OF
LOWERED INHIBITIONS

We think that drugs and alcohol lower our inhibitions, thus giving us

- courage to speak our minds;
- ability to express our true feelings;
- confidence to be bold, daring, and straightforward;
- freedom from social anxiety or embarrassment;
- ability to be ourselves;
- ability to get out of our own heads;
- ability to let down our guards and be real;
- unleashed creative abilities; and
- freedom from fear.

There are countless ways we can say it and thus countless *perceived* benefits that fit under this umbrella of lowered inhibitions. And the fact is that, if you have grown up within a culture that imbues drugs and alcohol with the power to lower inhibitions, then you can feel all these things while drinking or using drugs. But remember the lesson of *drug, set, and setting* and the lesson of *active placebos* (both in chapter 17). To this day, the only credible scientific explanation for how substances lower inhibitions is the sociological one discovered by Heath, MacAndrew, Edgerton, and others—these effects are not the product of substances but rather the product of the license to misbehave. That is, you have grown up learning that you will be held to a different standard of behavior while intoxicated so you feel empowered to behave differently while intoxicated.

As we said in our discussion of substances' perceived yet unreal ability to relieve emotional pain, you can go on thinking you need substances for all these wonderful benefits. You can continue to feel these things and think you need substances for these things if you choose to close your mind to the truth. However, if you are a person who feels a desperate need for substances and that need troubles you, then it pays to know the truth. The truth is that substances do not give you any of the courage, social ease, or other forms of lowered inhibitions listed above. Those are cognitive products. They occur as processes of the mind, as matters of belief. You effectively create these effects yourself. You do not need substances to achieve them, and you have already been achieving them on your own yet crediting drugs and alcohol for them.

If you want to let go of heavy substance use and adopt a "take it or leave it" mindset about substance use, then you need to stop imbuing substances with powers they don't have. You can remember this knowledge when you think you need substances. You can know that you don't need substances for these things that they do not do. You can take these things off your mental list of benefits of substances. It's your choice what to make of this new knowledge. If you're unconvinced, we welcome you to read the resources below where countless examples proving the point can be found. To this day, there is no better scientific explanation for lowered inhibitions under intoxication than this sociological phenomenon.

Substances don't lower inhibitions – the culturally granted "license to misbehave" makes us feel empowered to behave differently while intoxicated.

REFERENCES

Heath, D. (2000). *Drinking occasions: Comparative perspectives on alcohol and culture*. London: Bruner-Routledge.

MacAndrew, C., & Edgerton, R. B. (2003). *Drunken comportment: A social explanation.* Clinton Corners, NY: Percheron Press.

Marshall, M. (1978). *Weekend warriors: Alcohol in a Micronesian culture* (1st ed.). Palo Alto, CA: McGraw-Hill Humanities/Social Sciences/Languages.

Marshall, M. (Ed.). (1979). *Beliefs, behaviors, and alcoholic beverages: A cross-cultural survey.* Ann Arbor, MI: University of Michigan Press.

Zinberg, N. (1984). *Drug, set, and setting: The basis for controlled intoxicant use.* New Haven, CT: Yale University.

CHAPTER 20:
PLEASURE

W e talk about pleasure as if it's an objective thing or a quality inherent in things. This simplistic notion is taken for granted with substances and never questioned. The way substances are discussed, it's as if a blunt, a Percocet, or a shot of Jack Daniels *contains pleasure* in the same way that an apple *contains nutrients*. Nobody seems to realize how deeply this view of inherent pleasure rules the discourse on substance use habits, but it does. And it's important to pick apart. The notion of "addictiveness" is built on it. The idea that it's hard to quit or reduce substance use is built on it. The idea that it takes self-control or willpower to "resist" an inherently tempting quality of substances is built on it. The idea that "support" is needed to deal with the loss of this inherent pleasure is built on it. The obsession with the costs and consequences as a necessary focus of quitting is built on the idea that substances inherently *contain* pleasure. The sense of loss and deprivation that people believe they'll have to endure when changing a substance use habit is built on the belief in the inherent pleasure of substances.

But what if drugs and alcohol didn't inherently contain pleasure? What if it was a far more subjective matter than that? The entire approach to quitting or reducing substance use would change. It would no longer have to be about summoning strength and support to resist and avoid temptation. You would no longer have to approach this change with an intense fear of impending loss and deprivation. You could look forward to the potential of greater pleasure and happiness rather than a life of guaranteed lower levels of both.

The truth is that pleasure is entirely subjective in any realm. The idea that anything is *inherently* pleasurable is flat out wrong. Pleasure isn't a quality that exists within things. Pleasure is an experience that comes about in myriad ways but one that must always include the individual's mind.

PLEASURABLE THINGS

Let's start by discussing something that is commonly known to produce pleasure: *music*. Many studies have been done examining brain activity while people listen to music, and it has been found to produce "a particularly intense, euphoric response." In one study, neuroscientists asked people to provide a recording that gives them euphoric "shivers-down-the-spine" or "chills." Then they did PET scans of their brains while they were listening to it. They found the following:

> Subjective reports of chills were accompanied by changes in heart rate, electromyogram, and respiration. As intensity of these chills increased, cerebral blood flow increases and decreases were observed in brain regions thought to be involved in reward/motivation, emotion, and arousal, including ventral striatum, midbrain, amygdala, orbitofrontal cortex, and ventral medial prefrontal cortex. (Blood & Zatorre, 2001)

This sounds exactly like the jargon-filled talk about the power of drugs on the pleasure center or reward circuit of the brain because it is. The researchers noted that "these brain structures are known to be active in response to other euphoria-inducing stimuli, such as food, sex, and drugs of abuse" (Blood & Zatorre, 2001). Yet, in this case, this isn't a food, sexual act, or drug that they studied. It's *music*, arrangements of sounds and waves traveling through the air. Music has no physical substance, as the researchers pointed out:

> We have shown here that music recruits neural systems of reward and emotion similar to those known to respond specifically to biologically relevant stimuli, such as food and sex, and those that are artificially activated by drugs of abuse. This is quite remarkable, because music is neither strictly necessary for biological survival or reproduction, nor is it a pharmacological substance. (Blood & Zatorre, 2001)

This research regarding music can't be ignored; there is no *substance* going into your body, yet the euphoria you can feel when listening to it is intense. We've all had moments of intense pleasure that didn't involve the use of substances. Many people reading this will have had these experiences with music. Yet people think there's something supernatural or extra special about drugs because they experience euphoria while using them. I (Steven) feel like I am on the drug known as ecstasy/molly when I listen to a few of my favorite recordings of music, and that is no exaggeration. However, other people would feel nothing significant when listening to those same recordings, or they might even feel *displeasure*. And this brings us to a second point regarding pleasure.

To make the proper measurements, researchers also had to scan the brains of their subjects while they listened to a recording that did not give them euphoria, pleasure, or "chills" so they could compare and find the differences. Obviously, the brain activity while listening to the "less pleasurable" piece was very different and didn't show the same pleasure response. For this other piece of music, they were offered several pieces from which to choose, which incidentally were made up of recordings the other test subjects had chosen as their euphoria-producing recordings. (Blood & Zatorre, 2001)

This meant that each piece of music used in the study was shown to produce euphoria, "shivers-down-the-spine," and "chills" for one person, while producing no such effects in the next person. If a piece of music were "inherently pleasurable," then that pleasure should be transferred into anyone exposed to it, the same way the nutrients from an apple are transferred into anyone who eats it or the pleasure from a drug is supposedly transferred into anyone who takes it. But it isn't. The pleasure is subjective; it is not *inherent* in the music—it has everything to do with the individual.

This isn't surprising. All people form their own unique tastes for their own reasons. There are various associations that individuals make with music, personal histories involved with developing these tastes, and special personal meaning to some pieces of music. That these variations are in the realms of the mind and personal experience is no small point. The pleasure isn't coming directly from the music nor necessarily from the brain either. Instead, it's coming from your mind, from how you interpret the music, and then the pleasure is physically acted out through the brain. An inherent pleasure model could never sufficiently explain the euphoria people get while listening to their favorite music.

But maybe the inherent pleasure model can explain the euphoria of sexual experiences? Many readers will instantly recognize this notion as absurd. Of course, we could get into the technical details of all the neurocircuitry involved in sexual arousal, pleasure, and orgasm, but it boils down to this: many of the same brain areas and neurotransmitters involved in pleasure with music, food, and drugs are fired off when people have enjoyable sex.

There are facts about sexual behavior that are easily observed by the naked eye, which demonstrate that no sexual act is *inherently* pleasurable. All you need to do is peruse the items available at your local sex shop or the genres of pornography available online. You'll find countless things that you are not at all interested in and would feel no pleasure in using/watching and many things that directly repulse you and turn you off. Yet these things are available for a reason: because there are many people out there who find them intensely pleasurable.

What's more, you could think of a sex act that you enjoy, perhaps your favorite thing to do sexually. Is it *inherently* pleasurable? You could probably come up with many exceptions where it would not be pleasurable. There are times and places where you would not enjoy doing it. And there are certainly people with whom you would not enjoy doing it. In a model of inherent pleasure, if for example, a stroke of your thigh created arousal, then it should create arousal no matter who does it, where it's done, and when it's done. But the who, where, and when of sexual acts matter as much as the what in whether you will find it pleasurable. *Set* and *setting* matter, and a simple stroke of the thigh is just the "drug" part of the equation (see explanation of the "drug, set, setting" model in chapter 17).

Even with food, the picture is complex, and this is the example that comes closest to drugs because actual substances are going into our bodies when we eat. Much has been made of the role that sugar and fat plays in the enjoyment of food. In a report aired on *60 Minutes*, a scientist brought Dr. Sanjay Gupta into a lab with an fMRI brain scanning machine, put a tube into his mouth that would deliver a sip of sugary soda, and scanned his brain. They then showed brain scans demonstrating that dopamine was triggered in the "pleasure center" of

Dr. Gupta's brain when he ingested the soda. The report used the word "euphoria," compared sugar to cocaine, and said that it was "one of the most addictive substances we have."

Here, we see once again that pleasure is an inherent quality of a thing, and in this case especially, the parallels with substances have already been well drawn in the addiction-obsessed media. Using the same logic and research done on lab rats, later reports from Gupta said that Oreo cookies were "more addictive than cocaine," as if both addictiveness and pleasure are one in the same and inherent properties of things. Richard DeGrandpre (2010) cut right through these simplistic notions in his tour de force on the magical, mythical view of drugs, *The Cult of Pharmacology*:

> Consider another abused substance that involves dopamine: food. Drugs are not the only substances that affect the mesolimbic system. So are foods. The pleasure one receives from foods depends on various additional factors, including how hungry one is and whether one likes the food that he or she is eating. Physiological research has demonstrated this as well. In one study, when an animal was presented with food, researchers found neurons firing as a function of either the sight or taste of food, but with an important caveat: the neurons fired only when the animal was hungry. If pleasure were as simple as eating foods that triggered the release of dopamine, then one would never stop eating. The same notion applies more or less to drugs. Why should one expect cocaine to be pleasurable at all times or to all individuals when one would never expect this to hold true for even the most beloved foods, such as chocolate, ice cream, or pasta?. (p. 189)

Don't miss the point. Foods are supposedly inherently pleasurable because they contain "addictive ingredients," such as sugar and fat, which go straight to the pleasure center of the brain. Yet, even in a creature as simple as a rat, these addictive ingredients don't always produce pleasure. It should be common sense that, if you had, for example, chocolate ice cream day after day, then eventually, it would cease to give the same pleasure. Not to mention the fact that, while some other flavor of ice cream, such as bubblegum, might be filled with even more fat and sugar, you might find that eating bubblegum ice cream brings you no pleasure whatsoever.

Pleasure from food just isn't that simple. It's wrapped up in other factors just like every other pleasure we've discussed here. In psychologist Paul Bloom's *Pleasure: How It Works* (2010), there were no easy answers, but he offered several findings that struck right at the heart of simplistic notions of inherent pleasure in foods:

> There have been several studies showing that how you think about food or drink affects how you judge it. The design of these studies is usually simple. You get two groups of people, you give them the very same thing to eat or drink, but present it to the groups in different ways. Then you ask how they like it. Studies find, for instance, that
>
> • Protein bars taste worse if they are described as "soy protein."
>
> • Orange juice tastes better if it is bright orange.
>
> • Yogurt and ice cream are more flavorful if described as "full fat" or "high fat."
>
> • Children think milk and apples taste better if they're taken out from McDonald's bags.
>
> • Coke is rated higher when drunk from a cup with a brand logo.
>
> This last study has been replicated with a brainy twist, where subjects were in an fMRI scanner. When given a blind taste test between Coke and Pepsi, with the liquids squirted into the subjects' mouths through a tube, the brain's reward system lights up and people are evenly split. But when they are told what they are drinking, a different pattern of brain activation emerges: people's preferences shift according to the brand they like more. (p. 45)

Similar findings have been popularly reported with wine. When a cheap wine is described as more expensive, people enjoy it more, as reflected in brain scans that show more activity in the pleasure center than when it is presented as inexpensive. Again, what all this means is that the pleasure isn't inherent to the wine but rather is a product of the mind. This also means that people aren't faking it when they enjoy the same wine more because it was presented as expensive. They *are* enjoying it more because pleasure isn't in things—it's in the total experience as you put it together in your mind.

We don't need a brain scan or any other technical test to know that if a vegetarian is forced to eat thick-cut maple-glazed bacon, he won't get any pleasure from it. Nor does it take a rocket scientist to know that a health food enthusiast truly derives great pleasure from preparing and eating a healthy meal full of vegetables, with very little fat and no processed foods or refined sugars. We only need common sense. Pleasure is a subjective matter even if there are some substances that do a better job of going straight to the pleasure center of the brain than others.

Common sense cuts right through "sex and love addiction" too, as legendary addiction theorist Stanton Peele swiftly demonstrated. He exposed the inherent pleasure model as fiction by explaining that the 12-step model of addiction is "object-based," and

> it says that thing is so addictive, they couldn't resist it. You know, heroin and alcohol, who could resist it? But it's crazy to apply that to love, because as soon as you say that man or woman was so irresistible that anybody would have become addicted to them, you automatically know that's bullshit because you're probably the only person addicted to them. (as cited in Atkinson, 2017)

Peele has a history of using topics such as love addiction, food addiction, and gambling addiction to show the folly of the popular view of substance addictions. He's famously demonstrated that people often get the same feelings of attachment to many involvements where no substance is ever consumed, such as relationships, in his best seller *Love and Addiction* (Peele & Brodsky, 1975). In the example above, his point is clear. It's not the thing itself that's pleasurable or "addictive" (in this case, another person); it's the mind of the individual that imbues the thing with so much personal meaning. The pleasure, that great spike of reward, isn't just a matter of molecules, and *it isn't out there—it's in your mind.*

ATTRIBUTING PLEASURE TO SUBSTANCES

The lessons above apply to drugs as much as to anything else. Substances aren't inherently pleasurable. You can't put any drug into any person at any time or in any place and reliably produce a pleasure that all people find impressive and care to repeat. This truth holds for all drugs, even those deemed the most "addictive" because of their assumed inherent pleasure. DeGrandpre mentioned a British study from 1964 involving opiates to make this point:

> Two consecutive doses of morphine were given to 150 young males with no previous opiate experience. After finding that only three chose to have the experience repeated and that none believed they would seek out the drug recreationally, the authors concluded, "Opiates are not inherently attractive, euphoric or stimulant" in nature. Clearly, a love of opiates had yet to be cultivated for these individuals. (p. 214)

Right now, you might be a bit incredulous reading this because you've taken opiates, alcohol, cocaine, or some other favorite drug that you find to be more pleasurable than any other experience you've ever had in your life. We understand, but an open mind is essential if you wish to change. Remember, new thoughts are required to make new choices and develop new preferences. You might consider the idea that this pleasure is more of a love that you cultivated rather than the inevitable product of an inherently pleasurable or euphoric quality contained in the drug you're fixated on. You might choose to challenge the notion that the substance you prefer holds a magical key to your brain's pleasure center. You might apply your new knowledge of the "drug, set, and setting" model of drug effects and the idea that drugs act as *active placebos* to the issue of pleasure. By thinking critically about your favorite drug, you might find that it doesn't contain an inherent irresistible pleasure.

Please note that we don't mean to suggest that people don't feel pleasure when using substances. We're just suggesting that this pleasure is not as simple, reliable, and straightforward as it's been made out to be and that drugs aren't particularly spectacular or magical when compared to other potential pleasures. Drugs aren't special in the fact that they do things to the brain, including the so-called pleasure center or reward circuitry. All pleasures involve activation and can create "brain changes" in these same areas. The latter point shouldn't be overlooked because the recovery society has taught you that drugs are unique in their ability to change or "hijack" the brain. Plenty of nonsubstance activities do this, and yet we don't see these other activities as things that we're bound to for life or that ruin us for all other pleasures. As neuroscientist Marc Lewis (2012) put it, speaking of the "pleasure center":

> Every experience that has potent emotional content changes the NAC ["pleasure center"] and its uptake of dopamine. Yet we wouldn't want to call the excitement you get from the love of your life, or your fifth visit to Paris, a disease. The NAC is highly plastic. It has to be, so that we can pursue different rewards as we develop, right through childhood to the rest of the lifespan. In fact, each highly rewarding experience builds its own network of synapses in and around the NAC, and that network sends a signal to the midbrain: I'm anticipating x, so send up some dopamine, right now! That's the case with romantic love, Paris, and heroin. During and after each of these experiences, that network of synapses gets strengthened: so the "specialization" of dopamine uptake is further increased. London just doesn't do it for you anymore. It's got to be Paris. Pot, wine, music … they don't turn your crank so much; but cocaine sure does. Physical changes in the brain are its only way to learn, to remember, and to develop. But we wouldn't want to call learning a disease.

So you may have learned that your drug is what you need for pleasure, and it may be very pleasurable to you right now. But regardless of all the impressive neuro-jargon about how that pleasure is acted out in the brain, you still aren't fated to get your pleasure from only this one thing for the rest of your life. In fact, the norm is to change and to get pleasure from other things. We recognize this in so many other areas. We grow bored with many games, hobbies, activities, careers, people, forms of entertainment, places, and so on, but we put drugs in a different category. We think that we'll be stuck on our substance and that it will continue to bring us the same pleasure indefinitely. *Substances can get boring too.* The only thing that holds you back from realizing this is the belief in inherent pleasure, that drugs have a magical essence and that this has been proven by their chemical structure and activity on the "pleasure center."

Here is where I must use a personal anecdote. I (Steven) used many substances in a way people call "addictive," and I eventually quit that with the ideas of *The Freedom Model*. My main drug was heroin. This drug and all other opiates are supposed to produce an "irresistible high" (see Appendix D). After ending my "addiction," I'd gone 14 years having taken only a handful of opiates for dental procedures, and then I had to have a tonsillectomy. The doctors prescribed a dozen Percocets (an opioid painkiller) a day, and I was on strict orders to take the full amount for two weeks. That's a lot for someone with no tolerance and no recent history of opiate use whatsoever. As I recovered and the pain from the surgery dulled, I realized that I was in a foggy, sedated state. I recognized it as the same feeling from when I used to be an avid heroin user (minus the occasional head rushes I would've gotten from injection). However, I did not enjoy this feeling nor find it pleasurable at this point in my life. I didn't want this feeling. I wanted to be clearheaded and to get back to my work, my goals, and my hobbies. This wasn't pleasure; it was a burden, and I was happy to rapidly decrease the number of painkillers I was taking and replace them with over-the-counter Tylenol. I certainly didn't find anything about them "irresistible" or get "readdicted." This is because the pleasure isn't inherent in opiates; they didn't hold a special key to my pleasure center. In fact, pleasure is a highly subjective and personal feeling produced more so by the mind than by magical molecules.

THE NOT-SO-SIMPLE PLEASURE CENTER

Along with the simplistic notion of pleasure being inherent in things, we have the equally simplistic notion that there's a central spot in the brain that can be pushed by drugs and reliably produce pleasure. This is typically phrased something like this: "these powerful drugs go straight to the pleasure center of the brain, causing a spike of dopamine that no other natural rewards can compete with." This completes the magical drug mythology by granting them special access to a special brain region that only they can "hijack," turning people into drug-seeking zombies.

The myth of this simplistic drug/pleasure center interaction was deconstructed by DeGrandpre (2010) in his book *The Cult of Pharmacology*. The title of this work highlights our culture's obsession with the "drug" as well as our culture's dismissal or even ignorance to the elements of "set and setting" in producing drug effects. In it, he brings us beyond the pleasure center and magical drugs. He wields mounds of evidence that can point us straight back to set and setting as being greater determinants of drug effects, *including pleasure*. In a chapter important to our topic, he traced the discovery of the pleasure center, which began with a study in 1954:

> When animals' responses on a switch produced electrical stimulation in the brain's septal area, the animals responded as frequently as several hundred times per hour to keep the stimulation going. Among the many implications of the study was the possibility that certain drugs might be stimulating this "reward" area of the brain, and in doing so, encouraging or even inculcating addictive behavior. (p. 179)

This was found in rats first and then in other animals and humans. It seemed that any creature would just keep doing whatever it had to do to get those jolts into what became known as the pleasure center when given the chance. Similar studies were carried out where animals could work for jolts of morphine or cocaine to the brain, and they would keep taking doses if they could, even to the point of death.

The initial concept of a simple pleasure center didn't turn out to be so simple after all. Decades of uncertainty followed about where the center was, which neurochemicals acted most significantly upon it, and whether its effects were pleasurable or pain relieving. One of the main neurochemicals involved, dopamine, went from being the direct lever of reward, to being the anticipator of reward, to being far more multifaceted than either of those narrow descriptions allowed. None of this has been so simple as originally conceived, and it certainly isn't even close to being understood. Yet, more than 60 years later, the public and far too many professionals are left with the impression that there's a simple little button in the brain that can be pushed with magical drugs to make a spike in dopamine and produce pleasure. Case closed.

The evidence brought to bear in *The Cult of Pharmacology* pertains to the effects of set and setting. The most surprising development was that rewards had to be pursued voluntarily to be rewarding. So, although animals would work relentlessly for electrical stimulation when given the chance, the story changed when their brains were stimulated at the same frequency without their having a choice in the matter. *When offered the chance to work to stop the electrical stimulation, they would work just as hard to avoid electrical stimulation as they would have to attain it!*

> This indicated a serious hitch in the theory, for if brain stimulation connected to a single neural pleasure switch, why should it matter who throws it?
>
> Even if a pleasure center did exist in the mammalian and bird brain, it seemed pleasure could not be reduced, even in a basic animal model, to a simple matter of stimulating that area. (DeGrandpre, 2010, p. 184)

Further research showed that when rats voluntarily worked for doses of cocaine, they all survived long stretches of frequent doses but identical rats paired with them that received the same doses at the same times without working for it overdosed and died at an alarming rate (38%). The drug was *more toxic* to the rats that didn't choose when to take it. When similar studies were done with morphine, it was shown that there were drastic differences in brain activity upon drug administration dependent on whether the animal voluntarily worked for the drug or received it involuntarily. Such research sounds surprising, but it shouldn't. Even simple pleasures aren't so simple.

> A more interesting but also more complex theory was warranted, suggesting a dynamic interplay between the brain, behavior, and experience. And this made sense: in looking at one's own everyday experience, it is clear that one's sense of pleasure is intricately tied up with an engagement in the activity that produces it. (DeGrandpre, 2010, p. 184)

And that is what we've been presenting. We've shown that the pleasure found in several activities isn't inherent and constant but instead flexible and dependent on the individual's mindset, time, place, setting, and various other factors. We've seen this with sex, food, and beverages, and now we have research proving it's the case with drugs. There are plenty of commonsense ways to see it with substance use once you look for it. Most people don't like taking their preferred substances at just any time and in any place, yet we should if pleasure is just a matter of a drug entering our bodies. Unfortunately, the *inherent pleasure* model (or pharmacologicalism, as DeGrandpre calls it) dissuades us from seeing this truth. It portrays drugs as magical containers of ultimate pleasures.

> From the standpoint of modern pharmacologicalism, such results are upsetting indeed, for they undermine the fundamental notion that a drug's most socially significant effects, such as the mind-altering experience it produces, are derivative only of pharmacology. While modern pharmacologicalism presents a static model of drug determinism that is highly reductionistic—it reduces drug taking and drug effects to the level of molecules tickling a static brain—this research suggests a very different model: drugs do not have a single essence, whether good or bad, addictive or nonaddictive, weak or powerful, that transcends time, person, or place. Because drugs do not become "drugs" until they enter the ecological mix of environment, behavior, and brain, their status as "drugs" is always contingent and dynamic, never absolute. (DeGrandpre, 2010, p. 186)

The evidence that drug pleasure is a complex product emerging not just from pharmacology but more so from the mindset of the individual taking them and from various factors of social, cultural, and physical setting, not to mention a product of learning, has been mounting for years. And beyond that, drug effects aren't the de facto, most rewarding pleasures in existence. Rather, they exist in comparison to other options perceived by the individual (remember the Positive Drive Principle), such as in my own case mentioned above where I wanted to get off my prescribed painkillers and back to what I liked about my normal life before it was interrupted by a painful surgery with a more painful recovery period.

Whether a drug will be pleasurable is dependent on far more than the chemical makeup of the drug and the existence of a pleasure center that it can act upon. As mentioned earlier, morphine wasn't perceived as pleasurable by unknowing users. Alcohol researchers have demonstrated in several experiments where "alcoholics" had access to alcohol that they often ceased drinking in response to stress or the absence of a drinking partner. Shouldn't they always go after that pleasure regardless of whether they have a friend to do it with (especially in a lab situation, where there isn't much else to do)? And it has often been observed and demonstrated in controlled experiments that first-time marijuana users don't get high. How can this be?

When sociologist Howard Becker (1997) investigated marijuana in the 1940s, a time when less was known about the plant, he found that new users went through a process of learning to perceive the effects of THC (the cannabinoid found in the plant that is purported to produce the psychotropic effect) as pleasurable. They learned how to perceive its effects from others pointing out to them that they were high or by hearing about other people's physical effects, such as feeling heavy or drowsy, and checking whether they too felt the same way. Perceiving a high is learned. As Becker puts it:

> He must learn to enjoy the effects he has just learned to experience. Marihuana-produced sensations are not automatically or necessarily pleasurable. The taste for such experience is a socially acquired one, not different in kind from acquired tastes for oysters or dry martinis. The user feels dizzy, thirsty; his scalp tingles; he misjudges time and distances. Are these things pleasurable? He isn't sure. If he is to continue marihuana use, he must decide that they are. Otherwise, getting high, while a real enough experience, will be an unpleasant one he would rather avoid. (p. 53)

The phenomenon of people not feeling high the first time they use marijuana has decreased over the years, but the reason for this is simple: our cultural products of music, movies, television, and books are now full of references to marijuana and what to expect when using it, and cultural knowledge affects people's experience of substances. Becker also uncovered the fact that when marijuana was introduced into the United States as a recreational substance in the 1910s, admissions for psychosis from marijuana were at their highest rate. This steadily dropped until sometime in the 1940s when barely anyone was being admitted for marijuana psychosis. This was because a sufficient subculture had grown to initiate new users to marijuana. When little was known, many people interpreted the effects of marijuana as madness. Once people knew it was supposed to be pleasurable and wouldn't destroy their minds, they stopped having these negative reactions. The same eventually happened with LSD. Cases like these show that the psychological effects of substances are wide open for interpretation and more a matter of the mind than pharmacology.

Not all people like all substances. We've interviewed plenty who never liked marijuana, but as they described their tales of trying it, patterns emerged. Many who didn't like it were extremely apprehensive about it before trying it. It was their first substance, and they were scared. They felt pressured into trying it to fit in. They had built up such a negative expectation that, when they felt the effects, they hated it and didn't feel any pleasure whatsoever. Their mindset ensured that it wouldn't be pleasurable. Yet, if pleasure were just a matter of pharmacology, then mindset shouldn't matter. Another trend that emerged was that first-time users expected a fantastically overwhelming experience, and when it didn't turn out that way, they either thought it was barely good or, in some cases, felt nothing whatsoever. One person we interviewed had become a challenge to his friends. Throughout college and at parties many years after, they tried relentlessly to get him stoned. They upped the dosages from bowls to blunts, from bongs to gravity bongs, from low grades to the highest grades of marijuana, and nothing ever seemed to work to get him high. Ten years later, he finally felt high from a marijuana cookie and realized he had always been expecting more from the experience.

We've talked to plenty of people for whom marijuana and drugs, such as ecstasy, cocaine, opiates, alcohol, and LSD, eventually became unpleasant. Again, if it's just a matter of molecules tickling the brain, this shouldn't occur, but it often does. Alcohol goes from being a fun feeling to a run-down and groggy feeling. Cocaine and other stimulants often go from being a high to simply being a state of being awake and anxious. Opiates can go from feeling euphoric to feeling like mere sedation. Marijuana can go from a pleasurable high to one of disorientation and/or paranoia. Over time, the effects of any substance can go from pleasurable to boring or even entirely unpleasant. Sometimes, it seems to happen overnight as people get disenchanted and question what they really like about it. It often happens when a bad experience turns people off so that any further use is just stressful. Again, if substances were inherently pleasurable, none of these changes in experience would ever occur, yet they do regularly.

SUBSTANCES ARE SUBJECTIVELY ENJOYED

Substances are perceived as pleasurable by people with particular mindsets at particular times and in particular places. This is no different than various recreational activities, relationships, careers, and other involvements that we move in and out of throughout life in which we find fluctuating levels of pleasure and happiness. The fact that substance use can bring a spike of dopamine or endorphins or any other brain chemicals doesn't guarantee that they'll forever be pleasurable or any more pleasurable than other things. As we've already seen, this principle holds across all pleasurable things. Riding roller coasters and skydiving both cause massive spikes of brain activity, and yet we don't consider them to be addictive in the same way we consider substances to be addictive. Our society doesn't have magical views about such activities like it does about substances, and that's the difference.

Throughout these past four chapters, we've questioned everything you thought you knew to be cold, hard facts about substances. They are not magical or supernatural. They cannot get into your mind to take away emotionally painful thoughts; they cannot make you loving or violent; they don't make you suave, outgoing, or otherwise lower your inhibitions; they don't "addict" you, turning you into a substance-seeking zombie or possess you in any other way; and finally, they aren't pleasurable unless you want them to be and fixate on them as the thing you need to feel good. They are simple chemicals that slow down or speed up bodily functions, including neurotransmission, and cause other changes in brain activity.

Literally anything can be pleasurable if we want it to be. Pain can be pleasurable, and many people find it so. Pain as pleasure is a practice in sex and with eating spicy foods that burn. People have odd hobbies that they take great pleasure in whether it's an intellectual pursuit in a strange, obscure topic or collecting all kinds of things. It's also true that people often change the objects of their pleasure. The things we find pleasure in contain no special pleasure molecules. We know they aren't magical. The challenge for you is to be willing to let go of the magical, romanticized view of substances as being so especially pleasurable that they ruin all other pleasures. This just isn't the case.

The fact that heavy substance users can find plenty of pleasure without substances has readily been on display in our retreats for the past three decades. We have always organized activities for our guests—playing volleyball, playing musical instruments, hiking in the mountains, spending time at parks and local beaches, and even going to movies, museums, amusement parks, and plenty more. A good time is generally had by all (even in the museums!). The people who come to our retreats have quit substances for just weeks or sometimes just a few days, and they begin finding pleasure without substances. Many attest that it's the most fun they've had in a long time.

Fear sets in for some though, and they say "It's easy to have fun without drugs here at the retreat, but you don't know what it's like at home." Well, we know this: your brain isn't so destroyed that you're constitutionally incapable of finding pleasure without substances. So one of two things is going on, either your home is hell on earth where no pleasure is possible, or you just want to stick to a simplistic pleasure. If your home really is hell on earth, then for God's sake, move. If not, then own your decision, whether to use or abstain, and stand by it. But please don't believe in the lie that your past substance use has robbed you of the ability to find any pleasure and enjoyment in life wherever you may be. It simply isn't true and would be a shame if you let this misinformation discourage you from seeking greater happiness.

You are not destined to keep seeking pleasure from the same objects and activities for eternity because the pleasure isn't in the thing—it's in you and created by your causal mind. This should be great news to you. It was great news to us as we learned it and moved on from our own heavy substance use habits and expanded our lives and levels of happiness.

Our goal has been to show you that substances are neither as awful nor as great as our culture has made them out to be. We want to give you the most realistic view of their effects and potential, and indeed they're very small. They basically offer a cheap thrill by tickling your brain and body, which you might perceive as pleasurable if that's what you're seeking. But they are not magical. Use this information to make your decisions going forward and you will find that adjusting your substance use will result in far greater happiness if you're willing to give that a real shot.

REFERENCES

Atkinson, S. (2017, March 21). Why a sex addiction isn't as sexy as it sounds. Retrieved from http://www.highsnobiety.com/2017/03/21/sex-addiction-net-flix-love/

Becker, H. S. (1997). *Outsiders: Studies in the sociology of deviance* (new ed.). New York, NY: Free Press.

Blood, A. J., & Zatorre, R. J. (2001). Intensely pleasurable responses to music correlate with activity in brain regions implicated in reward and emotion. *Proceedings of the National Academy of Sciences of the United States of America, 98*(20), 11818–11823. https://doi.org/10.1073/pnas.191355898

Bloom, P. (2010). *How pleasure works: The new science of why we like what we like* (reprint). New York, NY: W. W. Norton & Company.

DeGrandpre, R. (2010). *The cult of pharmacology: How America became the world's most troubled drug culture* (1st ed.). Durham, NC: Duke University Press.

Lewis, M. (2012, November 12). Why addiction is NOT a brain disease. Retrieved from http://blogs.plos.org/mindthebrain/2012/11/12/why-addiction-is-not-a-brain-disease/

Peele, S., & Brodsky, A. (1975). *Love and addiction.* New York, NY: Taplinger.

Sugar expose 60 Minutes Dr. Sanjay Gupta. (2013). [Video file]. Retrieved from https://www.youtube.com/watch?v=bYDlHUnyZ9o

CHAPTER 21:
THE BENEFITS OF ADJUSTED SUBSTANCE USE

Typically, when people make a formal attempt to address a substance use problem through treatment or support groups, they strongly believe that they must quit completely. If they don't arrive at this conclusion themselves, the helpers in the recovery society often try to force it upon them using scare tactics, and they face ultimatums from loved ones or the legal system to fully abstain. The result is that they hastily jump to abstinence as their goal, with little thought of the potential *benefits* of abstinence. In fact, from the substance user's point of view, the goal of abstinence doesn't usually appear to have any benefits, and instead they see it as a significant loss. They think it's what they "have to do" or "should do" and don't see it as something they "want to do." Proceeding with a hastily chosen goal that you don't really want is a recipe for failing at that goal. There is no personal investment in such a goal; there is no real motivation, which means that as quickly as the goal is adopted, it is often just as quickly abandoned.

Throughout our history of running the retreats, our specialty has been helping those who've been in and out of multiple rehabs—the "hopeless cases." Even now, most of our guests come to us because they've failed with recovery society methods many times and we promise a truly different approach to the problem. For many in this group, we are their last shot. As such, we refuse to encourage yet another hastily chosen attempt at abstinence that ends in failure and leaves our guests feeling even more hopeless.

Please don't misunderstand us; we're not advising against abstinence, and we should mention that if you're in a very destructive and dangerous pattern of substance use, abstaining completely can be a wonderful decision to make. It is a fast and relatively easy way to immediately remove a massive amount of risk from your life, and so, hasty or not, it can be a great and effective choice. However, we're also concerned with the long-term and bigger picture. We're concerned with your finding a lasting solution. To that end, a key difference in *The Freedom Model* approach is that we have always asked our guests to contemplate making a change for greater personal happiness. We asked them not to adjust their substance use because they fear consequences or feel like they are obligated to but to adjust it because it may be the more enjoyable way for them to live. Are you ready to consciously make a choice for greater happiness?

ADJUSTED SUBSTANCE USE—A NEW CHOICE

Traditionally, the only acceptable goal for people with substance use problems was lifelong abstinence. This was based on the idea that those who've become "addicted" can't "control" their intake of substances, that "one drink equals a drunk," and that some drugs are so "addictive" that any usage whatsoever creates a trap that causes users to keep using. Decades of research have conclusively shown these ideas to be completely wrong. But then there's also the sense of a moral and social obligation to abstain, where it is felt that "addicts" have essentially *lost the right* to use substances. This thinking holds that you've caused so many problems and so much pain in your own life and for others that you "owe it" to the people in your life to never even think about touching substances again. Even if you were to use at low, nonproblematic levels, the memories this behavior evokes in your loved ones would be hurting them a second time so you have lost the right to use at all.

While we can't say whether you should feel such a moral obligation to abstain, we can say that choosing abstinence purely on these grounds often lacks the element that abstinence is a personally beneficial and happier option than some level of substance use. So whether you choose to feel morally obligated, we're still going to point out that to make this choice based on *The Freedom Model*, you'll need to add the element of seeing it as the happier option for you. You'll need to see benefits in it that are personally motivating so you feel a true desire to follow through on it and sustain it. Moreover, if you continue to see heavy substance use as desirable and yet you deprive yourself of it because you feel you "owe it" to others, you will likely feel a growing hostility and resentment toward those people.

As we start to dissect these issues, hopefully you can see what our research team has learned during our decades of observing people making these choices: putting prepackaged options in front of people, such as abstinence, runs the danger that they will jump into a choice in which they're not truly invested. There's been limited recognition of this in the recovery society in recent years, so some alternative programs of recovery have started to entertain and add "moderation" as an option. This is an improvement, but because of their lack of understanding of the problem, they've added moderation while also keeping the addiction and recovery rhetoric and beliefs alive. This is obviously an incomplete and dangerous method to use to adjust one's substance use.

Whereas "addicts" once faced the binary option of abstinence or "active addiction," which usually scared them into an abstinence attempt, they are now sometimes given the option of "moderation." However, moderation is usually offered with the caveat that "some people can moderate, and some can't." This is dangerous and misleading. What's more, those who offer moderation also often say "but abstinence is the safest choice." What they imply when they say this is that you might still "lose control" of your substance use if you attempt moderation. The effect is that whether abstinence or moderation is chosen, problematic substance users still proceed on the grounds of trying to inhibit and deny rather than change their desires. People who choose moderation with these beliefs proceed full of self-doubt, suspecting they may "relapse" into heavy use at any given moment. Fear still rules the day. They still believe that substances have supernatural powers.

What's more, the term "moderation" is highly problematic. Moderate use technically means an "average" level of use, so it's a normative term, based not on what works for individuals but on trends that emerge when the habits of thousands of people are depersonalized and statistically averaged over time. To put this in perspective, imagine you decide to raise an average (i.e., moderate) number of children. Well, according to the Pew Research Center, mothers now typically have 2.4

children. Do you know anyone who has 2.4 children? Could *you* have 2.4 children? That's a meaningless number that can't even be chosen; it reveals the folly in trying to model your life after averages. The "average mother" with 2.4 children simply does not exist. Some mothers choose to have one child, some won't be fulfilled until they have six—the possibilities for what will be preferred and manageable for a given family is subject to countless factors unique to them. People choose when to have children based on what they think they can personally handle, such as how the children may affect their other life goals, how they predict their finances will change, and where they plan on living. There are countless factors and individual preferences and opinions that play into these choices. People simply don't choose how many children to have based on what the average is.

Likewise, averaging out the typical number of drinks or hits people have on an occasion or the number of days they use per week or month to use as a guideline for what you should do is equally silly; it's just as detached from the reality of you as an individual and what works for you personally as "2.4 children" is detached from parenting choices. The same goes for choosing your substance use based on which substance is most popular or accepted or choosing your style of substance use based on what people your age "should" do.

Moderation is a term full of *shoulds, have to's*, and social mores. It is a contextual term that will differ by your local culture and peer group. For example, moderation could mean two to three drinks every night and pot on the weekends in a town full of academics in California. Meanwhile, moderation could mean one to two drinks only on special occasions, such as weddings or holidays, in a religious community in the Midwest. In Brooklyn, among young men who work in masonry, moderation can mean as much alcohol as you want every day (even some on the job) and cocaine on Friday and Saturday nights at the club but never touching any opiates whatsoever. Among wealthy housewives in Connecticut, moderation may mean as much alcohol as you want if you're with friends, an opioid painkiller here and there when stressed out, and some Xanax when anxious, but even one drink alone by day is taboo and qualifies you as an alcoholic.

We asked some friends on social media recently, who are all very successful people, how they would define moderation, and a few defined it as simply "not blacking out." As you can see, there are as many meanings of moderation as there are places and peer groups. But the key point here is that these are popular meanings among these groups, and while such "moderate use" may win *social approval* among these groups, their versions of moderation don't address the full range of needs and desires of you as an individual.

Again, we see both moderation and abstinence as *prepackaged options that can encourage people to choose without thinking things through on a personal level.* These options often depersonalize the process of change, result in low commitment, and leave people proceeding in fear anyway. So we're not going to recommend that you choose between moderation or abstinence, based on the baggage these terms have. This isn't to say we're against these terms, but to communicate our message and *The Freedom Model* approach, we're going to use a different term: adjusted substance use.

This term, *adjusted substance use*, is not about just a matter of semantics. The point of it is to get you to think of what you would have to *adjust* about your substance use to get better, happier, more satisfying life results for yourself. It's time to brainstorm about what adjustments you could potentially make and what the potential benefits of those adjustments would be.

Here are some potential adjustments that can be made to substance use habits:

- Using less per occasion.

- Using on fewer occasions.

- Using only legal substances.

- Using less expensive substances.

- Using less physically damaging substances.

- Using substances for different reasons.

- Using substances in safer environments and in safer ways.

- Using safer substances.

- Slowing your rate of usage on a given occasion—spreading the same amount of substance intake over a longer period.

- Choosing to use substances with people who are less apt to cause trouble when intoxicated and less apt to encourage troubling behavior from you when you are intoxicated.

- Using only on occasions when you have no other responsibilities to tend to.

- Using only in situations where you don't expose yourself to law enforcement.

- Using without unearned shame and guilt.

- Having a glass of water with each drink.

- Ceasing substance use until you've reached full adult age and don't have to answer to parents.

- Being honest and straightforward about your substance use—not hiding it.

- Being discreet about your substance use.

- Ceasing all substance use until you've learned how to not feel like you need it emotionally.

- Never using again.

- Using only to celebrate.

- Never using substances that can produce intense withdrawal syndromes.

- Never using a withdrawal-producing substance more than a day in a row.

- Using without excuses.

- Using only at parties.

- Waiting to use until you've stabilized the other parts of your life.

This list is by no means exhaustive; there are infinite adjusted forms of substance use that you could imagine. The point is that there are many adjustments that could be made to your substance use habits that could result in greater benefits to you and that any proposed adjustment can be made from a place of seeking greater personal benefits and outcomes rather than from a place of doing what you should do according to others' standards. There are many ways to approach adjusted substance use from a personal level that really speaks to your exact needs and desires. Rather than adopting some cultural idea of moderation, there is another way to think about it. You could think about the potential adjustments and benefits. Now that we've got you thinking about the adjustments, let's think about the benefits some of these adjustments can bring.

THE RELATIVE BENEFITS OF ADJUSTED SUBSTANCE USE

Since most people wish to adjust their substance use to reduce costs or mitigate consequences, the benefits are a relative matter—that is, they exist in contrast to your current costly pattern of substance use. For example, if walking around with illegal substances leaves you feeling constantly paranoid and in fear of the police (i.e., a cost), then if you made the adjustment to using only legal substances, you would experience the benefit of feeling safer.

The default position is to think of this as only a reduction in costs, but it can realistically be a benefit or gain as well. Consider this: if you have been paying a 35% income tax rate for 10 years and Congress passes a 5% tax cut, then it will feel as if you are getting a 5% *raise* in income. You are now taking home 5% more per year than you were previously taking home. You have been living your life on a budget of 65% of your earnings. You have had a car and an apartment and developed spending and saving habits that could all be afforded on that rate. But now, you keep 70% of your earnings. Yes, you are technically *losing less* of your income to taxes now, so the tax cut is removing a loss. Regardless, you legitimately experience it as a gain because it exists in comparison to what has been your norm. This perspective is what we could call *The Freedom Model* attitude—to see a reduction in costs as a gain. This kicks in the Positive Drive Principle to move in this "gaining" direction.

Even though your costs decrease when you adjust your substance use habit, you will experience the reduction in costs as a gain. I (Steven) mention this example because it was a highly notable personal one for me. I used illegal substances for years, was arrested many times, and lived in constant fear and paranoia of being caught with those substances. Of the countless times I was arrested, only a few were for possession. One time, I was arrested because the police found empty heroin bags and managed to scrape some minuscule amount of substance out of them. Another time, I was arrested for possession of syringes. So, even when I didn't have substances, I was worried I might have the remnants of substance packaging in my car somewhere or paraphernalia that could land me in jail. I lived in constant fear of the harsh sentences I could face in jail time. I was constantly looking over my shoulder for the police. I changed many things about my daily life to try to cut down on any potential contact with the police. I was always trying to become cleverer about hiding my drugs, and in fact, I forgot where I stashed them more than once. It took a massive amount of mental energy and left me in constant pain. When I stopped using illegal substances, that all went away. I still had some habitual responses for a few months to seeing a cop car. But then I would think about the fact that I had nothing to hide and nothing to fear, and I would feel such comfort. Suddenly, I felt free. I had more mental and emotional energy to channel into all the other things I wanted to do with my life. It's truly liberating to no longer fear being arrested for possession of substances.

This principle of relative benefits applies in countless ways for different individuals. One of our program guests, Sandra, often drank to blackout. Among her experiences while blacked out, she had woken up in someone's home she didn't remember going to, and more than once she had woken up on a subway train at the end of the line in the middle of the night. She had sent texts and made social media posts while blacked out that she later deeply regretted. She looked at her call history after blackouts and saw that she'd made calls she didn't remember making to old flings and angry calls to family members. During this period of her life, Sandra constantly feared that she'd done something extremely embarrassing in blackout or, worse, been victimized without knowing it. She was obsessed with getting STD/STI tests as her imagination ran wild about what she might've done while blacked out. The constant anxiety was eating her alive. After a few years of living with the costs of drinking to blackout, feeling freedom from that anxiety when she adjusted her drinking to nonblackout levels resulted in a wonderful gain for her. She experienced it as a newfound freedom and a great benefit. Again—this is *The Freedom Model* attitude—to see fewer costs as gains!

But here's where framing this in terms of benefits is truly important. For years, Sandra had been beating herself up about what she might've done or what might've happened to her while blacked out. When she thought about drinking, she'd tell herself *Don't do this; you'll regret it* or *Don't do this; you might get raped or murdered.* Sandra kept trying to scare herself out of drinking to blackout with the absolute worst-case scenarios and very realistic fears, and yet she kept repeatedly drinking to blackout. A complicating component was that she thought alcohol *helped* her with her anxiety, so ruminating on these fears only increased her anxiety level and made her want to drink that much more. When she finally adjusted her drinking with *The Freedom Model* attitude, her fear subsided, and she focused on the benefit of freedom from blackout anxiety as a positive gain to making a change. She had chosen to swear off drinking for at least a year, and when she contemplated drinking a few times in those first few weeks, she reminded herself how much she'd been enjoying living without this anxiety. She mentally celebrated this benefit often, taking notice of how good she felt now. Within a month, she *knew* she didn't have to struggle anymore to resist drinking; she was truly enjoying her changed habit more because she was recognizing benefits now instead of focusing on fears. This is a big shift but a simple one too! Can you see how much easier it is to live by the motive of benefits rather than running from fears?

Jeff was a friend of mine who had overdosed on heroin and been revived so many times that he had lost count. He was a serial abstainer who had also lost count of how many times he'd sworn off all substances and eventually gone back to tragic levels of heroin use yet again. Jeff didn't formally use *The Freedom Model*, but it's now been years since he's overdosed on heroin. I'm including his story because it contains the principles we're now discussing. The last time he swore off all substances, he found himself wanting to use heroin yet again, but he did something different. He realized he really liked getting high, and he thought about whether there was a better way he could get high. So instead of going back to heroin, he decided to smoke pot instead, a substance with no known risk of overdose. And instead of lying to his family yet again and pretending to be abstinent of all substances, he told them he was smoking marijuana and would use this rather than heroin. They didn't love the idea, but they welcomed the openness. They just wanted to be free of the craziness of his overdoses, so they accepted it as his choice. He smokes pot now quite a bit, but he holds down a steady job and enjoys his life. He doesn't conform to other people's views that he should be totally substance free. Instead, he does what he thinks works best for him. *He's happy, and he's alive.* That's his goal, not other people's goals. It's not that Jeff *can't* abstain; he can. It's that he doesn't want to, and he also wants not to overdose. These are not mutually exclusive goals. Jeff utilized *The Freedom Model* attitude to decide what options would bring him the benefits he was seeking. It works!

Hopefully, the picture is getting clearer: *the (reduction of) costs of heavy substance use are the benefits of adjusted substance use*—if you *choose* to see it that way.

And if you do see it that way, then you'd be amazed at the genuine motivation it gives you to make a change. Instead of continuing your years of being mired in fear and panic of what might happen and the costs of your substance use, you can be excited about all you stand to gain by making a simple change. This is a way that you can proactively use the Positive Drive Principle to your benefit. You have an endless supply of motive power in the PDP, and all you need to do is shift gears by changing your view of where the most happiness lies for you; this power is then instantly redirected away from the old choices that weren't working to new choices that work better.

We know the costs are going to be a concern to you; if they weren't, you wouldn't be seeking help. Although our goal in *The Freedom Model* is for you to be benefits oriented, we must also address the costs. Beating yourself up with shame and fear about the costs isn't effective for any length of time. So we're proposing a better, more constructive way to address concern over costs. We'll give you a brainstorming exercise designed to stretch your thinking into looking at your options and costs from new angles.

THE FREEDOM MODEL IS NOT HARM REDUCTION

This exercise shouldn't be confused with "harm reduction," which is an approach to helping people with substance use problems that has recently become popular. While well intentioned, help that comes under the banner of harm reduction often comes with the assumption that people are incapable of fully stopping so the best that can be done is to reduce the harms of substance use for those poor, unfortunate, addicted souls. Of course, this is false, and we want to be clear on that point. All options, including stopping altogether, are possible in *The Freedom Model*; no option is more difficult than any other whether that be adjusting your use or abstaining.

From *The Freedom Model* standpoint, no one is truly addicted (addicted meaning enslaved to continue to desire and use substances), so everyone, from the "highly functional alcoholic" to the homeless man at the bus station begging for money to get more crack, is equally capable of fully quitting or adjusting his or her use. Remember this truth because it makes this an exercise in imagining happier options rather than simply reducing harms. There is a motivational difference in these competing frames; we advocate moving forward based on the benefits of various options without fear involved, whereas harm reduction implies that addiction is a real thing that must be fought. Now, with that said, the exercise follows.

REFRAMING COSTS TO THE FREEDOM MODEL PERSPECTIVE OF BENEFITS

First, you're going to write down the larger costs that you regularly worry about, the ones that you are no longer willing to pay. Then imagine you've found an adjusted form of substance use that doesn't include those costs. You don't need to know what that adjusted form of substance use is yet; just pretend you've found it. Wiping those costs from your daily life will be experienced as a benefit once you do it. So the next step is to frame them that way. Allow yourself to imagine living with these new benefits, and write them down from this perspective.

Here's an example from Michael, a daily heroin user:

Cost I no longer want to pay	Benefit of living without it
Getting arrested	Moving about without worry; having a sense of freedom and security.
Spending all my time getting heroin	I'll have so much time and energy to do other things that make me happy, including rebooting my career, getting my own place to live, and finally making music again.
Spending all my money on heroin	I could finally go out and do things again. New things, different things, more exciting things. I can have new experiences with all that extra money.

Here's an example from Marie Angela, a heavy drinker:

Cost I no longer want to pay	Benefit of living without it
Being hung over and run down	Waking up every day feeling better and more energetic than I have in 10 years.
Embarrassing myself while drunk	Feeling free to be more social, get out more, and be involved with more people.

Now, it's time for you to give it a shot. Turn your biggest fears into benefits of change. It doesn't matter that you don't know yet whether you want to change or, if you do, what change you want to make. In fact, it might be better if you don't know. Just allow yourself to imagine those costs could instantly disappear and how you would experience this as a benefit.

Cost I no longer want to pay	Benefit of living without it

Now, how will you come up with an option of adjusted substance use that will bring you these benefits? That's for you to figure out. Maybe it's available, maybe it isn't. Maybe it takes abstinence to best achieve it, or maybe there's some other adjustment that does as good a job at providing these benefits. Maybe you'll decide to accept those costs. The point is for you to start the process of opening yourself to the idea that an adjustment could be a better, happier option. You can't find one if you don't look for it.

Always remember—addiction isn't real unless you believe in it. It's a construct of our culture; it's not an inevitability. So all options are open to you. Convert all fear and costs into a viewpoint of finding benefits just as we did in the charts above.

The following chapters will continue to provide ways to reevaluate your options and shake up your perspective so that, if you decide to change your substance use, you can harness all the motive power of your PDP to do it.

CHAPTER 22:

THE HIDDEN COSTS

A lthough you make your choices based on perceived benefits, the costs are also a factor when deciding to make a change, so discussion of them can't be avoided. That is why we have written this chapter, but before we dive into the costs, let's make sure we're clear about the benefits. The Positive Drive Principle motivates you in the direction where you see the most benefits. Until now you've been moving toward some problematic level of substance use. What is it that moves you there? What are the benefits that you see in it? What are your reasons for preferring this style of substance use? We ask that before reading ahead, take some time to think of what you like about heavy substance use and write down your reasons on the next page. (Please note: If you've come to think there are no benefits and you no longer want to use substances, then write from the perspective of when you were still using. What were the benefits you perceived at that point in time?)

WRITE DOWN YOUR REASONS BELOW

_____

_____

_____

_____

_____

_____

_____

_____

_____

_____

_____

_____

BENEFITS OF SUBSTANCE USE

The PDP operates on the comparison of options. To choose means you're seeing more than one option and then judging one of the options as the best and then doing it. This means that, if you're choosing excessive substance use, you see it as the best option available to you. Naturally, then, this means you also see the option of going without such excessive substance use as worse in some way. People often wonder *How can this be? My substance use is costing me so much that I shouldn't want it.* But the fact is, on some level, you *do* want it. You want it at least in part for the list of reasons you wrote down on the previous page.

What you don't realize about costs is that you see costs *in both choices*—in both continuing heavy use and discontinuing it. You've worked so hard to become and stay conscious of the costs of your substance use that you've overlooked the fact that part of your calculation that makes continued heavy substance use look so attractive is that you see equal or even greater costs in discontinuing it. In a sense, you could also say *Why would I ever quit? It would cost me so much.* Yes, you read that right. I want you to read that again: *Why would I ever quit? It would cost me so much.* Now, sit for a moment and let that statement digest. It's true, isn't it?

What costs could there be in quitting? Well, *you just wrote them on the previous page.* Every benefit you see in heavy substance use, you may also view as something you lose by discontinuing heavy substance use, that is, it is *a cost* of quitting. So go back to the previous page. Above the line that says "Benefits of substance use" in big letters, make a slash, and then write "Costs of quitting." Look it over, and think about it; that list represents both these things. This is part of the puzzle of why continuing has seemed worth it despite all the costs.

Your list doesn't have to be long. You might have only one reason listed, such as "It's the only thing that makes me happy," and thus quitting comes at the cost of losing "the only thing that makes me happy." That's a massive cost. Or maybe your list also includes "It helps relieve my stress." Depending on whether you think you need it for this purpose or it's just a minor aid in relieving stress, this could be a major cost of quitting, or it could be insignificant. It's all a matter of perspective.

YOU'RE NOT STUCK

Recognizing your perceived costs of quitting or adjusting your substance use doesn't mean that you're stuck continuing heavy substance use. You might come to believe that some of those benefits are less significant than you previously thought they were. You might come to believe you can get some of the same benefits you feel you're getting from using while discontinuing heavy substance use. You might come to believe there are ways other than using substances to acquire the same benefits. You might even come to believe that some of those benefits you thought you were getting were never actually there. You can dramatically change your perspective on your options if you exercise the courage to open your mind to new ideas and think critically. You might want to critically rethink some of the things on your list by going back to chapters 17-20.

CHAPTER 23:

A HAPPIER VISION

"I know I will never be an addict again."

That was an amazing thought that I (Steven) had shortly after finishing my stay at Saint Jude Retreats (Freedom Model Retreats) having studied an earlier version of *The Freedom Model*. I was surer of the fact that my troubles with substance use were over than I had been about anything in years. However, at that point in my life, my health was failing, I had built up a lengthy criminal record, I was on probation yet again, my arms were still covered with track marks, and I would be without a driver's license for a few more years because I was still paying the price for an episode where I had tried to outrun the police and crashed into a telephone pole. Beyond all that, I had been looking around at my peers for the past few years and saw that they'd graduated college, started careers, and were buying homes and having children. I had betrayed everyone in my family, and I was generally a goofball (and still am) who must've appeared unstable to everyone around me. I had sobered up for short periods in the past, and I'm sure many people thought this would be yet another temporary stop on my way to total self-destruction. Yet I *knew* different. I knew I would never be an addict again, and knowing this felt great.

I hadn't even totally sworn off drugs and alcohol forever. The deal I had made with myself was that I would just take a year break from substance use and make a genuine effort to see if I could be happier without using substances. This deal was broken very early on with a few single instances of substance use. I used marijuana once, heroin once, and alcohol once, all within two or three months after arriving at the retreat. However, since I no longer believed in addiction or relapse, those uses were now seen as just choices, isolated incidents, and were really cases of my testing the waters. Each of those instances confirmed that substance use was only a mild amusement and no longer what I wanted to focus on in my life. They either led to or strengthened my conviction that I would never be an addict again.

It's been 15 years, and I've never been an addict again and never doubted that conviction that I reached right after my retreat stay. Since that time, I have desperately wanted to give this same feeling to as many people as possible. I have wanted to develop a surefire way to make sure everyone seeking help is able to achieve it. I thought I could make a clear path—*a set of steps even*—that anyone could follow to get there. The tough realization is that there is not and never will be any clear set of steps that can be followed to get there. It's more intangible than that because it's a realization. It isn't like dieting, working out, cooking dinner, learning a trade, or getting a college degree. There is no set path. It's a personal discovery and realization. It's a change of mind.

I learned that all I can do is look at how my thoughts changed during that time and look at how other people change their thoughts as they get over their substance use problems for good. Those of us who have used programs, methods, treatments, medications, and plans of recovery to try to change tend to become focused on the concrete trappings of those formalized solutions. Meanwhile, the majority of people who have ever had these problems get over them without any formal system of help; they just figure it out on their own. I think their insights are more valuable than the small minority of people who receive formal help because those insights aren't as tainted by the recovery ideology that has failed our society for much too long. Luckily, such people present themselves to me often in my day-to-day life since they know what I do and that I have a unique take on addiction that honors and respects their experience. They firmly reject any notion that they were *addicted* and helpless. Some went through a stage of thinking that through because of self-doubts created by addiction ideology in the culture. But many rejected the idea of addiction outright with no doubts whatsoever. When I ask for their story, it boils down to a few points:

- They realized their drinking/drugging just wasn't working for them anymore.

- They realized they were capable of change.

- They realized they wanted and could have more happiness than they were getting out of using.

- They decided to change.

As I think back on my realization that I would "never be an addict again," these are the same ingredients, except that I thought I needed help—and this is a key difference for everyone who seeks help. Those people who seek help are bogged down in the addict self-image and the addiction and recovery mythology. This false belief system stands as an obstacle keeping them from making those realizations that the self-changers make. To help this demographic (of which I was a part), there is an extra element—*those obstacles must be removed*. And once they are, making those realizations is a matter of human functioning and can occur just as it does in the minds of all the self-changers. Changing one's mind and behavior is an inside job for which we use our free will, mental autonomy, and the PDP. It's a matter of seeking knowledge and new thoughts and exploring possibilities.

What thoughts and knowledge can help? By working through the text I studied at the retreat and my many conversations with the presenters and founders of Baldwin Research Institute, I realized that I was indeed fully free to change and that this battle I'd been waging against the bogeyman of addiction was in fact a fool's errand. Learning that I wasn't addicted allowed me to realize I didn't have to keep using substances. I already knew coming into the retreat that my substance use wasn't working out well for me. But the next realization that sealed the deal is the one that's harder to pass along. I had to believe that it was possible for me to be happier without using substances heavily. This is the magic element that you can't give to or force on anyone; you can only try to inspire and persuade people to open their eyes to the possibility and hope they give it a shot.

For me, I can think of two things that helped me get there. The first started a few months prior to the realization that I would never be an addict again as I spent a month in jail. During that time, I started thinking deeply about life and what I wanted. I started *dreaming*. I didn't plot out a career path or a set of goals. My dreams were simple. I thought things like *God, it would be great if I could just start spending time again with my friends Brian and Diane and the people I love, my nieces and other family. I really miss doing things like skiing, snowboarding, going swimming at the gorge, and I'd be so happy to do all that again. I'd like to get back to making music. I want to finally make something of myself.* What would I make of myself? I had no idea, except that it would be more rewarding than what my recent life had been. It took another 10 years to finally decide what to really make of myself, but I knew all along it would be something that made me happier than revolving around substance use made me. These thoughts were the elements of a happy life that I had long since abandoned in my all-consuming quest to stay intoxicated. This envisioning of a happy life was the beginning of my realization that I would never be an addict again, but I still wasn't there.

The final realization came months later when, through talks with the people at the retreat, I learned that life after substances didn't have to be a miserable letdown. I learned that I wouldn't have to wait for happiness, that it was instantly available. I left the belief behind that my heavy substance using past had permanently ruined me for other things. I embraced the belief that there are nearly infinite other ways I could be happy. These ideas were in opposition to what I'd been learning in treatment programs, that I just needed to work on self-control, focus on recovery, and struggle one day at a time to resist *irresistible* substances. The folks at the retreats conveyed through their attitude that all that talk about addicts being in for a lifelong struggle and life of deprivation was complete garbage. Compared to the dire attitude of those in the recovery society, the folks at the retreat were flippant: "You don't have a disease; you're just doing what you think will make you happy." What they did with that attitude was teach me that change is only a matter of *my wanting it*. I took that idea and ran with it straight to the conviction that the world was my oyster if only I would choose to grab it. This in turn helped me to finally reach the conclusion that I could and would be happier letting go of heavy substance use. Thus, I finally realized that I would never be an addict again. I knew it. In my sick, emaciated state, with no record of success and a lengthy criminal record, I knew I was going to be happier and never wear the label of addict again. There was no doubt in my mind.

Change was so easy after that point. It didn't take the ongoing work and suffering that the recovery society always led me to believe it would. It just took a change of mind. Everything I wanted in life hasn't worked out, and there have been difficulties over the years, but I always knew that a return to "addictive" substance use wouldn't make me happier. It truly was a choice to quit my problematic substance use habit.

Throughout the book, I have provided as best I can, a focused presentation of what I got from the informal environment of positivity and inspiration that was the Retreats in 2002 when I attended (but stripping out the things we taught at that time that were problematic). However, I can't give anyone dreams or a vision of greater happiness. This is a highly personal and individual matter. All I can say is *try it, and you won't be disappointed.*

With that, I give you the final chapter of *The Freedom Model* and the final part of a sequence of chapters designed to help you challenge yourself to positively weigh out your substance use options differently than you have in the past. You can tip the scales away from heavy substance use like I did (you can make them crash!). If you are willing to do the intangible act of envisioning greater happiness, I know you can find that vision, and with it, will come a sense of freedom and motivation to change like you've never felt before. You are free to make that happen. I hope you will give yourself what I cannot—a dream.

Sincerely,

Steven Slate, coauthor of *The Freedom Model*

WEIGHING YOUR OPTIONS

With the Positive Drive Principle (the fact that all people constantly move toward what they see as their happier option), the scales are tipped toward any given option by the overall *benefits* we see in it. The only way the scales will tip in a new direction is for you to see your options differently, and the past several chapters have offered several ways to shake up your thinking to achieve that end. As we wrap up *The Freedom Model* lessons, we need to go back to our three basic options, (1) heavy substance use, (2) adjusted substance use, or (3) total abstinence, and make sure we've given each one a fair hearing. This chapter will bring all you've learned together, offer another way to add weight to the options, and help you avoid a few more common pitfalls involved in reassessing these options. If you apply yourself here now, this groundwork will pay great dividends as you move forward, allowing you to make lasting preference change that guides your future decisions toward greater happiness.

THE BENEFITS OF SUBSTANCE USE REVISITED

Remember what you've learned about substance effects throughout this book because that is one of the most powerful pieces of information that nobody else will give you. Our pharmacology-obsessed culture portrays substances as magical elixirs with all manner of benefits that are just too good to be true. When you believe in these magical powers, you give the heavy substance use option far more weight than it deserves, and your view of the options is distorted by falsehoods. Let's briefly review the truth about substances:

1. *Substances don't relieve emotional pain:* Although they can alter some of the physical symptoms that are experienced from emotional pain, they can never change the emotions because emotions are a cognitive product, a result of how we judge the conditions of our life. At best, intoxication can be used as a distraction from negative circumstances and events that we'd rather not focus on, but anything could be used this way. Thus, the substances aren't relieving your emotional pain by any special pharmacological power. If you're unclear on this, revisit chapter 18.

2. *Substances don't lower inhibitions:* They don't make people more courageous, social, or outgoing or otherwise allow people to do things they're normally repressed from doing. Although this effect may be seen sometimes in some places and in some people, it is a result of the *license to misbehave* rather than a pharmacological effect of substances. You don't need substances to "unleash your real self." If you're unclear on this, revisit chapter 19.

3. *Substances aren't inherently pleasurable:* While they do perturb the body (including the brain) in ways that can be perceived as pleasurable, there is no one-to-one correlation that putting a drug into a person will result in guaranteed pleasure. Rather, drugs are perceived as pleasurable by some people in some places at some times, which is because of the many factors that dwarf the pharmacology of the particular drug. Like any other pleasure, they can lose their luster, become boring, and have diminishing returns. Particularly, if altering consciousness is your goal, then with continuous use, the alteration of consciousness becomes the norm and thus, less novel. Continuous use of substances is like eating your favorite meal every day; eventually, it will no longer be special. In this case, sobriety can become far more pleasurable, and intoxication can become unpleasant. The availability of pleasure from intoxication is far more fluid than you've been led to believe. If you're unclear on this, revisit chapter 20.

Substances aren't all they're cracked up to be. Knowing this, the weight you give to any substance use as an option can change dramatically.

The Magical View of Substances	The Realistic View of Substances
• Takes away my depression • Takes away my anger • Takes away my stress and anxiety • Numbs all emotional pain • Makes me forget troubles and trauma	Might be used as a distraction like any other activity
• Makes me more social and outgoing • Relieves shyness • Allows me to speak my mind • Gives me courage • Allows me to be more sexual	Intoxication serves as an excuse to behave differently
• Brings euphoria, a pleasure greater than anything else known to man • Will always make me feel good • Makes any activity more enjoyable	Perturbs the brain and body in ways that can be perceived as pleasurable

Again, the PDP being operative every moment of our lives, the weight that tips the scales toward any choice comes from the benefits we see in it. There is no doubt that, if you truly understand the information reviewed above, then any substance use option can now have far less weight in your mind. This, however, does not guarantee that you will see abstinence or adjusted substance use as your happier option. To do that, you need to sort through what benefits those options offer to see whether there's a way to give them more weight than heavy substance use.

THE BENEFITS OF ADJUSTED SUBSTANCE USE OR ABSTINENCE

There are two ways we know to analyze the other options. One is to make sure you understand that if you adjust or eliminate your use of substances, then as the costs of heavy substance use are eliminated, you will experience real gains, both immediately and in the long term. This principle was discussed in chapter 21. If, for example, your heavy drinking left you with little quality time for your family, you will experience a gain in potential quality time with your family when you cease it. If your cocaine use was leaving you strapped for cash to dedicate toward other activities, then ceasing it allows you more money to do other things that may end up being far more enjoyable than cocaine. If your opiate use has kept you tethered to a drug source to stave off withdrawal every day, then getting out of the withdrawal cycle gives you greater mobility and frees up time to expand your life. If your drinking has been slowly destroying your health, decreasing or ceasing it allows a return of health and greater energy to enjoy life. These are only a few of the gains. There are as many gains to be made by altering your substance use as there are costs involved in continuing it. So, instead of solely eliminating costs, the other options will bring immediate and long-term gains into your life compared to what you would experience by continuing heavy substance use. The choice is to recognize these potential gains and thus bring weight to the other options or to think of them as only an elimination of costs, which keeps you focused on only the heavy substance use option. Make the positive choice to see benefit in change. It's there if you look for it.

The next method of building up the other options takes daring and imagination.

VISION

So many people feel hopeless and desperate, blinded by years of discouragement, and mired in low self-esteem that they've given up on any possibility of a life that's any better than what they know now. Their efforts are focused on trying not to sink any lower. With no vision of anything better, all they can do is cling to the methods of happiness they already know. When that method is heavy substance use, any efforts they make to change tend to result in cycles between painful abstinence and troublesome binges of heavy substance use that lead to worse pain. The recovery world says that these people "can't stop" or that their "disease is strong." But the fact is that these people are capable of changing; they just lack the vision of a change worth making. If you can imagine greater happiness, you can develop solid motivation to change.

Only you can do the work of dreaming your happier life and allowing yourself to imagine that there could be far greater happiness in some life that doesn't revolve around substance use, flesh out this possibility in vivid detail, and dare to experience a real vision of more happiness than you've ever known before. This exercise will be more work for some readers than for others, depending on where you sit on the spectrum of desperation and hopelessness.

On the mild end of the hopelessness spectrum, your happier life may look much like your current life, with just a few tweaks. On the extreme end of the spectrum, you may be so down and troubled with a life torn apart by legal, health, and relationship problems and such a small record of success that it may take a great effort at imagination to envision something better. No matter where you are on the spectrum, you can dream of something better and hold onto that vision to drive you forward. The authors were on the extreme end of the spectrum and have known plenty who were even more hopeless, yet they dared to dream and catapulted themselves into greater levels of happiness.

Dreaming matters. You will move in the direction where you see the greatest potential for happiness. Part of the difficulty in making this choice to see greater happiness comes from the myths of addiction, yet we've done away with those myths throughout the book. Some of the most damaging myths follow:

1. *You will forever desire substances, so you will face a lifetime of fighting this desire.* We did away with this myth in chapter 1 and appendix C, showing you that far from being chronic, heavy substance use is a problem that well over 90% of people move beyond.

2. *Your other life problems will keep pushing you uncontrollably back to heavy substance use.* This myth was reviewed in chapter 7. The problems you've been taught to connect causally to heavy substance use are in fact common problems that most people face without feeling compelled to use substances. The recovery society and treatment professionals have latched onto these problems because they don't know how to directly help people to change their substance use choices. They've complicated the issue. You can let go of these connections and simplify your substance use choices by recognizing that "addicts" aren't unique in having such problems, and substance use doesn't solve them.

3. *"Natural rewards" and other pleasures won't do anything for you now that you've destroyed your pleasure center with substance use.* This is pure hogwash.

   If it were impossible to experience pleasure after a period of "addiction", then how do more than 90% of people leave these patterns of substance use behind permanently? How do the majority of them do it in their twenties and thirties when they have a whole lifetime ahead of them? If it were a lifetime of misery, they'd surely "relapse" - yet they don't. (see chapter 1 and appendix C) We have witnessed most of our retreat guests having fun and enjoying themselves within days or weeks of being substance free.

Far from being a dead end that dooms you for the rest of your life, changing a heavy substance use habit has been an enlightening experience for millions of people. It brings new vigor and offers an opportunity to completely reinvent your life. Where many others without substance use problems stay settled into comfortable ruts, those who make a big change like this have the perfect excuse to make other exciting changes to their lives. The further you've fallen, the greater the opportunity to seize the day and change several other things in the process. Through making this radical change in mindset, you will gain new awareness of just how much power of self-determination you possess. Although we wouldn't recommend that people knock themselves down just for the experience of getting back up, if you find yourself there like so many of our guests have over the years, you'll see that it's a transformative experience that can elevate you, leaving you *better* for the experience.

Are you willing to believe that your life can be better? Are you willing at least to *try imagining* that there's greater happiness available to you? Again, some of you may already know it will be better with just a few tweaks. But some of you will have to get out of your comfort zone to envision greater happiness. However, this won't be the first time you've done so. At some point, you did not know exactly how you would feel if you took up substance use, but you went out on a limb and tried it. Then, you tried it in more situations and more often, and you grew a preference, making the move from suspecting it would make you happier to knowing it did. But now you're at a point where the happiness it provides may be greatly diminished. Are you willing to go out on a limb yet again? Now is your chance to do just that. If you can allow for the possibility of greater happiness, then you can change.

That you shouldn't let fear hold you back from dreaming is a given, but there's another obstacle that deserves special mention: shame and guilt. This blockade to dreaming comes in a sneaky form, under the guise of "delayed gratification." We hear it all the time: "Addicts need to let go of instant gratification and learn how to delay their gratification." Many who are wracked with shame about their past grasp onto this, thinking they need to "grow up," which in the instant/delayed gratification dichotomy gets defined as denying yourself *all* pleasure, exercising "self-discipline," and toiling away in misery. Everyone has immediate gratification as a part of his or her daily life. *Everyone.* You're here to deal with a substance use problem, not to become a monk or nun (that life is the dream of only a handful of people). If it's your dream to become a monk or nun, that's fine, but if it's not, please don't let shame and the idea that you have to do your penance stop you from the dreaming that could motivate you to change. Now, it's time to dream.

There are many ways to dream, but here is what we suggest: just think of what your ideal happier life would be like if it didn't revolve around heavy substance use. You don't have to imagine abstinence right now, and in fact it's better if you don't count substance use into this vision at all. Just begin picturing all the other things you want in your life, and write down a fully fleshed out vision of that life below. Do this before reading further because it's an extremely important exercise regarding your vision.

ANALYSIS OF YOUR OPTIONS

How do you think the level of substance use in each of the three options will complement your vision and help you to fulfill it? Don't be afraid to give fully truthful answers. This isn't for others to judge; it is for you to motivate yourself toward greater levels of happiness. Write a brief description of how each option would work with your vision:

1. Heavy substance use (your current level):

_____

_____

_____

2. Adjusted substance use (define the adjustment, and then describe how it would meld with your vision):

_____

_____

_____

3. Abstinence:

_____

_____

_____

As you judge how your vision melds with the various substance use options, think about *compatibility*, not incompatibility. Which substance use option works best with your vision? As you put that vision next to the other potential benefits you see in the options, which one seems to hold the greatest potential for happiness?

This is the way you add weight to the other options. For you to be motivated to change, it doesn't matter in concrete terms what your vision of greater happiness is. All that matters is that you identify the option that fits best and is most in alignment with your achieving your vision.

Again, it doesn't matter what the vision is or whether you achieve it. All that matters is that you dream of something sufficiently motivating so you can give yourself the chance of discovering greater happiness. This is about making discoveries, developing motivation, and making more discoveries as you use the power of the PDP to act on your new perspective.

One thing this exercise is not about is *going through the motions*. We will not be assisting you in developing a "plan of action" to pursue your goals for a good reason. The point of *The Freedom Model* is to show you your freedom and to show you how to use it to make new choices about substance use. You are resourceful. You will find a way to set and pursue goals if that is what you decide to do after learning *The Freedom Model* (and we certainly encourage that), but there are pitfalls to doing goal setting within a model of help for substance use that we want to avoid.

PITFALLS OF GOAL SETTING

People assume that goals will change them from the outside in. If we send you out the door with a goals list, it might distract you from the matter at hand, which is to answer one simple question: *Do you believe that you can be happier reducing/quitting your substance use than you can be by continuing it as is?*

That's it. That's all you need to know. If you don't believe you can be happier, then you will not be motivated to change. If you came up with a goals list without answering yes to the question above, then you wouldn't pursue the goals or your pursuit of them would be a half-hearted attempt. It would be a case of going through the motions to feel like you're addressing your problem when in fact you aren't. Then, you would think *I tried setting goals, and they didn't work* or *I tried preoccupying myself with other things, but it didn't work.* If you've sparked your dreams by coming up with a potential vision and decided that there must be something better than continued heavy substance use, then you will change regardless of your goals working out and any difficulties you hit along the way.

The vision exercise is about opening your mind to possibilities, adding weight to the other options, and seeing greater happiness. That's all that's required to initiate change. Coming up with a goal set prematurely can distract from that process. Coming up with a vision that grabs you emotionally can enhance that process.

The other pitfall of goal setting is a reliance on the idea that you can create a lifestyle that is incompatible with substance use that will then guard you against yourself and guarantee that you'll never choose to use substances again. This gets the order of things wrong. It assumes that without ever thinking through your substance use options differently, you will somehow proceed to make different choices about it.

Let's consider *the ultimate substance-use-incompatible goal: becoming an addiction counselor.* The recovery society is teeming with addiction counselors who are in recovery, and a large percentage return to heavy substance use. In fact, more than a few eventually become guests at our retreats. Famous television interventionists, among others, have had very public *relapses.* While editing this chapter, a big news story broke about two addiction counselors who were responsible for overseeing a sober-living facility in Pennsylvania. They simultaneously overdosed and were found dead in their rooms at the sober-living home. All we can assume is that they still believed they'd be happier using heroin. News reports say they "succumbed to their addiction" and "lost their battle with the disease of addiction," but in fact, they freely made the risky choice to use drugs of unknown composition and purity acquired through the black market. No goal would protect them from making this choice. What the goal of being a counselor did is give them a false sense of security and distracted them from digging into their preferences to change.

Finally, and this is a topic we've had trouble communicating in the past, a goal set as part of a "recovery plan" can promote the idea that you must become happier *first* to make your desire for substances go away. Again, this idea gets things in reverse order, but it's a common misperception in *The Freedom Model* because the model is based around the pursuit of happiness. Let us be clear about this: The Freedom Model *does not say you need to be happy* first *and that happiness will then stop you from using substances. It says that you will do what you see as your happiest option and that you have the power to change the way you see things, to cease seeing heavy substance use as your happiest option.*

All you had to do initially to get motivated to start using substances was *believe it would be worth it.* In fact, many people's early experiences with substance use are painful and involve vomiting, coughing, and other problems and miserable outcomes, yet they persisted because of a belief that they can do it in the right way to acquire happiness. All you need to do to change your substance use is believe it'll genuinely be worth changing. You need to believe that a change offers you the chance of greater happiness, and you will then persist on this new path if you believe it's a viable possibility. Building this new preference starts the same way you built the old preference.

The creation of a goals list can also promote the idea that you need to do spectacular things and achieve spectacular levels of happiness to replace the happiness lost by decreasing/quitting substance use. We've shown you that the benefits of substance use are highly subjective and that there's *little to nothing* to be lost by letting go of heavy use. Therefore there is also little to nothing that needs to be replaced if you choose to decrease your substance use.

Your vision was an exercise in waking up to the possibility of greater happiness. The visions will be unique to everyone. The grandmother whose drinking upsets her children and comes between her and her grandkids may simply envision cutting her drinking back to a point that makes her family comfortable and trusting again. That vision can be promising and motivating. The 25-year-old heroin user who feels like he's thrown his life away already and there's no getting it back, no "catching up" with the progress his peers have made in life, may have to flesh out his vision a bit more to convince himself. Both these people are fully capable of envisioning greater happiness. Neither of them will see greater happiness in change just by setting and accepting goals that they believe they "should" pursue and going through the motions. They will change when they believe in their hearts that change is worth it, when they've used their free will and mental autonomy to set their sights higher and the PDP kicks in to motivate them in a new direction.

The term "dependence" is often used to describe people's strong preferences for substance use. The term is misleading because, to be dependent, means to have a genuine need or requirement for something. The benefits of substance use are few and subjective and thus change on a dime as a matter of personal perspective. In fact, there is no genuine need; substance dependence is a matter of the mind. You shed your mental dependence as soon as you believe that you don't need heavy substance use, there's little to lose by not doing it, and there are many costs to be avoided and many gains to be made by quitting/decreasing it. Since this is a matter of the mind and your mind is autonomous, it's up to you to answer this question: *Do you believe that you can be happier reducing/quitting your substance use than you can be by continuing it as is?*

When you can answer that question in the affirmative, then you can *know* that you will never have to feel an "uncontrollable urge" to use problematically again. If you can't, then you might try dreaming more, making sure you aren't focused solely on costs and that you don't have any addiction/recovery mythology holding you back from assessing your options.

MOVING FORWARD

We've shown you that the enslavement to substance use, which so many people feel, is entirely a matter of the mind. There is no genuine entity of "addiction" that people have or get, but rather there are strong preferences that people develop for various activities and involvements throughout life. Like so many other preferences, a love of substance use is fluid and changes throughout life as people reassess its value to them. This process is usually invisible and incremental whereby people slowly grow bored or disenchanted with substances and slowly modify their use and come to prefer less of it. They may barely notice these changes happening, but that isn't always the case. Sometimes people change suddenly because a change of mind is often abrupt when new information or experiences give people a reason to take a deeper look at things and change their thinking.

With controversial or questionable behaviors, such as substance use, societal forces often step in to interfere with the natural change processes of the individual, which badly complicates things. The complication comes from the fact that various figures in society try to control and override the mental autonomy of others. They try to control people's wants, desires, likes, and dislikes. This is an impossible task, and people get hurt in the process. The most poisonous attempts to control others involve shame, fear, and misinformation. The shame people attach to substance use leads the people who like substances to hate themselves, hide their behavior, and develop a negative self-image that often drives them further into heavy substance use. Viewing themselves as constitutionally bad for having a forbidden want, they become convinced of their subhuman status and then resign themselves to a deviant life. In hiding their substance use, the activity seems only more precious and valuable because they must wait for times to sneak it in. Fear and misinformation about the "addictiveness" of substances, including the legend that heroin or crack is "so good, you shouldn't even try it once," create self-fulfilling prophecies that change people's perceptions of drug effects.

Reacting to this coercion, people often try to categorically swear off substance use. They mirror society's view that it must be an all-or-nothing choice, that substance use is categorically bad and should be categorically despised and rejected. The truth is that very few things are categorically good or bad in life. As economist Thomas Sowell pointed out in his 1995 work, water is both necessary in moderation for life and deadly in inundating circumstances. In a poignant example, he points out the absurdity of categorical thinking, saying that, while few would disagree that food is more important than music, we wouldn't demand that Bach, Beethoven, and the other masters of the art be put to work in the fields growing potatoes. He goes on to say that

> a world where food had a categorical priority over music would be a world of 300-pound people, whose brief lives would never be brightened by a song or a melody. (p. 138)

In yet another brilliant example taken from his work *Basic Economics* (2011), he states that

> one may believe that health is more important than amuse-ments but, however reasonable that may sound as a general principle, no one really believes that having a twenty-year's supply of Band-Aids in the closet is more important than having to give up all music in order to pay for it. (p. 84)

Please don't take this as a recommendation for moderate substance use. I raise this point of categorical thinking in the final paragraphs to recommend moderation *in how you think through the issues*. The real-ity of life is that things have value to us incrementally, and I believe the closer our understanding of the issues is to reality, the better the chance we have at making the most effective choices. The categorical injunctions against substance use do not fit the reality of substances. Substances aren't inherently bad or good; they are bad or good only to the degree that we find them useful in furthering our happy exis-tence. There is a point when substance use may have no more value to someone. All people should be allowed to reach that insight on their own, to fully and accurately assess the reality of their own lives and how using substances enriches or detracts. The categorical swearing off of substances or labeling oneself as an "addict/alcoholic" shuts down thinking and doesn't allow for a convincing and reality-based conclu-sion to be reached in someone's mind. The immense failure of this belief system can be seen in addiction education programs for chil-dren that fill their minds with misinformation about substances and are designed to scare them and paint all substance use as categorically bad. Based on the consistent increase in problematic substance use and overdose deaths, these tactics fail miserably.

This method especially backfires when adults try to do it to themselves. Having had a history of substance use, any passing whim for substance use is then experienced as an "irresistible craving" for something they "shouldn't want," which is then taken as a sign that they're "addicted." It's not addiction; it's ambivalence, confusion, and likely just a passing thought that results from habit. Decrees against substance use won't clear it up and do away with it. The knowledge that you are free to reassess and think things through realistically will. Please don't try to coerce yourself with categorical decrees; they just don't work. Try taking on the attitude of a freely choosing intelligent person who doesn't need to rely on being scared into submission. After all, that's what you are, and with the knowledge you've gained through *The Freedom Model*, you're better prepared to make decisions about substance use than most people (definitely more prepared than most addiction counselors!).

The ultimate and most insidious attempt to coerce people to stop what is considered unaccepted levels of substance use comes from the psychiatric and treatment establishment, which uses the mantle of science to convince people that their desires for certain substances and behaviors are literal diseases. Using the faith our society puts in the institution of medicine and people with an impressive set of letters behind their names, these mental health professionals hope to inculcate submission and obedience. They hope we'll turn ourselves over to their authority and that our wants will magically disappear as a result. But the science behind their methods isn't there, and their attempts to force people to change their desires and behaviors often end tragically. Millions of people wrongly come to believe they are sick and diseased and that their plight is hopeless. As a result, they dive further into heavy substance use. Sadly, all too often, this downward spiral ends tragically. We know this because we've seen that substance-related deaths have skyrocketed with acceptance of the therapeutic state's authority on this matter.

When you're caught up in the recovery culture, hope is lost, but you don't need to lose hope. We have shown you the way out. Your wants and desires are your own. You don't have to rely on the recovery society and its doctrine, and you can let go of shame, fear, and self-hate to try to motivate a change in yourself. Being aware of your mental autonomy, free will, and positive drive, you now know that substance use is just a choice and that it is fully yours to make. You are free to reassess your options at any time. We've given you information that helps you to do that more accurately. You may have already found your answer. Many find their answers before they come to us for help, and they simply need to be reassured that they are free to change. Many find it in the early chapters of the book, and many find new perspectives that allow for an abrupt and sweeping change of mind about substance use. Others take longer and want to test the waters some more after learning *The Freedom Model*.

If you're still unsure of what you want, you will not resolve the issue by wearing the self-image of the addict and beating yourself up with shame. Nor will you resolve it by making demands of yourself to just stop, use willpower, and grow up. It will be resolved by letting go of panic, slowing down, and moving forward with an open and inquisitive mind, intent on finding your happiest options. The knowledge gained here can put you on the road to incremental change if you're willing to stop seeing substance use as a matter of addiction, recovery, and relapses and start seeing it as a matter of freely discovering and making your happier choices. Whatever your path, we wish you the best.

REFERENCES

Sowell, T. (1995). *The vision of the anointed: Self-congratulations as a basis for social policy*. New York, NY: Basic Books.

Sowell, T. (2011). *Basic economics: A common sense guide to the economy* (4th ed.). New York, NY: Basic Books.

APPENDIX A
THE MYTH OF LOSS
OF CONTROL

> "Adherents of the disease model posit that the alcoholic's ingestion of any alcohol activates an underlying addictive craving for more alcohol that is impossible to resist. According to this approach, it is impossible for alcoholics to ever control their drinking."
>
> —Alan Marlatt, pioneering addiction researcher

In this quote, Marlatt (1985) is describing Alcoholics Anonymous' theory that alcoholics have an *allergy to alcohol* whereby any ingestion of any amount of alcohol begets a physiological response that then causes further unstoppable involuntary drinking. It's summed up in the slogan "one drink equals a drunk" and by the belief that once so-called addicts or alcoholics start drinking, they cannot stop using until they are forced to by some force or condition outside themselves. The same logic was also eventually applied to other substances, and has ruled conceptions of heavy substance use since AA first theorized it in the 1930s.

This theory is the basis of the myth that moderation is impossible for those deemed to be addicts. If it were true, it would mean that addicts have only two options for substance use—abstain or use substances recklessly and disastrously. One good thing about this theory is that it's coherently stated and lays out clearly testable terms. The theory states that addicts and alcoholics have a biological/genetic flaw that causes the allergic/loss-of-control reaction and that choice is not possible once a drug enters the system of an addiction victim.

Think of what happens when someone with a nut allergy eats something without realizing that it contains nuts. It's very simple: their symptoms occur regardless of their knowledge. They may swell up, have trouble breathing, and even go into shock. If "uncontrolled" substance use is the same type of biological reaction, then we can test it by giving addicts their problem substance without their knowledge and see what happens. If they respond by relentlessly seeking the substance or express a sudden burst of intense craving, then there's something to the theory. If that doesn't happen, then the craving can't be a physiological reaction like that in an allergy and there must be something else going on. This is exactly what Marlatt did in a now legendary 1973 experiment. Here's how one review summed up the simple experiment:

> Nonabstinent alcoholics and social drinkers were given either alcoholic (vodka and tonic) or nonalcoholic beverages (tonic only) in a taste-rating task. In each condition, half the subjects expected to drink alcohol and half tonic. Consumption increased only when subjects expected alcohol, regardless of actual beverage content. (Marlatt, 1985)

The test subjects had access to pitchers full of the drinks and were told they could have as much as they wanted. The researchers came up with a mixture of alcohol that could not be detected by taste. If the allergy model were true, then the presence of alcohol in the mixture should have resulted in more drinking. In fact, consumption increased only when test subjects were led to believe they were drinking alcohol but did not increase when they were led to believe they weren't drinking alcohol. This gets right to the core of the idea of an allergy-based loss of control and disproves it. Again, people with a nut allergy don't need to know that they've eaten nuts to have the allergic reaction, yet alcoholics do need to know that they've had alcohol to react "alcoholically."

This experiment wasn't the first of its kind; it was just one variation of several "priming dose" experiments carried out since the 1960s. They're called priming dose studies because addicts are "primed" with a first dose, and then their response to that "first drink/hit" is observed and measured. Remember, the theory goes that a single drink or hit is supposed to trigger uncontrollable craving and substance use and that the "addict/alcoholic" has no choice in the matter after that point.

The earliest priming dose experiment mentioned in the research literature was carried out in 1966. Here it is as described by Nick Heather and Ian Robertson (1983) in *Controlled Drinking*, a book that covered many such studies:

> Nine inpatients diagnosed as gamma alcoholics with loss of control were given one fluid ounce of vodka disguised in orange juice and presented to subjects as a vitamin drink at breakfast. Pilot work had established that the presence of vodka in the mixture was impossible to detect. In the control condition a similar proportion of water replaced vodka in the mixture. Subjects acted as their own controls and were given either mixture in two-day sequences over sixteen days. During the late morning of each day of the experiment subjects were asked to record any degree of craving experienced on a simple five-point scale (no craving, slight, moderate, strong, very strong craving) by nursing staff who were unaware of the purpose of the experiment and of the fact that alcohol was being secretly administered to patients. The results showed no difference in average craving scores between the alcoholic and nonalcoholic mixtures. There was also no significant difference in the number of occasions when any craving was experienced; indeed, there were slightly more such occasions following the nonalcoholic mixture. (p. 97)

In this variation of the experiment, the test subjects didn't have direct access to more alcohol, but the desire for alcohol (craving) was measured and didn't increase after the first drink. So now we see both parts of the equation represented in two controlled experiments. When alcoholics don't know they've taken alcohol, they don't crave more, nor do they actually drink more when given the chance. Several other experiments with slightly different designs all show the same results, which are that alcohol doesn't pharmacologically trigger increased craving and drinking. Where the increase is seen, it's a product of expectancies and other cognitive factors—not biology. *Drinkers are craving and choosing because of what they think and believe, which means that they're choosing.*

Another way to discern whether addicts are still freely choosing after the first drink or hit is to bring into the experiment the same sorts of things that affect other freely chosen behaviors. Namely, you can manipulate the costs and consequences of substance use as well as the availability of other options. If the addict really becomes a zombie hell bent on relentlessly consuming substances, then manipulation of costs and competing options shouldn't affect their behavior.

Some priming dose experiments carried out at Columbia University in recent decades used competing options to understand addicts. There, neuroscientist Carl Hart brought crack and methamphetamine "addicts" into the lab, gave them a priming dose of their substance, and then offered competing options. Here he describes his experiments:

> In one study, we gave methamphetamine addicts a choice between taking a big hit of methamphetamine (50 mg.) or five dollars in cash. They took the drug on about half of the opportunities. But when we increased the amount of money to twenty dollars, they almost never chose the drug. We had gotten similar results with crack cocaine addicts in an earlier study. This told me that the addictive potential of methamphetamine or crack was not what had been previously claimed; their addictiveness wasn't extraordinary. Our results also demonstrated that addicts can and do make rational decisions. (Hart, 2014)

What's important to realize is the money they were offered went into an account they could access only weeks later. So it's not as if they could take the 20 bucks and walk out of the lab to buy more drugs with it five minutes later. They had to wait for it. They had to be able to "delay gratification" as many people put it. Within the loss of control model, this is an ability that "drug addicts" lack altogether or at least lose temporarily after they start taking drugs. If their further substance use wasn't a choice, then no amount of money could have persuaded them away from taking another hit, but it did.

Dr. Hart's experiments offer further proof that addicts aren't turned into substance-seeking zombies when they get high but that they remain active choosers. When *they believe they have better options*, they can and do make different choices. When they believe that substance use isn't worth the cost, they make different choices. Dr. Hart began his career believing that crack and other substances had, by their phar-macological powers, addicted people and destroyed poor communities, such as the one in which he grew up. He thought that research in neu-roscience would provide the answers to fighting the influence of these powerful substances, but he concluded that "The more I studied actual drug use in people, the more I became convinced that it was a behavior that was amenable to change like any other." (Hart, 2017)

The same sort of manipulation of costs and options that Hart did with users of substances such as cocaine and methamphetamine was also done decades earlier with alcohol users in behavioral research labora-tories, such as the National Institute of Mental Health (NIMH) in Maryland. Similar results were shown. The test subjects at NIMH did not have mild drinking problems—they all had between 5 and 30 years of a history of "alcoholism"; they all experienced tolerance and with-drawal. The researchers found the subjects at a local correctional in-stitution, and they were "for the most part, homeless men with a his-tory of repeated incarceration for public drunkenness." (Heather & Robertson, 1983)

At the time of the experiments, they lived in the ward of the hospital, and while the researchers tightly controlled their access to alcohol, they still gave them *plenty* of access to it in exchange for completing various tasks in behavioral experiments. It was decisively shown through several experiments in this laboratory that drinking, in alco-holics, is a behavior affected by costs, consequences, and other envi-ronmental factors just like any other normal human behavior. It was shown that the worst of the worst "alcoholics" can clearly be seen to have control over their drinking when we look for it.

One of the NIMH studies that makes the case well was extremely sim-ple. Eight subjects could drink as much as they wanted, but they had to earn it. The work to earn it was simple. They each had a box with a button that they had to push one thousand times to earn a single pok-er chip, which they could then trade for either a cigarette or an ounce of whiskey. Heather and Robertson, (1983) describe it here:

This task was so simple that it could not be impaired by alcohol intoxication and could be performed while watching television, eating or talking. Under these conditions, all eight subjects showed a very clear and surprising dissociation between drinking and work periods. Typically, they would work during periods of abstinence of one or two days' duration until they had earned enough tokens to drink for two or three days. The cycle would then begin again. During the abstinent working periods subjects frequently displayed withdrawal signs, ranging from mild to moderate in severity and associated with rapid falls in blood alcohol level. However, it is important to note that, despite the occurrence of these partial withdrawal phenomena, subjects did not immediately start drinking to abolish them even though alcohol was available, but generally preferred to continue working to amass more tokens. (p. 84)

What's shocking about these results is that withdrawal symptoms are widely believed to compel substance use, but this assumption was clearly defied by these drinkers. This is not uncontrolled behavior that is seen in this experiment. It is goal-driven behavior. And when you think about it, it's not very different from the weekend-warrior type of substance users. They work all week and then "lose control" of their substance use on the weekend. But do they really lose control? If so, how do they stop using and go back to work on Monday?

The timing is obviously goal driven. We see plenty of cases like this. We have met CEOs of large businesses who display this pattern, which is clearly goal directed. They drink moderately during the week at family and business dinners, but then come Saturday, they "lose control." Based on their weekend behavior, they are convinced that they aren't "in control" of their drinking and need to "regain control" of their drinking. The truth is simply that they find the weekend to be a more convenient time for heavy drinking and "losing control" at that time rather than midweek allows them to maintain the level of financial success they desire. They don't ever "lose control" midweek or on the weekend. The truth is that they are in control at all times.

YOU CAN'T REGAIN WHAT WAS NEVER LOST

The test subjects at NIMH showed many surprising results. They ceased drinking when angry. They ceased when a drinking partner was taken away. They modified their intake in response to costs. They did all this and more. The work there inspired many other researchers to carry out similar experiments, which show that "alcoholics" modify their drinking according to various costs/constraints. When the cost is pulling a lever 3,000 times per drink, they moderate; when the cost is 5,000 pulls, they abstain. In a situation where experimenters promised alcoholics the price per drink would go up if they had more than two drinks per hour, they slowed their drinking to no more than two per hour so the price wouldn't go up. When alcoholics were allowed up to 10 ounces of alcohol per day while living in a barren hospital ward, they drank the full 10 ounces per day. But when offered to live in better quarters containing a TV, pool table, and other games if they limited themselves to 5 ounces of alcohol per day, they moderated their drinking to 5 ounces or less per day. When the contingency was taken away again, they drank the full 10 ounces per day. What sort of a genuine disability disappears and reappears in the face of various contingencies like this? Can you persuade paraplegics to walk by offering them better living conditions (Heather & Robertson, 1983, pp. 88–89)?

In the experiments above, the costs and incentives are very clearly controlled and presented. Those substance users know exactly what is available to them, so the choices are stark. This allows us to see that choice is clearly at play and they really are in control (i.e., they aren't alcoholics/addicts at all; they are people who freely choose their own level of substance use). In life, things are much more flexible and less predictable. Your wife may threaten to leave if you drink, but you suspect she's bluffing. You choose to take the risk and drink heavily, calling her bluff. You are in control as much as the alcoholics in the labs, but the terms of your options are murkier. Don't let this hide the fact that you are freely choosing your behavior and trying to maximize your positive outcomes like everyone else in the world—and indeed like the test subjects of the experiments we've mentioned here, who were, in most cases, the most extreme "addicts and alcoholics."

Finally, another fact that destroys the loss of control theory is that there are plenty of former "addicts/alcoholics" who are now moderate users of substances. If they truly had a genetic handicap that made them lose control, then moderation should be impossible. Yet epidemiological surveys find that about 50% of former alcoholics become moderate drinkers (see Appendix E).

Less research exists on problematic users of other substances, but when researchers look for such users they can be found. For example, (Zinberg, 1986) set out to find moderate heroin/opiate users in the 1970s and found plenty. Forty-eight percent of his sample had previously been heroin "addicts" and then proceeded to use heroin moderately for a mean of 3.5 years, which was more than twice as long as their period of "addictive" opiate use. Only 5% of the total sample (both former "addicts" and those whose use had only ever been "controlled") eventually became "addicted" or "readdicted" in the eight years of the study.

We know that alcoholics don't "lose control" of their use, so the fact that half of them take up moderation later affirms this fact. *They didn't regain control because they had never lost it. They simply came to prefer moderate use.* The case is the same for the former heroin addicts. We have no reason to believe they are ever "out of control" or that they "regained control." They simply found a pattern of usage that worked better for them and carried it out. We do not know of the same sort of priming dose studies being carried out with heroin users, but there are relevant anecdotes to be found if one looks for them. Here is one recounted by researcher Alfred Lindesmith (2008):

> In a personal communication to me, a physician reported that a woman patient about to undergo a painful operation had asked him not to administer opiates under any circumstances, explaining that, although an abstainer, she had once been addicted and that a single injection might cause a relapse. Even if it were a matter of life and death, she begged that no opiates be given her. The doctor agreed, but after the operation the patient suffered such intense pain that a narcotic prescription became absolutely necessary, and was administered orally disguised in liquid form. It made the patient more comfortable and relieved the pain. Since she was not aware that she had received the opiate there was no relapse into the former habit. Later she thanked the doctor for his support of her program of abstinence. (p. 36)

The mindset of the substance user is what matters—the thoughts, beliefs, and expectancies. So-called addicts and alcoholics don't literally lose control of their substance use. It is a way they learn to think of their substance use that then cognitively affects their habits and reactions to substances going forward.

We see forms of this phenomenon occur in hospitals across the globe every day. Thousands are provided intravenous opiate medications for pain, and many of them are given these drugs for weeks or even months depending on the condition or surgery they have undergone. After the period of acute pain has subsided because of the body healing, they are taken off these medications by their doctors or they stop taking them on their own because they feel they are no longer needed. In the majority of these people, they do not seek opiates because they never built a preference for them. In many of the long-term cases, these patients even experience intense withdrawal when the opiates are stopped. Yet, with no knowledge that it is withdrawal symptoms they are experiencing, they do not mentally equate getting relief from these symptoms with taking more of the substance. They simply feel like they have the flu or a cold. After the typical 72-hour period, their symptoms abate, and they move on with their lives no worse for the wear. It's the myth of a substance's "addictiveness" that drives people to believe using opiates causes uncontrollable use and withdrawal symptoms drive more use. Without knowledge of the myth, people easily move past opiate use and the withdrawal just the same. Simply stated, substances don't drive use; a personal preference for substances does. The belief in the addictiveness myth drives this preference to new heights. Without that myth intact, people never get "addicted."

WHAT DOES "OUT OF CONTROL" MEAN?

The best thing we could ever do is to completely remove the word "control" from discussions of problematic substance use altogether because it confuses the issue. Many people come to us saying they agree that they can choose, but then they refer to their drinking as "out of control" or "uncontrolled" and express a desire to "regain control." This all implies that they aren't choosing their level of substance use, and indeed many of them feel truly *out of control*. This confusion in thought and feeling comes from the fact that phrases such as "out of control" are used in two different senses.

You *lose control* of a car if the brakes and steering fail. You can try to pump the brake pedal and turn the steering wheel all you want, but the car continues moving in the direction it was going before those systems failed until it runs out of momentum or crashes into something. In this situation, you have literally lost control of where you were going. It doesn't matter what you want to do. It doesn't matter whether you see another street you'd like to turn down or a place you'd like to park and get out. The car lands wherever it's fated to land, and you have no further say in the matter. For those who've had this experience, it is truly terrifying.

Addiction theorists are fond of saying that "addicts can't put the brakes on," directly comparing substance users to cars, evoking the situation mentioned above. They mention various systems and regions in the brain and claim to know that these areas are broken just like a car that won't stop. Choice is not possible in this model just like the driver of the car with no brakes could not choose to stop the car. This is the sense in which most people say that addicts and alcoholics are "out of control."

However, the evidence we reviewed shows that this isn't the case at all. When addicts or alcoholics see another path they'd rather take, they steer their way there. When they don't feel like going farther down the road of substance use, they hit the brakes (or more accurately, they stop hitting the gas). This happens on a situational level when people decide to bring an end to a drinking/drugging session, and it happens on a whole-life level when people quit or dramatically adjust their substance use for good, as the epidemiological evidence on "recovery" rates proves (see chapter 1). So the idea of being out of control is patently false and should not be used nor should the idea of "regaining control." You can't regain what you haven't lost. You can't regain control of your uncontrollable car by offering it money, yet "out of control" substance users can be persuaded to "control" their substance use with monetary offers, both in and outside the laboratory.

There is another, nonliteral sense in which "out of control" is used, and it gets mixed up with the one we just discussed, leading to much confusion. If a young child at a park starts misbehaving by swearing, name-calling, drawing crude pictures of body parts in the sand, and repeatedly refusing to obey his mother's demands to stop this behavior, we say the child is *out of control.* He is flouting the attempts of his mother to control him. He's flouting the subtle attempts that other parents make to control him through menacing looks. He's flouting what he already knows are standards he's expected to live up to. *He is in full control of himself in those moments.* He is doing exactly what *he wants to do*—as opposed to what *others want him to do.*

When we say the child is "out of control," what we really mean is that he's out of *social control.* He is behaving contrary to the standards he's expected to live up to in his social environment. He refuses to obey social norms and the desires and commands of others. He isn't doing what society deems he "should" do.

This latter sense of the phrase "out of control" more accurately describes problematic substance use than the literal sense of the phrase. "Uncontrolled" substance use is simply that which breaks accepted norms of behavior. If a college student gets fall-down drunk at a keg party, we don't suggest that he isn't freely choosing to because it is acceptable behavior from a college student in our culture. We might say those kids at the kegger are "out of control," but we don't mean it literally—we just mean that they're acting wildly. However, if a 40-year-old mother of two gets fall-down drunk at a party in front of the wrong people, we say she's *literally* "out of control," and she may be shipped off to a rehab in short order. The dividing line is the fact that our culture says 40-year-old mothers shouldn't behave this way but college students should. We say that the college kids are "out of control," and the 40-year-old is "out of control." But the same phrase means different things when applied to these different people and situations.

People whose substance use is described as uncontrolled or out of control are simply using in a way that is socially unacceptable. They are still in full control of themselves and their behaviors. The meaning of the phrase is switched for people to treat them like children while pretending they are not. When we say a child is out of control, we all know what that means and what the remedy is. They aren't behaving as we, *their superiors*, demand they should behave, and bringing them under control means disciplining them, scaring them into following our demands of how they should behave. This coercion makes children angry, but they are forced to accept it because of their powerless status as children.

Adults, on the other hand, have a different status in our culture. Adults are supposed to be free and independent to do whatever they like if it doesn't directly harm others. With respect to substance use, people can't be as open about saying that they are the substance users' *superiors* and that they know better than the substance users, nor can they say that the substance users must follow their orders and direction as they show them how they should live their lives. This attempt to control and direct another adult's freely chosen behaviors creates a thousand times the opposition that it does in children.

None of us want to be told how to live as adults, and we rebel against it at all costs. Therefore, it is thought that the commands by *those who know better* must be subtle and disguised to be effective. The claim that someone's drinking or drugging is "out of control" is thus used in the literal sense with adults (and some adolescents who've matured to a level of intellectual independence) to cover up the coercive dynamic. That is, what's really going on is that the substance users' freely chosen, fully controlled substance use goes against the wishes of others and those others are demanding they stop it. The demand/coercion is reframed as an offer of help, a diagnosis of the "loss of control" and "treatment for the disease of addiction." It is said to be a way to help the substance users "regain control" that they've literally lost because of their own behavior. It's all a ruse and a giant cultural charade. It allows the coercers to hide their coercion and the substance users to submit to the coercion while saving face and not appearing to be lower status individuals who are being bullied into living their lives on terms set by others.

Of course, it doesn't usually work so smoothly because people inherently know they are doing what they want to do, that their substance use isn't involuntary even though the results may be troubling. When substance users argue with the suggestion that they are literally "out of control," they are then said to be "in denial," which is just another symptom of the disease—*it hides from you the truth that you are truly out of control!* Now, the substance users have a second chance to acquiesce by "realizing" that they're "in denial" and "admitting" that they cannot control their substance use.

You get to decide whether you take part in this charade. Unfortunately, you may have come to believe it's reality and not a charade. In this case, you may feel truly out of control; but that's just a feeling, and it will change when you decide to change the thoughts and beliefs underlying it. Know this: the claim that substance users lack control of their own behavior is just a tool of control used by others. It is used to try to manipulate substance users into making the choices those other seemingly more powerful parties want them to make. It is not a scientifically true claim; *it is a socially convenient one.*

About half of our readers have personally faced this Orwellian doublespeak and will recognize it as formative of their own downfall. About half of you have not personally experienced it but have likely witnessed it if you think back on the experiences of friends and family. Whether you've experienced it personally, it's important for you to understand because *what you think you know about addiction is based on it.* The majority of research on "addiction" and views of what it is, how it works, and what is needed to overcome it are based on these coercive interactions. Support groups and treatment programs were invented as places to send people whose loved ones or the legal system decided to intervene and coerce them into making changes that they did not, of their own volition and judgment, wish to make. Those people then became the research subjects and the face of addiction.

Meanwhile, those who didn't face coercion yet discovered that their substance use was troubling and that they needed to make a change in it went under the radar, unnoticed by most researchers. Some of this population, the self-changers, do struggle and find it difficult to initiate and maintain change, but they do it without treatment, on their own timetable, and by their own voluntary exploration of their options. They also seem to do it with much less ongoing struggle and emotional upheaval.

The substance users forced into treatment have traditionally made up only 10% to 20% of those who fit formal diagnoses for addictions/substance use disorders. They've been misled into believing they can't control themselves. They've been coerced into playing the charade. And then the results, that they continuously struggle, "relapse," and require ongoing support, treatment, and aftercare, confirm the addiction model of problematic substance use as they then attest to it.

Those coerced into abstinence struggle more because they haven't been allowed to make their own decisions. They "need support" not to battle addiction because addiction doesn't exist. Rather, they need support to deal with the fact that they're being coerced to quit substance use when they really want to continue it. Their "support systems" don't magically transfer strength into them, which then helps them to remain abstinent. Instead, the people in these systems are more like *supporting players* in a film that help to make the whole scene more believable. Their life has become about playing this charade of being addicted and battling addiction (i.e., liking substance use and being deprived of it because of coercive involvements). For those who do experience a time of abstinence, they, exactly like the self-changers, have decided during that period that not using is more beneficial to them than using. Many become the memoirists, the activists, the counselors, and the general spokespeople for the charade of addiction and recovery. Sadly, many "addicts turned helpers/experts" continue to struggle throughout their lives because they truly believe in the loss of control myth and continuously reinforce it in their own lives. The other 80% to 90% are the self-changers, those who avoid the system and stay silent, unnoticed, and unresearched (for the most part), and most of them have no subsequent struggles with substance use.

The popular "loss of control" idea about addiction is based on a ruse and doesn't represent the reality of what a substance use problem is. Yet it's the only framework you've been offered for understanding what you're going through. More important, those who face coercion are put in a situation where it's not worth arguing with this model. If they say they're free, they're sanctioned for it. If they agree to it, they're granted some leeway. Agreeing to speak of their substance use as an "out of control" behavior has benefits for heavy substance users. They can then "lose control" and "relapse" occasionally if they explain it this way (that is, they get a pass to occasionally do what they want instead of what others demand).

This is the reason we end up with so many cases whose experience clearly defies the addiction model but who continue to believe in it at the same time. Remember our CEO discussed earlier? We'll call him Jim. When drinking midweek, he'd have only a few. When drinking with business associates, his demeanor was pleasant. But when drinking on the weekend, Jim "lost control" of both his drinking and his other behaviors, becoming "nasty" in interactions with his wife, as he put it (alcohol doesn't really cause nasty behavior; see chapter 19). He was not acting; he was *genuinely* convinced that he lost control of his drinking. The ruse of addiction made it worth seeing himself this way. Without the ruse, he'd have to admit that he likes having a lot to drink on the weekend and wants some time to himself to do so. He'd have to admit that he doesn't want to devote as much of that free time to his family as his wife wants him to. He'd have to admit that he just wants to tell his wife off after a particularly nasty argument. If they both saw this behavior as freely chosen, they'd be at a serious impasse, they couldn't blame the alcohol or "his addiction" for their problems. This would demand a tough discussion about whether or not they can continue to be together, whether they can forgive, whether they can learn to get along and make the marriage work given his wants. But if they both hold onto the charade of his being a victim of alcoholism (i.e., lacking control), they can avoid that tough conversation.

The truth is that, when Jim, or anyone else, uses substances heavily/frequently/problematically, he is doing exactly what he wants to do. Jim never truly lost control, but when the idea of addiction was introduced to him, it made convenient sense of an inconvenient conflict of wills between him and his wife. As he began to think of his drinking as an addiction, he began to feel genuinely out of control. This confusion and inaccurate understanding of his own behavior impede his self-perceived ability to change so that, even when he begins to think it might be worth changing, he struggles. This isn't mere conjecture; it has been revealed in research over the years, some of which we described in chapter 1.

The research and the truth are inconvenient to Jim's (and his family's) immediate situation; acknowledging he isn't powerless would force him and his wife to face some hard truths. The truths are even harder to face for those whose situations are more extreme. A drug user facing incarceration for illegal drug possession is benefited by softened sentences he receives by invoking the specter of addiction. A drug user who faces conflict with his family who has a zero-tolerance policy against drugs can temporarily benefit from the addiction charade too because it allows him an excuse to continue using drugs and escape at least some sanction from them. Much harder for him would be to tell them "I am an adult now; this is what I want to do, and you can take it or leave it."

It's even harder to accept for the parents who've built their self-esteem on the dream of raising the perfect child. They too would be at an uncomfortable impasse. They'd have to let go of control and release the strings, and the adult child would have to let go of material support from the family if he were to assert his independence. This has become hard enough as our culture has moved toward many families financially supporting adult children into their late 20s and 30s, but cutting the strings becomes even harder when it means openly accepting that your offspring may use drugs. Many parents won't let go and keep trying to exercise control over their children well into adulthood. In the most extreme case, when loved ones die from an overdose, the addiction construct helps families avoid the disappointment and anger of realizing that their loved ones freely made a choice that ended so tragically. It's much more convenient to think of them as the victims of a disease and not as having made that choice willingly.

The myth of "loss of control" helps those who work in treatment do their jobs and serve their *real* customers, who are in most cases not the clients/patients themselves but rather their loved ones, employers, or law enforcement agencies. Those parties want to buy abstinence, and treatment providers sell it. This isn't a cynical view; it's a historical and an economic fact that has incentivized the treatment industry/recovery society to function in a way that satisfies those parties. These entities don't exist to empower problematic substance users to discover their most rewarding choices. They exist to manipulate them into abstinence. So the recovery society and treatment providers present a false alternative designed to corner substance users into choosing abstinence—either you abstain or you go out of control using substances to disastrous ends. To make their false alternative real, they created family programs in which loved ones are trained to make disastrous consequences come down on the substance user with "tough love." These methods are designed to make the choice to abstain a no-brainer. They don't want substance users to think about their options at all; they just want them to accept their (the helpers') conclusions of what they (the substance users) should do. (This was discussed in chapters 8 and 9.)

Treatment professionals and their helpers have decided you need to abstain and that they need to trick you into doing it by telling you that you are incapable of anything between abstinence and reckless disastrous substance use. We have had conversations with some of the loudest, most influential voices in the recovery society, and while they all concede that heavy substance users are in full control of themselves and that the evidence presented above proves this, they still oppose telling them this truth because they see it as equivalent to "recommending moderation." This is very revealing of how they see their role. [Note: There are of course caveats and nuances to the situation, and we do not wish to indict all those who work in treatment. But the loss of control theory stays alive even though it has been completely disproven because it serves the interests of these other parties.]

The Jims of the world, their family members, the anti-drug crusaders, and the professional helpers in the recovery society go to great lengths to keep the ruse of loss of control and addiction alive because it serves many interests. The one interest it doesn't serve is to make people fully informed of the truth so they can make their own best decisions. To insulate their views and methods from scrutiny, the recovery society has made any other opinions on problematic substance use politically incorrect. It has ruled the way that many of you feel because you've been told that to think about it in any other way is ignorant, insensitive, and just plain crazy. And how can anyone fight that? We're told that we're disrespecting the dead or "morally judging" those who currently struggle with "the disease" if we question the scientific validity of these views. So instead, we all roll over and politely accept it, and then it becomes the common knowledge and practice.

Thankfully, not everyone is onboard. The fact that the recovery society needs to keep pushing for acceptance of their vision of involuntary substance use means that there are a great many people out there who just won't accept the doublespeak. Most problematic substance users reject treatment because it just doesn't make sense to them.

Any phrase that suggests substance users aren't in control of their own substance use is scientifically inaccurate and should not be taken seriously. Such phrases are a social invention, used to portray problematic substance use in terms that allow for excuses and coercive social arrangements. If we let go of this faulty belief, then we can talk about substance use in realistic terms. Substance users who seek help or are being coerced into seeking it can recognize that they simply like substance use enough to pay a high price for it and to do it to the exclusion of other things. When thinking about it in this way, they can consider whether they still like it enough to be worth the price they pay and whether they might prefer doing it less or not at all. Their loved ones can say what they really mean, want, and desire—they are afraid for your safety, they don't think you're giving them enough attention/priority, and they think you can use your resources in a way that helps you to attain a happier and longer life. These are hard conversations to have. These are hard is-sues to directly tackle. The construct of addiction seems to offer a more convenient solution to everyone involved, but in the long run, it causes more harm, as all misinformation does.

Without the charade of addiction, treatment, and recovery, some par-ties would also have to tell you that they just don't like your decisions and are unwilling to allow you to live in a way that they find unac-ceptable. Like any social construct, it takes two to play this game. You don't have to play along. You can opt out. Embracing the truth, that you do have control—always have and always will—opens the door for you to make fully informed decisions for your life.

REFERENCES

Hart, C. L. (2014, March 10). As with other problems, class affects addiction. Retrieved from http://www.nytimes.com/roomfordebate/2014/02/10/what-is-addiction/as-with-other-problems-class-affects-addiction

Hart, C. L. (2017). Viewing addiction as a brain disease promotes social injus-tice. *Nature Human Behaviour, 1*(55). https://doi.org/10.1038/s41562-017-0055

Heather, N., & Robertson, I. (1983). *Controlled drinking*. London: Methuen.

Lindesmith, A. R. (2008). *Addiction and opiates* (reprint). New Brunswick, NJ: Aldine Transaction.

Marlatt, G. A. (1985, May 6). Loss of control drinking in alcoholics: An experi-mental analogue. *Current Contents/Social & Behavioral Sciences, 18*. Retrieved from http://garfield.library.upenn.edu/classics1985/A1985AFW2300001.pdf

Zinberg, N. (1986). Drug, Set, and Setting: The Basis for Controlled Intoxicant Use (1st ed.). Yale University Press.

APPENDIX B
THE BRAIN DISEASE MODEL OF ADDICTION

Twenty years ago (1997), the head of the National Institute on Drug Abuse (NIDA), Alan Leshner, declared addiction a brain disease in a seminal paper and statement titled "Addiction Is a Brain Disease, and It Matters." It was quickly picked up and celebrated by the media and has dominated the discourse on addiction ever since. Unfortunately, the scientific substance to support the paper was entirely lacking. The case it made for the brain disease model consisted of two elements:

1. The same emotional rhetoric that's been used for every other version of the disease model of addiction, painting the disease model as compassionate and any other view as heartless and cruel.

2. Innuendo full of neuro-jargon and incomplete explanations that sound convincingly scientific to the layman but say nothing of substance.

THE EMOTIONAL RHETORIC

NIDA's paper provides a prime example of the logical fallacies known as "appeal to emotions" and "appeal to consequences." Throughout the paper, the author pits the brain disease understanding against punitive criminal approaches to substance use. After painting the average person as a heartless, unsympathetic moralizer who wants to send all substance users to jail, Leshner explains that the cause of this cruel attitude is ignorance of science:

Many, perhaps most, people see drug abuse and addiction as social problems, to be handled only with social solutions, particularly through the criminal justice system. On the other hand, science has taught that drug abuse and addiction are as much health problems as they are social problems. . . .

One major barrier is the tremendous stigma attached to being a drug user or, worse, an addict. . . . the more common view is that drug addicts are weak or bad people, unwilling to lead moral lives and to control their behavior and gratifications. To the contrary, addiction is actually a chronic, relapsing illness, characterized by compulsive drug seeking and use. The gulf in implications between the "bad person" view and the "chronic illness sufferer" view is tremendous. As just one example, there are many people who believe that addicted individuals do not even deserve treatment. This stigma, and the underlying moralistic tone, is a significant overlay on all decisions that relate to drug use and drug users. (Leshner, 1997)

First, let us say that the compassion versus punishment rhetoric is an apples to oranges comparison since the question of why people use substances heavily and whether substance use should be punished as a crime are independent issues. This false dichotomy suggests that if you think heavy substance use is freely chosen, then you must also be in favor of draconian laws related to substances. Please note that, when you hear this rhetoric, it's creating a bogeyman. "Addiction" isn't a formal crime, and those who believe that heavy substance use is freely chosen are not proposing laws that specifically target heavy substance users. As unjust as they may be, the laws against dealing or possessing substances and paraphernalia, public intoxication, and driving while intoxicated, to name a few, apply equally to those who've only dabbled in such behaviors and those "addicts" who do them daily. Such laws are supported by some who consider heavy substance use a choice and some who consider it a disease. Meanwhile, the only laws that aim to *specifically imprison "addicts*" are involuntary commitment laws passed in state legislatures under the banner of compassion and "treating addiction as a disease rather than a crime."

Contrary to the suggestion that a choice view underlies punitive approaches to substance use, the brain disease model has been and continues to be used to justify harsh laws against substances and substance users based on the idea that some drugs are especially "addictive" and radically transform the brain, causing "addiction" through exposure. The brain disease model is also used to support laws and regulations that unfairly single out younger substance users as well. Such rules take away school sports eligibility, federal financial aid for college, and driver's licenses. This is all justified by the claim that young people's brains are still under development and thus especially vulnerable to the "addictive powers of substances." Again, the brain disease model is used to support punitive measures even though it's continually portrayed as being the antidote to such attitudes.

You can be a supporter of either decriminalization/legalization of substances or harsher punishment regardless of whether you believe in the disease model of addiction. To wit, most serious critics of the disease model that we've met or followed tend to be in favor of some form of *loosening the laws* rather than more punishment.

The claim that anyone who disagrees with the disease model is a moralizer is downright insulting and a case of projection. The view that heavy substance use represents "immorality" or "badness" is not dependent on seeing it as a choice. *You may see it as a choice and yet believe it isn't your place to pass judgment on what others should do with their lives.* We know many choice proponents who hold this position (including us).

"Moralizers" are people who push their moral ideals (views of right and wrong/bad and good) on others. The real moralizing is smuggled into the disease model and conveniently goes unstated. First, the disease model contains the judgment that no one would freely choose the substance uses that it deems to be "addiction." This includes various levels/frequencies of substance use ("binge use"/"risk drinking," using to the point of tolerance, etc.), any use of illicit substances (such as heroin or methamphetamines), and using for unapproved reasons ("nonmedical use" of prescription drugs or using to deal with negative feelings). In all these situations, the "moralizers" are deciding what is considered good/bad and right/wrong (i.e., moral) and calling anything that goes against this code so wrong that it must be the product of disease and couldn't possibly be preferred and freely chosen by any-one in their right mind. *That's moralizing.*

Furthermore, the diagnostic criteria outlines a list of priorities (or *val-ues*) so that any substance use that goes against these priorities is la-beled a sign/symptom of an "addiction" in need of treatment. If your substance use "interferes" with work and social obligations, it breaks their code. If your substance use is the subject of an argument with a loved one, it breaks their code. If it leads to arrest, it breaks their code. If it costs more money than they believe should be spent on sub-stance use, it breaks their code. On and on and on. You can even break the code by thinking about substance use more often than they deem proper. Since their code (diagnostic criteria) determines that certain substance use is bad, should be stopped, and shouldn't be desired by anyone, it is a moral code. It says that you should value/prioritize things the same way they do, thus pushing their moral code on you. They just push this code under the guise of disease and medicine.

Add this to the fact that the brain disease model is used to support laws that can have you involuntarily committed if you break their code (fit the diagnosis for a "substance use disorder") and determine who can and cannot use drugs and for what reasons. It's clear to see who the real moralizers are.

Finally, the following circular logic from NIDA is stupefying:

> The gulf in implications between the "bad person" view and the "chronic illness sufferer" view is tremendous. As just one example, there are many people who believe that addicted individuals do not even deserve treatment.

The issue here is whether addiction is a disease. Any notion of whether people "deserve treatment" for addiction hinges on its status as a dis-ease because it's impossible to medically treat a nonmedical problem. Yet the NIDA plows ahead emotionally blackmailing people into be-lieving the disease model lest they become cruel monsters who com-mit the moral crime of *denying people treatment for a nonexistent dis-ease!* Absurd!

That final example demonstrates the level of discourse used to per-suade people into believing that addiction is a brain disease. There's no logical argument here, and thus there is no truly scientific case being presented. There is only emotional and political rhetoric. They paint their disease model as the compassionate position and the alternative of a free choice model as the cruel, moralizing position. This says nothing about whether there truly is a brain disease that causes heavy substance use. Furthermore, the disease model is full of moralizing and regularly used to support punitive legislation against substance users of all stripes.

This is an argument without a sound, logical premise. It commits the logical fallacy of appealing to consequences. Yet the consequences they appeal to don't follow the logic either. To be clear, disease proponents primarily argue for acceptance of the brain disease model by claiming that it will reduce stigma, leading to better treatment of "addicts," and that it opens the way for "addicts" to get the treatment they need. Since this major push began in 1997, rates of addiction have gone up, and overdoses and substance-related deaths have multiplied. Many more billions of dollars have been spent on treatment, and success rates haven't gotten any better. On the question of stigma, one study compared surveys from 1996 and 2006 measuring acceptance of a brain disease conception of depression, schizophrenia, and alcoholism, endorsement of treatment, and stigma associated with the conditions. The researchers concluded that:

> More of the public embraces a neurobiological understanding of mental illness. This view translates into support for services but not into a decrease in stigma. (Pescosolido et al., 2010)

More specifically, they found that:

> Social distance and perceived danger associated with people with these disorders did not decrease significantly. Holding a neurobiological conception of these disorders increased the likelihood of support for treatment but was generally unrelated to stigma. Where associated, the effect was to increase, not decrease, community rejection." (Pescosolido et al., 2010)

The questions used to gauge this were interesting. They asked whether people would be willing to have someone with alcoholism as a neighbor or to work closely with them, socialize with them, or have them marry into their family. These are very down-to-earth measures of stigma. They didn't significantly change over the 10 years. In fact, in some cases, they went up. For example, in 1996, 70% were unwilling to have someone with alcoholism marry into their family, and in 2006, 79% were unwilling (Pescosolido et al., 2010).

The idea that a brain disease model of a behavioral problem, such as substance use, would reduce such stigma is so often repeated that we don't even stop to question it. So let's question it now. Where's the logic? If you're a mother and your daughter falls in love with a man who is a heavy drinker, you won't be happy about that regardless of whether he's diagnosed with alcoholism. Furthermore, if he's an "alcoholic" who's "in recovery," that's not likely to make you feel better. If it's the result of a genuine genetic brain malfunction—*a chronic, relapsing brain disease*—then he is a ticking time bomb for the rest of his life, even if he does change his behavior for the time being. And furthermore, he could potentially pass down his defective genes to their offspring should they have any. Why should that be comforting? But if it's a matter of choice—*one of learning and personal growth*—then he may have realizations about his behavior. It may be a phase that he can permanently move on from in his life. And you won't be concerned that his faulty genes will continue into future generations. If anything, a choice model should be more comforting (unless of course you believe in stable, unchangeable character traits).

THE NEUROSCIENCE EXPLANATION

When the brain disease proponents shift out of their emotional appeals for a moment and focus on selling their model based on actual evidence, the logic is equally lacking. They churn out a lot of neuroscience jargon, such as talk about the midbrain, prefrontal cortex, mesolimbic reward system, neurotransmitters, metabolic activity, and more. They show colorful brain scans that they claim prove that substance users' brains or free will has been "hijacked." They talk about how the exposure to substances changes the brain in lasting ways. They make dramatic comparisons to well-known, indisputable diseases. Yet the one thing they never truly do is connect the dots in a logical way. Their arguments are incomplete, rest on several shaky premises, and defy well-established facts from other branches of science, such as epidemiology and behavioral research.

NIDA invested heavily in the brain disease model, replacing Leshner with Nora Volkow, a neuroscientist plucked straight out of a brain-imaging laboratory. Under her, NIDA went full bore with the brain disease model. In its signature piece by Volkow promoting the brain disease model, *Drugs, Brains, and Behavior: The Science of Addiction*, they define addiction as follows:

> Addiction is defined as a chronic relapsing brain disease that is characterized by compulsive drug seeking and use, despite harmful consequences. It is considered a brain disease because drugs change the brain—they change its structure and how it works. These brain changes can be long lasting, and can lead to the harmful behaviors seen in people who abuse drugs. (NIDA, 2014)

Boiled down, the basic claim is that substance use changes the brain, and then those brain changes cause the continued substance use. NIDA offers scans of "addicted brains" to make its case to the public in the same paper:

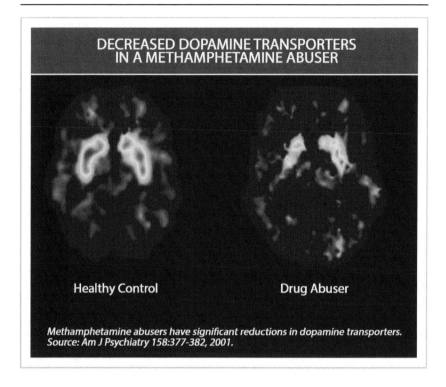

DECREASED DOPAMINE TRANSPORTERS
IN A METHAMPHETAMINE ABUSER

Healthy Control   Drug Abuser

Methamphetamine abusers have significant reductions in dopamine transporters.
Source: Am J Psychiatry 158:377-382, 2001.

The average person sees the brain scans that NIDA shows and just accepts the conclusion that follows: "case closed; that's the evidence of disease!" This uncritical reaction is in fact codified in research that found that *most people will believe nonsensical explanations of psychological phenomena if the phrase "brain scans indicate" is inserted into it.* (Weisberg et al., 2008). It sounds scientific and it looks scientific, so we don't think too much about it and just accept it. Let's not fall into that trap here; let's not shut down our critical thinking in the face of something we think the top scientists must have figured out. Instead, let's think about this "evidence" by starting with a great definition of the term:

> Evidence is fact that discriminates between one theory and another. Facts do not "speak for themselves." They speak for or against competing theories. Facts divorced from theory or visions are mere isolated curiosities. (Sowell, 2007, p. 6)

Does the evidence offered support the brain disease theory? The brain scans are interesting. They certainly must be able to tell us something, yet by themselves they do not prove that addiction is a brain disease. They don't prove much of anything regarding substance use. While there is evidence demonstrating that some changes to the brain do occur with continued, repetitive use of substances, it takes more than that to prove the theory that these brain changes "can lead to the involuntary, harmful behaviors seen in people who abuse drugs." This is a very serious claim of causation. To reach the conclusion that these changes in the brain cause heavy substance use and rob the user of free will, we need something that shows that people are physically unable to stop without medical intervention once these alleged brain changes have occurred. We need scans to show that the brain is changed yet again before people stop using substances.

The brain scans shown above are from a study of heavy methamphetamine users and have been used in many media and public presentations of the brain disease model of addiction. Later studies on the same group of subjects showed that, with sustained abstinence, their brains changed back to look more like the brains of people who had never used methamphetamine problematically. It leaves us with an important question: Did their brains change back *before* they stopped using or *after* they stopped using? For their assertions to hold water, you would have to see changes to the brain prior to stopping usage, not because of it.

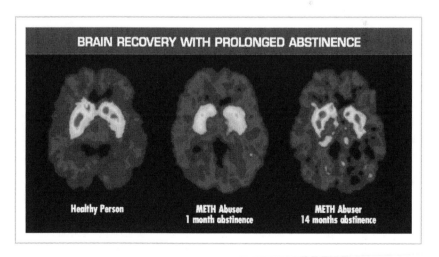

Think about this because this single point is enough to tear apart the brain disease model as it is regularly presented. If we are to believe that the brain state labeled as "Drug Abuser" in figure 1 causes "addicts" to use substances "compulsively" (without any choice in the matter and unstoppably), then those users would not be able to stop until their brains had been altered to once again look like a "Healthy Control" brain. However, they do stop usage, even while having a supposedly "unhealthy" and "addicted" brain, as shown in the scans of figure 2. The "powerless addicts" in this very study were not powerless at all; they stopped using methamphetamine while they were in the purported diseased and powerless state.

Furthermore, they did not have a scalpel put into their brains to surgically alter it, nor were there any medications used at the time to alter brain activity related to meth use. The subjects of these studies were gathered from run-of-the-mill treatment programs, where the treatment likely consisted of group counseling and 12-step meetings, among other nonmedical, talk-based treatment. Talking doesn't remove tumors. Talking doesn't restore dopamine function to Parkinson's patients. Talking doesn't eradicate infections or change insulin levels. Talking doesn't make a paraplegic's legs work. But we are asked to believe that talking made the "diseased" subjects able to stop while they were still supposedly diseased! How can that be true when the disease proponents' main criterion for the disease is that the subjects cannot stop while in the diseased state? You can clearly see that their rhetoric backfires and exposes the ruse.

Conversations aren't medical treatment. They are human interactions in which ideas are communicated. *Ideas.* Those ideas may persuade people to behave differently and to make different choices, but the premise of the brain disease model of addiction is that addicts' brains prohibit them from making different choices about drug and alcohol use. Yet here we see in NIDA's main piece of evidence for their brain disease model of addiction that "addicts" (of what we're told is one of the most "addictive" substances) do make different choices even while their brains are in an *unhealthy/addicted* state.

What this brain scan data demonstrates is a correlation. When people have been using heavily for a significant period of time, we see these brain changes. When they cease using heavily for a significant period of time, we see these changes go away. That is correlation: "a mutual relationship or connection between two or more things." The question that could point us toward a potential answer about causation would be about which comes first—the brain changes or the behavioral changes? The data above shows us that the significant brain changes come after behavioral changes. This doesn't answer everything, but it does negate the notion that addicts are prohibited from stopping substance use without a *medical* intervention.

It's important for you to know that almost everything we do repetitiously causes long-term changes to the brain. A few examples are that learning to play a musical instrument changes the brain; driving a taxi in London changes the brain, such that the longer you do it, the larger your hippocampus grows; learning and practicing juggling for 6 weeks results in increased white matter in the brain. We could go on and on with examples, but suffice it to say that anything people do can change their brains. Certainly, none of the behaviors listed in this paragraph are involuntary behaviors. Yet, with each of them, you can see "lasting changes to the brain." Many activities have been found to specifically change the same areas of the brain involved in "addiction," such as the nucleus accumbens (NAc), as discussed in the following passage written by neuroscientist Marc Lewis, an outspoken critic of the disease model of addiction:

> Every experience that has potent emotional content changes the NAC and its uptake of dopamine. Yet we wouldn't want to call the excitement you get from the love of your life, or your fifth visit to Paris, a disease. The NAC is highly plastic. It has to be, so that we can pursue different rewards as we develop, right through childhood to the rest of the lifespan. In fact, each highly rewarding experience builds its own network of synapses in and around the NAC, and that network sends a signal to the midbrain: I'm anticipating x, so send up some dopamine, right now! That's the case with romantic love, Paris, and heroin. During and after each of these experiences, that network of synapses gets strengthened: so the "specialization" of dopamine uptake is further increased. London just doesn't do it for you anymore. It's got to be Paris. Pot, wine, music ... they don't turn your crank so much; but cocaine sure does. Physical changes in the brain are its only way to learn, to remember, and to develop. But we wouldn't want to call learning a disease. (Lewis, 2012)

He goes on to call addiction "an extreme form of learning." That is to say, the changes to the brain that we're told cause addiction are a normal form of brain functioning, *not a malfunction on a cellular level, as in a genuine disease and traditional pathology.* "Addiction" is a way of being that society considers detrimental, but it isn't a unique product of biological forces.

As evidence mounts, the things that happen in the brain simply look increasingly routine and less special. The brain disease model continues to fall apart upon the most cursory investigation of its premises. For example, public presentations of the brain disease model have often included studies where a cocaine "addict" has her brain scanned while researchers show her pictures of cocaine-related cues/triggers, such as a straw or rolled-up dollar bill, some lines of cocaine on a mirror, or people using cocaine. This line of research was summed up in the press release for a recent experiment carried out at McGill University: (Cox, et al.,, 2017)

> Researchers have known for many years that cocaine use triggers the release of dopamine, a neurotransmitter involved in the brain's reward system. In people with addictions, cues associated with drug use create the same effect. Visual cues—such as seeing someone using cocaine—are enough to trigger dopamine release and lead to craving.
>
> Scientists have long believed that, as addiction progresses, cue-induced release of dopamine shifts to the dorsal striatum, a structure deep inside the brain extensively studied for its role in the way we respond to rewards.
>
> "This area of the brain is thought to be particularly important for when people start to lose control of their reward-seeking behaviours," Prof. Leyton says. "The dorsal part of the striatum is involved in habits—the difference, for example, between getting an ice cream because it will feel good versus being an automatic response that occurs even when it is not enjoyable or leads to consequences that you would rather avoid, such as weight gain or serious health hazards." (McGill University, 2017)

The traditional line of reasoning says that these neural responses are evidence of an abnormality in the brain which causes cocaine addicts to "lose control." Now, here's the rub—the researchers in this current experiment looked for the same brain response in *recreational cocaine users*, and they found it!

> Even among non-dependent cocaine users, cues associated with consumption of the drug lead to dopamine release in an area of the brain thought to promote compulsive use, according to researchers. (McGill University, 2017)

If both "compulsive users" (i.e., addicts) and "non-dependent cocaine users" (i.e., recreational users) have the same thing going on in their brains, then this can't be evidence of a neural mechanism causing "compulsive use." This brain activity isn't a special feature of cocaine addiction; *it's a feature of liking cocaine*, a fact which doesn't do anything to establish or support the notion that cocaine use is ever involuntary. That is to say, it is evidence that people who like cocaine have these kind of neural responses to "cocaine cues," and nothing more. You can have this response and be an "addict" or a recreational user.

What's more, cocaine is the substance people quit most often without treatment; it is the shortest lived among all substance use habits and has the highest lifetime recovery rate (greater than 99%). Yet we're routinely told that it has the power to create this special brain response that pulls people into a lifetime of addiction from which they can't escape. Like so many of these claims about addiction, this claim is debunked, even before you get to analyzing the neuroscientific data, by simply looking at the real-world life results among "dependent" cocaine users. Nevertheless, that didn't stop the university from concluding that the results found by its researchers should make us more afraid of cocaine than we were previously. They go on to say that:

> The findings, published in Scientific Reports, suggest that people who consider themselves recreational users could be further along the road to addiction than they might have realized. (McGill University, 2017)

Or they just might like cocaine today, grow bored with it tomorrow, and eventually quit. The latter is extremely more probable since it is what more extreme users, the so-called "cocaine addicts" do in real life. Cocaine "addicts" (seen as people who are stuck with a lifelong obsession with cocaine, inability to quit, and a lack of control over the choice to use) don't really exist in the way the recovery society has portrayed them. They quit, on average, quicker than any other "addicts", they do so permanently, they do it most often without treatment, and they show the ability to choose cash rewards over cocaine in laboratory settings (Appendix A).

All of this gazing at neural responses and brain scans ends up being a quest to find evidence of the causes of something that doesn't even exist (the "powerless addict in need of treatment"). When you get a look at a fuller range of data, as we have shown you throughout The Freedom Model, the people touting the "hard science" all begin to look a little superstitious. They almost look like those ghost hunters on television, with all sorts of electronic gadgets that go haywire, making lights and noises, spitting out numbers and readings – yet we still never see the ghost. One of the researchers responsible for those famous cocaine cue experiments was recently interviewed by National Geographic for a story on the brain disease model of addiction. They described her looking at brain scan images, and she said she just sits and looks at them for hours trying to figure them out, eventually saying that "it's like reading tea leaves." Indeed. (Aguilera-Hellweg, 2017)

This chapter has focused on one version of the brain disease model of addiction, the one that is the *currently* fashionable version of that model. We're not going to waste your time digging any deeper into the intricacies of the more specific neurological claims that make up the full model. To do so would give the model too much credit, being that its most fundamental claims aren't even true. Any model of heavy substance use that portrays it as a disease or some other involuntary state that people are stuck with for life is patently false. The experimental evidence on loss of control (appendix A), the epidemiological data, and basic logic already disprove these models, as researcher Gene Heyman, after having reviewed the evidence, succinctly stated in a critique of the brain disease model of addiction:

There are no published studies that establish a causal link between drug-induced neural adaptations and compulsive drug use or even a correlation between drug-induced neural changes and an increase in preference for an addictive drug. . . .

Most addicts quit. Thus, drug-induced neural plasticity does not prevent quitting. . . . [An analysis of epidemiological studies] shows that the likelihood of remission was constant over time since the onset of dependence. Although this is a surprising result, it is not without precedent. In a longitudinal study of heroin addicts, Vaillant (1973) reports that the likelihood of going off drugs neither increased nor decreased over time (1973), and in a study with rats, Serge Ahmed and his colleagues (Cantin et al., 2010) report that the probability of switching from cocaine to saccharin (which was about 0.85) was independent of past cocaine consumption. Since drugs change the brain, these results suggest that the changes do not prevent quitting, and the slope of [an analysis of epidemiological studies] implies that drug-induced neural changes do not even decrease the likelihood of quitting drugs once dependence is in place. (Heyman, 2013)

In plainer terms, Heyman showed with data about rates of quitting that the probability of quitting doesn't change whether you're an "addict" for 1 year or 20 years. Yet, if continued exposure to substances changes the brain in ways that make you more "addicted," as the brain disease model proposes, then addicts who have used for 20 years should be less likely to quit than their counterparts who have used for only one year because their brains should be more changed (i.e., more addicted). But that's not the case because the probability of quitting stays the same regardless of how long the substance has been used. This especially debunks the notion of substances containing a quality of "addictiveness." People who supposedly can't quit regularly do so—in massive numbers and percentages. Every way you cut it, traditional claims about addiction don't hold water.

While tragic stories of addiction are heartbreaking, they are in fact anomalies rather than the norm. The neuroscience and other experimental evidence give us no reason to believe that those sad cases involve a disease that "hijacks the brain" and causes "compulsive use." What we're left with is emotional rhetoric without scientific substance, and it is being boldly called out by more and more scientists every day. For example, when Michelle Dunbar, a co-author of *The Freedom Model*, asked neuroscientist and drug researcher Dr. Carl Hart what he thought about the idea that addiction is a progressive, incurable brain disease, his answer was clear and unequivocal:

> Ask the person who says that "Can you please show me the data to show that?" There is absolutely no data to support that fallacious sort of claim. It's a nice, sexy claim, and you can show brain-imaging pictures and you pretend that you're telling the person who's listening something that's remarkable when in fact you're not.
>
> It's one of the biggest frauds that's been perpetrated on the public—this notion of a chronic, progressive brain illness. (Hart, 2015)

What that answer leaves us with is that the brain disease model of addiction is misinformation and therefore harmful. It hasn't helped, it can't help, and it won't help people to solve their problems with substance use unless their only problem is that they need a socially acceptable excuse to continue using substances.

REFERENCES

Aguilera-Hellweg, M. (2017, August 22). How Science Is Unlocking the Secrets of Addiction. Retrieved August 27, 2017, from http://www.nationalgeographic.com/magazine/2017/09/the-addicted-brain/

McGill University. (2017). [Press Release]. Retrieved from <http://www.mcgill.ca/newsroom/channels/news/brain-area-involved-addiction-activated-earlier-previously-thought-recreational-cocaine-users-268258>

Cox, S. M. L., Yau, Y., Larcher, K., Durand, F., Kolivakis, T., Delaney, J. S., ... Leyton, M. (2017). Cocaine cue-induced dopamine release in recreational cocaine users. *Scientific Reports, 7*, 46665. https://doi.org/10.1038/srep46665

Drugs, brains, and behavior: The science of addiction. (2014, July 1). Retrieved from https://www.drugabuse.gov/publications/drugs-brains-behavior-science-addiction

Hart, C. (2015, January). Telephone interview with Michelle Dunbar, Saint Jude Retreats Blog Talk Radio.

Heyman, G. M. (2013, May 6). Addiction and choice: Theory and new data. *Frontiers in Psychiatry, 4.* https://doi.org/10.3389/fpsyt.2013.00031

Leshner, A. I. (1997). Addiction is a brain disease, and it matters. *Science, 278*(5335), 45–47.

Lewis, M. (2012, November 12). Why addiction is NOT a brain disease. Retrieved from http://blogs.plos.org/mindthebrain/2012/11/12/why-addiction-is-not-a-brain-disease/

Pescosolido, B. A., Martin, J. K., Long, J. S., Medina, T. R., Phelan, J. C., & Link, B. G. (2010). "A disease like any other?" A decade of change in public reactions to schizophrenia, depression, and alcohol dependence. *The American Journal of Psychiatry, 167*(11), 1321–1330. https://doi.org/10.1176/appi.ajp.2010.09121743

Sowell, T. (2007). *A conflict of visions: Ideological origins of political struggles.* New York, NY: Basic Books.

Weisberg, D. S., Keil, F. C., Goodstein, J., Rawson, E., & Gray, J. R. (2008). The seductive allure of neuroscience explanations. *Journal of Cognitive Neuroscience, 20*(3), 470–477. https://doi.org/10.1162/jocn.2008.20040

APPENDIX C
ADDICTION ISN'T CHRONIC

W e hear all the time that "addiction is a chronic, relapsing brain disease," and while we've taken on the disease notion in several chapters and thoroughly in appendix B, the "chronic" part of that statement is even more absurd. What is meant by chronic in the case of "addiction" is that it's ongoing and consistently recurring and thus needs to be managed or attended to for the rest of your life. In other words, "once an *addict*, always an *addict*." The recovery society compares addiction to diabetes, heart disease, or hypertension to convey this view. You don't stop having diabetes; rather, you spend the rest of your life adjusting to it through diet and managing it with medications, and it continues to be a problem for you. Addiction, they say, is the same way. However, the data disagrees with this version of addiction.

Here are the rates of addiction to all substances, by age, from the 2015 National Survey on Drug Use and Health:

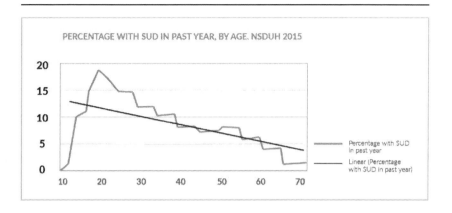

The results of this survey are similar year after year, for every year it's been done. What's more, they're similar to results found in other epidemiological surveys. The trend with addiction is that rates consistently go down as a function of age, and they go down sharply. Death rates do not even come close to accounting for this decrease in use. What this means is that people are *permanently* getting over their "addictions", which indicates this is not a chronic condition. To be clear, people once classified as addicted aren't continuously relapsing like recovery lore says they are. If this were the case, the rates would not go down with age, and they certainly would not go down so rapidly.

Contrast this with diabetes, a verifiably chronic disease to which addiction is constantly compared:

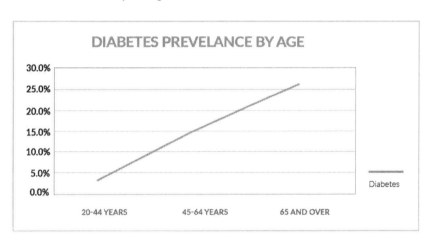

As you can see from this data acquired from the Centers for Disease Control (CDC), at increasing ages, more and more people are found to have diabetes. The same is true for coronary artery (heart) disease (CAD), another condition often compared to addiction:

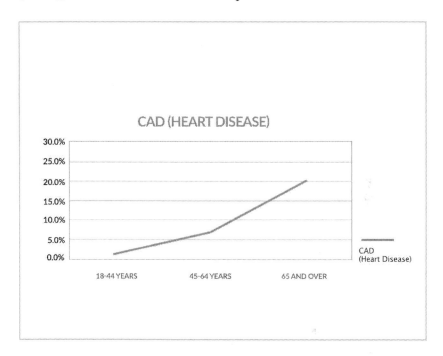

Heart disease and diabetes are chronic conditions that require ongoing treatment and management by the individual sufferer. The numbers grow because nobody is ever cured of heart disease or diabetes, but more people are diagnosed as they get older. Let's look at the trends for all three of these conditions against one another:

417

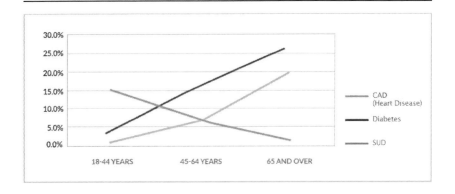

Clearly, the trend for addiction (SUD on the chart) goes down as a function of age, whereas the trends for chronic conditions go up with age. Despite that they're constantly compared by the recovery society, they are not at all comparable conditions.

Now, perhaps most important to this discussion, the people who get over their addictions are not constantly "managing their recovery" or working to prevent relapse. As we showed you in *The Freedom Model*, most people never get treatment or any formal help, and yet most of them get over these problems. If you haven't gotten help for "addiction," then you certainly aren't getting the form of treatment known as "aftercare." You aren't using "coping skills" taught to you in treatment programs. You aren't "avoiding triggers" that you identified in treatment programs, nor are you tied into a "support network" of recovering people. What you are doing is simply living your life, having moved on from heavy substance use because you've found that you're happier without it.

Contrast this with diabetes. You may have to monitor your glucose levels daily, radically alter your diet and exercise regimens, and administer medications such as insulin for the rest of your life. This is what managing a chronic disease looks like.

Getting over an addiction just looks like moving on with your life because that's what it is; it is not a chronic disease like diabetes or heart disease.

REFERENCES

Addiction: NSDUH 2015, Table 5.3b. Retrieved from https://www.samhsa.gov/data/sites/default/files/NSDUH-DetTabs-2015/NSDUH-DetTabs-2015/NSDUH-DetTabs-2015.htm - tab5-3b

Coronary Artery Disease (i.e., heart disease). Retrieved from https://www.cdc.gov/mmwr/preview/mmwrhtml/mm6040a1.htm

Diabetes. Retrieved from http://www.thefdha.org/pdf/diabetes.pdf

Hypertension. Retrieved from https://www.cdc.gov/nchs/data/databriefs/db220.pdf

HEROIN AND THE MYTH OF "ADDICTIVENESS"

> "At the turn of the 19th century any respectable person in Europe could walk into a pharmacy ... and routinely buy a range of hashish pastes, exotic psychedelics or morphine (complemented by a handy injection kit)" (Dikötter, Laamann, & Xun, 2004).

Moderate heroin use is possible, and it happens. Sustained heroin use without significant health, employment, legal, and social problems is possible, and it happens. Contrary to popular belief, these patterns of use are not just a temporary phase on an inevitable path to heroin "addiction"; just as with alcohol, some people are occasional and/or moderate users. This information flies in the face of the very notion that any substances are inherently "addictive."

Many people will be shocked and appalled that we offer this chapter. They think it's dangerous for us to give out this information and that it's an endorsement of heroin use. They'll say "It's just safer to stay away from heroin altogether, so why would you tell people they *can* do it?" It's important that you understand that to say that "anyone can" isn't the same as saying that "anyone should." It's simply stating a fact. And it's a fact that is important to know. There is no quality of "addictiveness" in drugs that is stronger in some drugs than in others – this includes heroin. So as much as people can use caffeine, marijuana, or alcohol "non-addictively", they can also use methamphetamine, cocaine, or heroin "non-addictively." The inverse is also true – all the less "hard" drugs can be used "addictively" because there is no quality of addictiveness; people don't get addicted to drugs, they choose to use them for reasons held in their own minds. The stronger a person's reasons supporting the substance use are, the more extreme their usage becomes. This holds for drugs, regardless of their pharmacology, and it holds true for activities where no substance whatsoever is ingested – such as sex, gambling, shopping, comic book collecting, fishing, cycling, running, et cetera. People don't want to face these facts. They think it's just safer to uphold the myth of addictiveness because drugs like heroin carry a danger of overdose that is greater than other drugs. So in their minds, anything that scares people away from it is good, and any fact that does away with the anti-heroin hysteria should be kept a secret.

Frankly, those people who believe that information like this should be kept from people are part of the problem. They actively spread misinformation, most of them ignorantly, some of them knowingly, to scare people away from all substance use. This tactic doesn't work because heroin users, and even those considering trying it for the first time, are usually already aware of the dangers, but more important, spreading the idea that heroin is so addictive that moderate use is impossible is also *counterproductive*. Believing this myth leads people to think change is impossible. It engenders self-doubt and leads people to feel controlled by substances. It leads people to give undeserved significance to a single usage of heroin or other opiates even for medical reasons. It bolsters the idea that drugs possess a power of "addictiveness" and distracts people from the important fact that they are actively making their own choices and are fully capable of making different choices.

To be clear, *we aren't recommending any heroin use.* We're remaining neutral on whether anyone should use substances because that choice is up to the person making it, and more important, changes in this choice can happen only in the mind of the person making them. It is imperative that you understand that we (the authors and this book) are not responsible for anyone's choices nor are we implying that his or her choices are in our hands in any way. It is imperative that the troubled users understand the choice is fully theirs, especially if their goal is to choose differently than they have in the past.

Clearly, it is safer to stay away from heroin altogether. You're far less likely to suffer a heroin overdose, be arrested for heroin-related charges, fall prey to the dangers of the black market, or suffer the judgment that often comes with heroin use if you don't actively choose to use it. These risks are abundantly clear, and we mention them only in the extremely unlikely chance that some readers may not know of them. However, risks are a normal part of life, and some people will see these risks as tolerable given the benefits they think they get from heroin use. These are judgments for each person to make for him- or herself. Our goal is simply to arm everyone with the most accurate information possible, specifically debunking the recovery society myths that substances are inherently "addictive" and that heroin and opiate/opioid use inevitably leads to uncontrollable use.

The legendary status of heroin as the "most addictive drug" props up the idea that other drugs have various levels of addictiveness. Thus, regardless of what substances a person uses, it infects everyone who believes it with the self-defeating notion that it's possible to "lose control" over substance use. Everyone is always in full control over his or her own substance use, and everyone can change his or her levels of substance use, even heroin users. If you can see through the legend of heroin, then you can see through the idea that anything is inherently addictive. You can then fully return your substance use choices to the realm of free choices. That is our educational goal with this chapter.

First, we'll review the basic stereotype of heroin use and users, and then we'll review the facts that dispel this fairy tale. Since the basic pharmacological effects of the various opiates/opioids (of which heroin is a part) are identical, we will mainly use the term heroin in this chapter, but when we do so, please know that we're referring to this entire class of drugs.

THE HEROIN MYTHOLOGY

Heroin has attained a rare, legendary status as an "addictive" substance, providing a high so pleasurable that no normal pleasures of life can ever come close to matching it. It's said that heroin feels like "love," "heaven," "being wrapped in a warm blanket on a cold day," and even "like kissing the creator," among other poetic quotes. It's often said that the high is so good you'll never forget what it feels like and you'll be stuck either painfully longing for it or chasing that feeling for the rest of your life once you try it.

But then, there's a darker side to heroin use that is revealed after a period of daily use: the withdrawal. The withdrawal is said to be so painful that it traps you, compelling you to keep using even when you know it's destroying your life – it makes you "crave" what you do not really want. The withdrawal turns users into drug-using zombies who will do anything for more heroin just to "feel normal," even as they cease to receive any pleasure from it.

It doesn't matter whether you manage to abstain for a while and fully withdraw; it is said that everyone always goes back. Now that you know that it "takes away all the pain of living" and is the only thing that makes you "feel comfortable in your own skin," now that you've lost your innocence and know this incomparable high, *irresistible* heroin will pull you back in like a siren song and make you use again. Then, the withdrawal will complete the trap again. There are no moderate heroin users, only those who haven't fully progressed to full-blown addiction yet, and liars.

If you haven't used the needle yet, you will once your tolerance gets high enough and you need a more efficient means of use. From there, it's game over. And you might dream of those early moderate days, but you can never go back; it was just a stage in your transition to full-blown addiction.

Should you somehow happen to achieve abstinence again, it'll only be temporary. You'll hear the siren song again and say to yourself *Just this once*. But "once" turns into "once every week," and then eventually, you'll slip up and use two or three days in a row, and the withdrawal will catch you again. Then, you won't be able to stop without treatment; you'll need to be on a replacement therapy, such as methadone or buprenorphine, for the rest of your life because your addiction has left you with a brain that permanently needs an opiate to fill in the deadened opiate receptors and hopefully keep you from craving but at least give you a permanent tolerance so it's harder for you to overdose. This is all inevitable because of the Pandora's box you opened by exposing yourself to the irresistible, incomparable high of heroin.

THE TRUTH OF HEROIN

The origins of the myths of heroin could fill an entire book and are beyond the scope of this section. Like most believable legends, those views are based on a few kernels of truth, but they're greatly exaggerated and mixed with blatant lies. Unfortunately, the mythology of heroin is so strong within our culture that it's become self-perpetuating. Current users are either trapped by the myth, or if they engage in behavior that runs counter to the mythology (such as moderate usage or quitting without professional help), they'd rather keep it secret than risk the judgment engendered by such recovery ideology. Here's the good news: we have the history and research to help you see through these myths and move past the dangerous idea of inherent addictiveness permanently.

THE IRRESISTIBLE HIGH

Heroin and the other opiates have been romanticized like no other substances have. The high is supposedly so good that it's "irresistible." That's a strong word. It means "too attractive and tempting to be resisted." To understand the depth of this thinking, let's remind you that to resist is to "succeed in ignoring the attraction of (something wrong or unwise)." The point is that when it's said that heroin provides an irresistible high, what's meant is that heroin is so inherently attractive that you can't possibly escape its magnetism. Like a black hole, heroin will pull you in, and there's nothing you can do about it. The best you can do is to permanently steer clear of that black hole. The extreme euphoric pleasure of heroin is irresistible—or is it?

> Looking back on it, I don't know whether it was a smart thing or a dumb thing.
>
> It was a whole different time and place. The whole country was different. I didn't know anything about (heroin), and I was too dumb to be afraid.

This quote is from newsman Dan Rather when in an interview he was asked about his choice to be injected with heroin a single time for a news report. He gave this statement to a reporter just before he got on stage for an anti-drug talk in 1990. At that point, it'd been about 35 years since he had used heroin a single time, and he'd had a stellar career as a journalist for decades. Had he in fact been too dumb? Was his ignorance about heroin a liability? Should he have been more afraid? Here's what he told another journalist in 1980:

> As a reporter—and I don't want to say that that's the only context—I've tried everything. I can say to you with confidence, I know a fair amount about LSD. I've never been a social user of any of these things, but my curiosity has carried me into a lot of interesting areas.
>
> As an example, in 1955 or '56, I had someone at the Houston police station shoot me with heroin so I could do a story about it. The experience was a special kind of hell. I came out understanding full well how one could be addicted to "smack," and quickly.

And more recently (2014), Rather said that heroin had felt "otherworldly," that he never wanted to go back to it, and "It gave me a hell of a headache" (Taibi, 2014). The only statement about heroin that fit with the mythology was when he said it felt "otherworldly." But apparently, it didn't feel otherworldly enough for him to ever feel the desire to use it again in nearly 60 years! And it gave him a headache? It was "a special kind of hell"? We never hear such statements about the effects of heroin in the press; he indicated that it wasn't that great. Rather says he understands how easy it is to get hooked, yet his own history shows no evidence of coming anywhere near being hooked on heroin, and that far from being an irresistible high, it was at best a mixed feeling for him.

Dan Rather's experience with heroin isn't all that odd. Opiates have been around for *thousands of years*. For most of recorded history, they were the only known effective medicine, mostly as a painkiller but also for coughs and bowel disorders, among other uses. Some historians date its use back to the Sumerians in 4000 BCE, and the agreed upon earliest written reference to their medical use dates to Greece in 1500 BCE, where they were widely used. Notably, "addiction" didn't appear until the 1800s, and its history is hotly contested. You can find statements by politicians in the late 19th century that mirror the rhetoric of today (Conrad, 1992) in which it is claimed that doctors are giving people opiates and they're accidentally getting hooked:

> The constant prescription of opiates by certain physicians ... has rendered the habitual use of that drug [in the Western states] very prevalent.

Here's a quote from a report to the Iowa State Board of Health in 1885:

> The habit in a vast majority of cases is first formed by the unpardonable carelessness of physicians, who are often fond of using the little syringe, or relieving every ache and pain by the administration of an opiate. (Conrad, 1992)

Nevertheless, the opiates were still widely and freely sold, and the rhetoric was as out of touch with reality as it is today. Millions of people are prescribed opiates today, and yet they do not find them to provide an irresistible high that permanently lures them in. Even those who try opiates for recreational purposes don't usually get hooked. And, as researcher Norman Zinberg (1984) found, people have a range of pleasant and unpleasant initial experiences with the opiates. Most people who try them do not become hooked. That's a fact. For example, data from the 2004–2006 SAMHSA National Survey on Drug Use and Health (NSDUH) found that only 31% of people who had tried heroin for the first time one to two years prior to the survey had used it again in the past year. That means 69% of people who tried it in one year *did not* feel "irresistibly" pulled to use it again the following year. Similarly, 56% of those who tried the nonmedical use of opiate pain relievers didn't bother to use them again in the following year. Furthermore, only 13.4% and 3.1% of those who tried heroin and opiate pain relievers, respectively, were "addicted" in the following year (SAMHSA, 2008) (several reliable surveys over several years show the same pattern, that only a fraction who try it continue to use the drug and that an even smaller fraction display "addiction").

We don't have an exact number, but tens of millions of prescriptions for opioid painkillers are written every year. In fact, the number of prescriptions in some U.S. states outnumbers the population of those states. Yet, when the Cochrane Group reviewed the available research to determine how many chronic-pain patients get "addicted" to painkillers, it found that it was less than 1%. The actual number was 0.27% (Noble et al., 2010). This information directly refutes the current narrative that people are getting "accidentally addicted" to opiates because of painkiller prescriptions. The more accurate explanation for such "accidental addiction" is that people who want a drug induced high find a good source of it in doctors, either accidentally or intentionally. Doctors then make for an easy scapegoat.

These numbers destroy the myth that the opiates provide an irresistible high that pulls you in once you try it. Dan Rather's experience with heroin turns out to be the norm, and it destroys this myth. His experience is in line with thousands of years of virtually addiction-free opiate use. Most people who use opiates don't find them to produce an irresistible high. The innumerable millions of people prescribed opiates every year and those given massive doses of morphine intravenously after surgery don't find these drugs to produce an irresistible high. If they did, we'd have well over a hundred million opiate addicts in this country alone right now. As it stands, we have approximately 2 million pain-reliever "addicts" (less than 0.6% of the U.S. population), and there's a much smaller amount of heroin "addicts". (Center for Behavioral Health Statistics and Quality, 2016)

To dig into some of the numbers more precisely, consider this: in the United States in the years from 2002 to 2013, approximately 170,000 people tried heroin each year. The number of people experiencing heroin "addiction" in any of these years has fluctuated up and down between approximately 200,000 and 500,000 per year, or approximately 0.1% of the population. If everyone who tried it during that period became addicted, we should have had approximately 2,040,000 heroin addicts on our streets by 2015; however, we had only 329,000 at that point. So is heroin irresistible? Clearly, it's not to most people (SAMHSA, 2014)

Note: We approached this section with the generous assumption that everyone who "gets hooked" finds heroin irresistible and, even if that were true, it would be the minority opinion on heroin. However, we don't even know that all those who use heroin in ways classified as addictive would even describe it as irresistible. Yet that is the narrative, and it's wrong. Don't believe the hype; heroin is not irresistible.

MODERATE OPIATE USERS

In the previous section, we saw that there are plenty of people who've used opiates but didn't become "addicted" and that in fact they are the norm. However, the mythology says that, if these people continue to use opiates, they will inevitably progress to "addiction." Is this true? Is it impossible to use opiates nonaddictively unlike the average American who drinks alcohol nonaddictively? You already know our answer is no, but we must explain it so you can confidently move beyond the addiction mythology.

First, in the survey previously referenced (SAMHSA, 2008), more than half of the people who continued to use heroin in their second year of use did so without meeting the diagnosis for addiction. We understand some will say that those people will all eventually become "addicted," that it's just a matter of time, and they will say that there is no such thing as sustained, moderate heroin use. A landmark study spanning from 1973–1981 says differently.

With funding from The Drug Abuse Council and National Institute on Drug Abuse (NIDA) Norman Zinberg (1984) set out to find and understand what he called "controlled users" of psychedelics, marijuana, and heroin/opiates. By controlled use, he meant "successful and consistent," and he specifically delineated this from occasional use. It's important to understand the criteria he used because it tells us much more than can be gleaned from SAMHSA's data. With SAMHSA's survey of people who used heroin over the past year or two, those surveyed could have used once, occasionally, often but sporadically, or regularly without dependence. There is no delineation; everyone is included. In contrast, Zinberg's nonaddicted users were regular users of opiates. The myth says that regular use always leads to addiction. He blew up that myth and many more with the data he collected.

Here are Zinberg's criteria for "controlled users":

- "They must have used an opiate at least ten times in each of the two years preceding admittance. If they did not fulfill this condition for one of the two years preceding admittance, they must have used an opiate within the last year and must also have met conditions 1, 2, 3, and 4 in at least two consecutive years of the preceding four.

- In each of the two years preceding admittance they must not have had more than three periods of four to fifteen consecutive days of opiate use.

- In those preceding two years the number of days of opiate use in any thirty-day period might have equaled but must not have exceeded the number of abstaining days.

- In those preceding two years they must have been using all drugs (licit and illicit, except tobacco) in a controlled way." (p. 48)

As you can see, the criteria do a good job at excluding extremely sporadic or one-time-ever users and binge users, and it sorts the regular users from the problematic regular users. It also excludes users for whom heroin is just a small part of a general addiction to other drugs. In short, it's a good description of moderate users (and we will refer to these subjects as "moderate users" from here forward because the term "controlled users" implies that heavier users are not in control of their use).

Despite limited funding, Zinberg's team located 61 moderate users in the Boston area who fit their criteria. They put the word out to colleagues who have regular contact with substance users and any social services agencies, placed newspaper ads, and then used a "snowball" collection technique whereby the initial users they found were asked to refer other users who may fit the criteria. Finally, they trained some of their subjects to interview and collect data from some moderate users who were unwilling to talk to researchers.

WHY WE DON'T HEAR ABOUT
MODERATE USERS?

The SAMHSA data shows there are more opiate experimenters than "addicts," and Zinberg's study shows moderate users can be found when a researcher specifically seeks them out. However, the average person and the average addiction professional don't believe in the existence of moderate opiate users. Most people in the recovery society, including many researchers, deny their existence, yet they exist. Why don't we know this?

First, before Zinberg's study, in the decades when the world's most extensive, organized research on drug use had just begun, the myth that no one could use opiates moderately was simply accepted as fact, and no researchers even bothered to look for moderate users. If they happened to come across them, they assumed they were lying or on their way to full addiction. Another big factor is that the myth that moderate use is impossible keeps moderate users from identifying themselves to others. Who wants to be wrongly identified as an addict and stigmatized?

Remember, one of the techniques Zinberg had to use to locate moderate users was to train other heroin users who knew them since they were so afraid to talk to researchers. Forty-two percent of the moderate opiate users were referred by someone else involved in the study. Most were aware that being found out could permanently ruin their careers and social lives. As Zinberg explained:

> as was expected in view of the more deviant status of opiate users, it was more difficult to contact and arrange interviews for controlled users of opiates than for compulsive opiate users or for any type of marihuana or psychedelic users. Without exception, controlled opiate users expressed much more concern about confidentiality than did any of the others. All of the controlled subjects [including marihuana and psychedelic users] were well aware of the illegality of what they were doing, but the controlled users of opiates were also aware of the extreme sense of deviance associated with their use; yet they lacked both the indifference regarding social acceptance shown by the marihuana and psychedelic users and the sullen disregard for consequences shown by the compulsive opiate users. (Zinberg, 1984, p. 60)

So, even when a researcher is specifically looking for moderate opiate users, they are harder to find than moderate users of other drugs because of the opiates' nasty reputation and the extreme stigma attached specifically to opiate use. One of his moderate-user subjects expressed it simply:

> When I have told people, they're always watching out to see if I'm doing it, and if I am, they'll give me a lecture. So it's not worth it to tell them. (Zinberg, 1984, p. 129)

And another gave a more detailed account:

> With one friend—one that's most adamant about it—there's a lot of concern involved. And lecturing … he started with this business about—he's my best friend—"I suppose I'm going to have to start watching my stereo equipment now." Just trying to lay it on like that. And then he started going into this lecture: "Once you start [injecting] you can't stop; you do it once, and you're going to be hooked for life; stop while you can." And I thought that the best way around this, I guess, is not to mention it. (Zinberg, 1984, p. 130)

In the second example, the friend doing the lecturing had even tried heroin himself, and yet he was still ready to shame his friend for using it. There's just no way around it in our culture. Moderate opiate users must keep their usage hidden or at least known only to other opiate users. The stigma of heroin/opiate use is too pervasive in our culture so they keep their use hidden not only from family members and acquaintances but even from friends who use other illegal drugs.

> The controlled opiate users in our study—most of whom used heroin but some of whom used Dilaudid, codeine, and other pharmaceutical opiates, all on an occasional basis—were painfully aware that they were perceived as deviant. They tended to keep their use a closely guarded secret from everyone except one or two dealers and their opiate-using friends. (Zinberg, 1984, p. 153)

Moderate users are out there, but they typically keep their drug use, and thus their existence as a class, secret.

The next big reason we don't know about moderate opiate users is because of the very fact that their use is moderate and secret, so they just won't end up in the places that average drug researchers find their subjects: addiction treatment programs, social services agencies, and law enforcement agencies. Simply put, researchers tend to study only opiate users with the most extreme problematic patterns of use that send them into the hands of professional helpers. Here, we see again that moderate users are invisible, but in this case, the invisibility is even more damaging because they're invisible to the intellectuals who drive the narrative about drugs and drug use. These researchers don't see moderate users, and thus, they present a picture in which moderate usage of opiates is impossible. Nevertheless, the moderate users are out there, and their moderate habits aren't just a phase on the way to addiction. They often use moderately for several years.

MODERATE USE DOES NOT INEVITABLY PROGRESS TO "ADDICTION"

In the recovery mythology, heroin or opiate use, if continued, must progress to the full picture of addiction. Once again, this isn't the case. Zinberg found users whose moderate usage career ranged between two and 20 years, with the mean length of usage being 7.2 years. Moreover, the average frequency of use in the 12 previous months for moderate users broke down as follows:

Average frequency of use in previous twelve months

Multiple daily	0%
Daily	0%
Twice a week	41%
One to three times a month	36%
Sporadic (less than once a month)	23%

Using sprees[5] in previous twelve months

No sprees	75%
Sprees only	6%
Sprees plus other use	20%

(Zinberg, 1984, p. 70, table 4)

Unlike many other studies, Zinberg collected substantial follow-up data, which found that:

> 49% had maintained their using pattern and 27% had reduced use to levels below those required for them to be considered controlled users. (Of these 24% had become abstinent.) Another 11% had maintained their controlled pattern of opiate use but had begun using other drugs too heavily for us to consider them controlled subjects. Only 13% (5 subjects) had increased their opiate use sufficiently to enter either the marginal (8%) or the compulsive (5%) category. (Zinberg, 1984, p. 71)

Here, we see direct evidence of sustained moderate use, with only a tiny minority of 5% eventually becoming "addicted" in follow-up.

---

5. Spree is defined as four to fifteen consecutive days of use.

Moderate use is possible. It happens. It doesn't inevitably progress to addiction.

A more recent longitudinal study located 126 long-term heroin users in Glasgow who had never received any formal addiction treatment. The researchers' aim was "to test whether heroin could indeed be used in a controlled, nonintrusive fashion for an extended period of time." Even though the study participants had been using heroin for seven years on average, it was found that:

> Participants had levels of occupational status and educational achievement comparable to that in the general UK population, and considerably higher than typically found in heroin research. At the conclusion of the study, six participants had entered treatment. While there was evidence of intensive risky patterns of drug use among the sample, there was equal evidence for planned, controlled patterns of use. Some drug-related negative health and social outcomes had occurred on a lifetime basis, but ongoing problems were rare, and heroin was not a significant predictor in either context. In contrast to typical samples of heroin users, high levels of negative health and social outcomes did not appear to be inevitable within this sample. (Shewan & Dalgarno, 2005)

These heroin users did not resemble what we usually think of as an "addict" other than the fact that they were using the most taboo drug. Although having been heroin users for an average of seven years, their lives did not fall into disrepair. Most were continuously employed, many in the highest levels; many were enrolled in college; half owned their own homes; and only 12% were staying with friends or parents. Most of the study subjects did not display the progression into "addiction" that we're told is inevitable with consistent heroin use. The researchers found this type of user because they made the effort to look outside the places where heroin "addicts" are usually found. We can't highlight enough the importance of this—most researchers look only for heroin "addicts" so that's all they find and present to the public as the face of heroin use. By looking outside jails and rehabs, these researchers discovered a sample in which three-quarters of heroin users fit into light- or moderate-use categories.

The above may seem surprising, but not to those versed in the history of opiate use. Numerous authors have documented a long history of regular opiate use without addiction. Regardless of the political propaganda, "most opium use in Europe, the Middle East and Asia was light and moderate," say the authors of a well-researched tome on the opium wars and narcotics in China. They continue:

> Opium was used by many people in moderate quantities: the relative absence of problematic users—rather than a proliferation of "drug fiends"—is the most striking feature of narcotic culture in late imperial China. Even heroin, which circulated as a substitute for opium in a climate of prohibition during the first decades of the twentieth century, was not used in life-threatening doses by a small circle of social outcasts, as conventional imagery might have it; rather it was taken by many social categories in relatively small and innocuous quantities. (Dikötter et al., p. 4)

Other authors have documented moderate use in many places. The truth is that continued moderate use of any form of opiates—from opium to heroin to oxycodone—is entirely possible and it's historically been the norm even if we don't think we see it around us now. "Addictiveness," as a quality of a drug, is a myth.

CAN MODERATE USERS INJECT?

> Opium pipes and morphine needles do not have lives of their own: they are granted social lives by their users, the sentient beings have disappeared behind the smoke-screen of the opium myth. (Dikötter et al., p. 7)

There is an idea that injection must lead to "addiction" and therefore moderate users can't be intravenous users. This too is a myth. It partly persists because of the invisibility of IV use in our culture. While people may smoke or even snort drugs openly in some social situations, syringes are almost never used openly except in front of others who also inject. The myth also seems to be founded on the idea that, since direct intravenous use of drugs is the most rapid and efficient route of use, it allows the "addictive" power of the drug to take hold quicker.

Smoking or oral administration is a less efficient path of use and so is said to be less addictive than IV use.

As we've seen through this discussion, opiates have a long and mixed history. Intravenous use has been around for well over 150 years. It wasn't always unanimously seen as the evil it is today. At the same time (circa 1900) that morphine injection kits were acceptable and easy for people to buy from the Sears catalog or pick up at their local pharmacy across the United States and Europe, the biggest concern about opiate use in the world was directed at opium smoking among Chinese people—one of the least efficient routes of opiate administration. This goes against the idea that route of administration is the most important factor in addiction. We should also note that, at the time, morphine injection was promoted as a cure for alcoholism. Injection was certainly demonized by some, yet it wasn't the taboo it is today. Ironically, smoking was more of a taboo, probably because of racism against the Chinese.

History and drug mythology are a riddle of contradictions. But here's what we learned from the hard data in Zinberg's study:

> Analysis of several relevant variables did not support the view that compulsive users inject opiates and controlled users do not. There were no significant differences between these groups as to whether they currently injected opiates, whether they injected heroin, or whether they had ever injected opiates. In fact, for all three variables the direction of difference was the opposite of what might have been expected, showing that a greater proportion of controlled subjects than compulsives actually injected the drugs. (1984, p. 73)

Zinberg's data directly contradicts the notion that IV use must lead to "addiction." He showed that IV opiate use can indeed be moderate and that it needn't be considered "more addictive" than other routes of administration.

In another study from 1992, researchers looked for intravenous drug users by community outreach (i.e., outside the treatment system) and located over 1,400 subjects. They found that 46% had no history of treatment, and they noted an important subgroup:

> Intravenous drug users who had neither a history of arrest since 1977 nor of drug treatment were more likely to be women and more educated, to have not received public assistance, and to inject less than weekly. (Alcabes, Vlahov, & Anthony, 1992)

This data directly contradicted the monolithic junkie stereotype of IV drug users and showed that a wide range of IV users exist, if only we have the will to look for them. Unfortunately, moderate opiate users and intravenous drug users undermine the talking points of anti-drug and anti-addiction zealots and organizations, so funding for this sort of research is slim to nonexistent. As one observer noted of some of Zinberg's initial study of moderate users, "the Drug Abuse Council of Washington had funded the study, assuming that 'controlled use' would prove to be nothing more than a transitional moment before the inevitable onset of addiction" (DeGrandpre, 2006, p. 113). Oops! Looks like they didn't get what they bargained for, and then some. Moderate use is possible and doesn't necessarily progress to "addiction" and even IV use doesn't cause a progression to "addiction."

Some readers may have experiences that seem to contradict what we've shown here; in fact, one of the authors does. I (Steven) used heroin nasally on and off, at various frequencies of use for three years. I understood fully that injection was the biggest drug taboo there is and declared it a line I would not cross. Then, I went to inpatient rehab because of an arrest. There, the counselors as well as fellow patients and local 12-step members who attended meetings at the facility confronted me about my heroin use often. They told me that I would soon be shooting up "because everyone does." They added that, once I did shoot up, there was no going back and I'd be addicted for the rest of my life (*odd strategy for helping people, don't you think?*). I ended up believing this stuff, and within a week of leaving rehab, I thought "screw it" and shot up for the first time.

My heroin use escalated wildly from there in terms of frequency, quantity, experience of withdrawal, and desperate behavior to sustain the flow of drugs (including much criminal activity). But does my story serve as proof that injection causes increased "addiction"? There was so much more going on differently in my mind after rehab that to blame the needle for my descent would be extremely shortsighted and untrue.

I had just been taught, and chose to give credence to, a deep well of addiction mythology. I had suffered an arrest that proved I was using heroin to my family. I took that as a totally devastating development. Because my family was so naïve to drugs, and heroin was such a taboo, and the image of the junkie was how I thought they would see me for the rest of my life, I began to take on the image and likeness of the "addict" I was taught about in the rehab. I began, for the first time, to feel hopeless and thought I'd ruined the rest of my life. There was only one thing that I thought would make me feel good at that point: more heroin. I figured everyone would assume I was doing it anyway, and I saw no other options for happiness because that is what rehab told me was now my only hope for happiness. So I dove headlong into extreme heroin use. I had my reasons of course. I was not caused to do this in any way, but I was beginning to take on that causal ideal because the "professionals" told me I was well on my way there anyway.

But again, let us look at what was really going on for me. Blaming the needle for my increased usage would be silly considering all the developments in my thinking at the time. It would be getting causation reversed by ignoring the many other important variables. Everything I just explained demonstrates that I had a massive change of mind and completely threw caution to the wind—in other words, I learned the concept of addiction, and then I *chose* to make that image personal to me. As part of my new, reckless attitude and increased preference for heroin use, I decided to start injecting. I "caused" my own increased drug use and injection with my thoughts—rather than the needle or heroin itself causing it. Don't forget this point: in my case, IV use was a result of my choice to use recklessly.

There are nearly infinite analogies that would demonstrate our point about causation. Consider a downhill skier who uses a basic set of all-purpose skis meant for intermediate skiers. He decides he wants to take up freestyle skiing, which involves making big jumps, skiing alternately forward and backward, and doing tricks such as flips. Upon making this decision, he buys a special set of skis meant to make these activities easier. It was his desire to take up this different style of skiing that led to the purchase and use of the specialized equipment. He had to put countless hours of effort into his new style of skiing. Simply putting someone on a set of freestyle skis wouldn't cause them to go for big air jumps and flips. They'd have to want to do those things. They'd have to have reasons in their mind for seeing this risky activity as rewarding enough to devote their time and energy to it. So again, don't get causation reversed. It would be absurd to think that if someone got his hands on the best set of golf clubs available, then those clubs would turn him into Tiger Woods. Equally absurd is the notion that access to a hypodermic needle would turn someone into the most extreme drug user possible. The equipment doesn't make the athlete, nor does the paraphernalia make the drug user.

But what about the potency argument? Intravenous use is a way to ensure that the entire drug makes it into your bloodstream thereby ensuring that the full potency of the drug would be experienced, whereas other methods may lose some of the drug along the way. This they say is why IV use should cause more addiction. This would be like saying that drinking a beverage with 40% alcohol like whiskey would more likely result in alcohol addiction than drinking a beverage with 4.5% alcohol like beer. Or more directly, it would be like saying that taking the "harder" (i.e., more potent opiates) is more likely to result in addiction than taking less potent opiates. In Zinberg's study, he classified heroin, methadone, morphine, and Dilaudid as hard opiates and codeine or Percodan as "soft" opiates. He found no differences between moderate users and "addicts" as to whether they currently used or had ever tried the various hard or soft opiates. Taking drugs of higher potency doesn't make you an addict. In fact, there have been various accounts of people continuing to seek out the same amount of drugs and display the same "addictive" behavior even when the potency of available street heroin dropped to near nonexistent levels. Although their tolerance must have gone down as they continued to use diluted heroin, they certainly didn't become any "less addicted" because of using less potent heroin. The desire for drug use simply isn't caused by potency or route of administration.

The historical perspective is extremely valuable in demystifying injection. Hypodermic needles appeared in the 1800s, at a time when medicine was still a crude art. Surgery was feared, far more than we could imagine today, because it often ended very badly. Medical practices were barbaric. Yet this device comes along that represents a quantum leap in medical technology. It didn't take long before hundreds of compounds were available for injection to treat countless medical conditions, and countless people were injecting themselves with medicines (Dikötter et al., 2004). It turns out that many of the medicines available for injection weren't effective (and some were countereffective). But if you understand the placebo effect—the power that taking an inert pill has to comfort people—then you can catch a glimpse of the effect that injecting something, anything, had on people worldwide in the 19th and early 20th centuries. The hypodermic needle itself was a placebo; it had a magical aura about it. It was serious stuff then, and as its use became limited mostly to the hands of doctors, its use by laypeople took on a darker meaning.

Nowadays, when we find out that people need to give themselves injections for a medical problem, even something as routine as insulin for diabetes, many of us often pity them, and we fear for them. Diabetes can take on the dark aura of cancer once we know self-injection is involved. And while it is a serious condition, self-administration of insulin is a perfect solution for some people with diabetes, and they come to see it as normal an activity as taking an aspirin. We all know people with diabetes are prolonging their health and life with injections, yet there is a negative atmosphere surrounding their use of the hypodermic needle. What of the drug user, injecting for pleasure? The negativity surrounding this practice is obviously far worse.

For the intravenous drug user in our culture, injection is now a mixed experience. The hypodermic needle carries both a placebo and a nocebo effect. Whereas a placebo effect is often positive, the nocebo effect is a negative (or adverse) effect caused by expectancy. Research has shown that many IV drug users will experience a high or even a reduction in withdrawal when they are injected with a saline solution. They're expecting a powerful drug and for it to hit them quickly and directly through the needle. These expectancies create powerful feelings even in the absence of the drug. Sadly though, the magical legend of the needle's power to addict can bring a nocebo effect at the same time. If people expect a needle to lead to addiction, if they see it as a symbol that they've lost control and have become trapped forever needing drugs, then when they start injecting, they will manifest feelings of being trapped forever as lifetime addicts. This combination placebo/nocebo effect puts the true believer in the magic of the hypodermic needle into a serious bind.

Throughout the 20th century, countless millions of people have been hooked up to intravenous supplies of morphine following surgery, and the overwhelming majority of them did not develop opiate use problems. This fact should remove the notion that IV use and/or withdrawal causes addiction. What separates those people, moderate users, and experimenters from problematic IV drug users on every level is their reasoning. They lack the belief that extreme opiate use is needed to satisfy them. Problematic users are those who've come to prefer drug use over anything else. This is a matter of thoughts, not one of mere contact with a needle.

CAN AN "ADDICT" EVER GO BACK TO MODERATE USE?

The most visible former drug "addicts" are those who embrace the recovery lifestyle of ongoing counseling and support group meetings where they are taught that a return to moderation is impossible. These folks embrace abstinence and proudly tout their abstinence, sometimes rattling off their abstinent time not only in terms of years but down to the exact number of days and hours. We hear the same from many "recovering alcoholics." They are the ones who become recovery activists. Their visibility paints a one-sided picture, and allows us to think that maybe the drugs are addictive to some people, but not addictive to other people, due to genes or some other biological difference.

The epidemiological data available on former "alcoholics" paints a different picture. More than half of former "alcoholics" become moderate drinkers—*more than half!* (Dawson, 1996). They are the people who either leave the recovery society or never enter it in the first place so they remain mostly invisible to those spreading the misinformation about substance use problems. While the same quality of data isn't available on former drug "addicts," there is no reason it should be impossible to become a moderate user of other drugs (alcohol contains the drug ethanol). All drug use is motivated by people's desire for happiness (their PDP) and their freely chosen belief that some level of drug use will fulfill that.

We have personally known formerly "alcoholic" drinkers who returned to moderate drinking; people who formerly overused opiate pain relievers and heroin who returned to using opiate pain relievers as prescribed; people who formerly overused their benzodiazepines, such as Xanax and Valium, yet returned to using these drugs as prescribed; and users of many "hard" drugs who abstained from those drugs but decided to use the "softer" drugs, such as marijuana and alcohol moderately or even to use psychedelics on occasion. When it comes to heavy marijuana use, most readers won't have to look far to find friends and acquaintances who were once total potheads yet now enjoy a hit of weed here and there. It appears that anything is possible when people change their mindsets about substances and addiction.

I'm sure you noticed that we didn't mention people returning to moderate heroin use. Zinberg studied this group of moderators though. Forty-eight percent of his moderate opiate users had previously had a period of "addictive" opiate use. That period of "addiction" (mean 1.6 years) was much shorter than their current period of moderate use (mean 3.5 years), but they experienced it fully and made the choice to moderate their opiate use (and keep in mind that only 5% of Zinberg's moderate users had changed their status to "addictive" use in follow-up) (1984, p. 71). Heroin "addicts" can become moderate heroin users. They do it in the same way "alcoholics" become moderate drinkers: they change their minds as to what level of drug use they believe will make them happy. The drug doesn't become less "addictive" and the individual's genes don't change (making them less susceptible to the fabled "addictiveness" of the particular drug). The individual's mindset changes.

DOES WITHDRAWAL MAKE HEROIN/ OPIATES ADDICTIVE?

Tales of the power of withdrawal are perhaps the biggest culprit keeping the heroin mythology alive. As we noted earlier, opiates have been around for several thousand years; they have been used for both medicinal and recreational purposes for thousands of years. The usage of any opiates, from edible opium to codeine, morphine, heroin, or oxycodone, can lead to a state in which stopping use can cause withdrawal syndrome. Yet, for most opiate users, throughout most of history, this withdrawal hasn't presented a major problem. It didn't make them "addicted," and most people who take these drugs don't appear "addicted" today. For example, surgery patients given a steady supply of morphine for long, sustained periods do not normally seek out drugs during withdrawal. Many who were not told of withdrawal upon release from the hospital have no recollection of withdrawal at all, and yet they were on heavy dosages for long periods of time. Why is that?

Well, listen to how a review paper on withdrawal syndromes in the *New England Journal of Medicine* describes opiate/opioid withdrawal:

> Opioid-withdrawal syndrome resembles a severe case of influenza. In addition, the symptoms include pupillary dilatation, lacrimation [tears], rhinorrhea [runny nose], piloerection ("gooseflesh"), yawning, sneezing, anorexia, nausea, vomiting, and diarrhea. Seizures and delirium tremens do not occur. Patients who are dehydrated or debilitated can have life-threatening complications. (Kosten & O'Connor, 2003)

That's right; the symptoms of opiate withdrawal are like those of the flu. We know there will be readers who will say it's worse, but physiologically it is like the flu. Symptoms can range from a mild flu to an extremely bad flu, but still, withdrawal is like the flu. It's important to note that it's dangerous for only a handful of people who are already on death's door. What's more, the duration of withdrawal is like that of the flu; the worst of heroin withdrawal is over within days:

> The time to onset of peak opioid-withdrawal symptoms and their duration after abrupt discontinuation depend on the half-life of the drug involved. . . . For heroin, symptoms peak within 36 to 72 hours and last for 7 to 10 days. (Kosten & O'Connor, 2003)

It does not cause "cravings." It isn't deadly, and it does not create a need for more opiates. It creates a sickness that resolves itself within days and is easily tolerable. Again, knowing the history is important. Withdrawal symptoms created by edible opium were easily tolerated historically by users in Europe, the Middle East, and Asia. By many accounts, when the famous patent medicines of the 19th century that contained opium as their main ingredient were made illegal, the regular "addicted" users of them, mostly stay-at-home women, stopped without becoming illegal drug users. Strong withdrawal syndromes were and currently are tolerated by most surgery patients throughout the history of the use of morphine. The Vietnam vets who were using massive amounts of some of the most potent heroin available historically, managed to go through withdrawal just fine, and 96% of them got over their "addictions."

Withdrawal can play a part in "addiction" because it increases the immediate value of drug use, but it doesn't enslave (i.e., addict) anyone to continue using. The groundbreaking discovery here was made by sociologist Alfred Lindesmith, who studied most of the facts mentioned above and more, as well as conducted original research in interviewing self-described opiate addicts. What he found was that withdrawal alone was not sufficient to cause anyone to become an "addict." For that evolution to happen, opiate users had to be taught the idea that they were addicted, or "hooked." They needed to begin to think of themselves as "junkies" or "dope fiends," and it was this cognitive shift that created opiate addiction. Without it, people stopped and tolerated withdrawal easily.

The individual's interpretation of withdrawal distress is a belief or attitude that exists as a cultural and psychological phenomenon. It tends to be imposed upon the addict by his social environment. The crucial fact of it is not its validity, but that the individual, once having accepted it, is subject to influences and social pressures of which he was previously unaware. The attitudes he assumes toward himself are altered. He realizes for the first time that he may be a "dope fiend," and in the privacy of his own thoughts he begins to entertain tentatively that idea of himself and to explore its implications. Further experience with the drug quickly impresses him with the truth of his notion, and he is soon compelled to accept it, though he usually struggles for some time and makes fruitless efforts to free himself. During this time the person is transformed from a nonaddict to an addict with all that that implies.

The essential process involved in the transformation and basic to it is a linguistic and conceptual one. It is through the use of the social symbols of language in conversation with himself and with others that the personality changes involved in becoming an addict are initiated and developed. The individual, when he uses the symbols which society provides him, also assumes the attitudes appropriate to those symbols when he applies them to himself. He calls himself a "dope fiend" and gradually hardens himself to the fact that he has become an outcast and a pariah to respectable people. He of necessity seeks the company of other addicts, both because they can solve the problems arising out of addiction and because he feels more at home with them. He attempts to quit because he accepts the general public disapproval of addiction and wishes to remove himself from the pariah category. It is this whole process which George Herbert Mead has described as "taking the role of the generalized other" or assuming toward oneself the attitudes of the group or society in which one lives. (Lindesmith, 2008, pp. 192–193)

We've confirmed this explanation in our interviews with many opiate "addicts" ourselves, and attributional research shows the same. The

Glasgow study of heroin users showed that the heavy users were more likely to describe their heroin use as *caused* by factors out of their control and the product of addiction, whereas the light and moderate users were more likely to describe their use as freely chosen. The authors of that study express the importance of psychology over pharmacology:

> The traditional model of addiction would suggest that when people use addictive drugs, then this cognitive component is at least reduced ... and that this particularly applies to heroin. . . . We would dispute that cognitions are somehow replaced by a physiological need to continue drug use that has an overwhelming effect on behaviour.
>
> The work of Davies (1992, 1997) and Orford (1984) in particular suggests that addiction is as much a cognitive state as a physiological one. The addicted set [see chapter 8], therefore, could be characterized by a narrowing of the repertoire of choice available to the drug addict, either subjectively or objectively: subjectively in that the addict believes he or she is addicted ... objectively in terms of the social pressures which come to surround the addict ... and indeed the tangible legal sanctions. . . . The contribution of psychological factors in addiction is rarely disputed. Regarding these factors as secondary is to neglect what would appear to be a component that is equally as important as drug pharmacology in the addictive process. (Shewan & Dalgarno, 2005)

Craving for substances is a matter of the mind, not the body. The opiates came to be "addictive" only when the idea of addiction was invented and propagated. Before that point, they were simply drugs that led to a withdrawal syndrome upon cessation. What you think about these drugs and the power they hold over you is far more important than the withdrawal effects they create when it comes to feeling "addicted."

In closing, we have provided this extensive, detailed information in this chapter so you can be fully informed and can make your decision regarding substance use knowing the truth, that heroin and opiates—just like alcohol, pot, psychedelics, cocaine, meth, cigarettes, caffeine, and chocolate—have no power to enslave you. None of the drugs are "addictive." By providing this information, we're not saying you should or should not use opiates. We're not advocating any level of usage, nor are we trying to persuade you to be abstinent. These decisions are yours to make based on what you want for your life. Because you are reading this book and seeking a solution to your substance use problems, we ask that you seriously consider all your options and be open to the possibility that your life could be happier with a change in your substance use.

Knowing this truth about opiates is essential to ending the fear/abstinence cycle that so many heroin and opiate users experience. In summary, here is how opiate use works: The myth of its inherent addictiveness is used to present a binary option of fear. The accepted narrative says that if you use opiates at all, you are guaranteed to descend into disastrous addiction so you must abstain. This misinformation short-circuits the PDP and any process of personally discovering whether abstinence or moderation is more attractive to you than heavy use. It also short-circuits the probability that you will question what's so good about opiate use. The idea of heroin and other opiates being so powerful that you can be enslaved to them is short-circuiting your mind; it's short-circuiting *you by taking your thinking abilities out of the equation!* The result is that you still see heavy use as your dream option and yet you try to stay afraid of it and deter yourself from it. Feeling deprived in abstinence, you eventually begin to see heavy use as being worth its heavy costs so you say "Screw it!" and go back to heavy heroin use.

Again, some of you will see this chapter as the authors' trying to tell you what option to choose regarding heroin use. That is not our goal at all, but we don't have control over your beliefs. So, if you are going to try to moderate your heroin use but are unwilling to let go of your fear of its supposed powers over you and your will, then we strongly urge you to use caution and absolutely recommend abstinence until you change your beliefs and fully accept that drugs are not "addictive." We also strongly urge you to be completely aware that *any* drugs bought on the black market can be tainted. Presently, there is a rash of drugs being tainted with Fentanyl, a slower acting, longer lasting opioid with which accidental overdose is a great danger. So again, do not take this chapter as license to use opiates moderately. This chapter is meant to demonstrate that no drugs are inherently "addictive" and that all substance use is thus freely chosen. By letting go of the myth of addictiveness, you can then focus on what really underlies your choices: the belief that certain types of substance use are what you need to be happy. You need to sort that out, because that is what will change you.

Attempting moderate use is a path to assured disaster if you are still holding onto the myth that you are weak and that heroin or whatever substance you prefer is "addictive." While you are a believer in these myths, there is no room for moderation—only abstinence is the safe option.

The myth of heroin's addictiveness is used as a virtual gun to your head to scare you out of using, but it can never convince you that abstinence or moderate use is any more enjoyable than heavy use. By discarding the myth and taking away that virtual gun, you free yourself from the fear and panic so you can make the decision for greater happiness, make positive discoveries, and retain your motivation to change if that is what you choose.

REFERENCES

Alcabes, P., Vlahov, D., & Anthony, J. C. (1992). Characteristics of intravenous drug users by history of arrest and treatment for drug use. *The Journal of Nervous and Mental Disease, 180*(1), 48–54.

Center for Behavioral Health Statistics and Quality. (2016). *Key substance use and mental health indicators in the United States: Results from the 2015 National Survey on Drug Use and Health* (HHS Publication No. SMA 16-4984, NSDUH Series H-51). Retrieved from https://www.samhsa.gov/data/sites/default/files/NSDUH-FFR1-2015Rev1/NSDUH-FFR1-2015Rev1/NS-DUH-FFR1-2015Rev1/NSDUH-National Findings-REVISED-2015.pdf

Conrad, P. (1992). *Deviance and medicalization: From badness to sickness* (2nd expanded ed.). Philadelphia, PA: Temple University Press.

Dawson, D. A. (1996). Correlates of past-year status among treated and untreated persons with former alcohol dependence: United States, 1992. *Alcoholism, Clinical and Experimental Research, 20*(4), 771–779.

DeGrandpre, R. (2006). *The cult of pharmacology: How America became the world's most troubled drug culture* (Kindle ed.; p. 113). Durham, NC: Duke University Press.

Dikötter, F., Laamann, L., & Xun, Z. (2004). *Narcotic culture: A history of drugs in China* (1st ed.). Chicago, IL: University of Chicago Press.

Kosten, T. R., & O'Connor, P. G. (2003). Management of drug and alcohol withdrawal. *New England Journal of Medicine, 348*(18), 1786–1795. https://doi.org/10.1056/NEJMra020617

Lindesmith, A. R. (2008). *Addiction and opiates* (Reprint). New Brunswick, NJ: Aldine Transaction.

Noble, M., Treadwell, J. R., Tregear, S. J., Coates, V. H., Wiffen, P. J., Akafomo, C., … Chou, R. (2010). Long-term opioid management for chronic non-cancer pain. In Cochrane Database of Systematic Reviews. John Wiley & Sons, Ltd. https://doi.org/10.1002/14651858.CD006605.pub2

Shewan, D., & Dalgarno, P. (2005). Evidence for controlled heroin use? Low levels of negative health and social outcomes among non-treatment heroin users in Glasgow (Scotland). *British Journal of Health Psychology, 10*(Pt 1), 33–48. https://doi.org/10.1348/135910704X14582

Substance Abuse and Mental Health Services Administration, Office of Applied Studies. (2008, March 27). *The NSDUH Report: Substance Use and Dependence Following Initiation of Alcohol or Illicit Drug Use.* Rockville, MD.

Substance Abuse and Mental Health Services Administration. (2014). *Results from the 2013 National Survey on Drug Use and Health: Summary of National Findings*, NSDUH Series H-48, HHS Publication No. (SMA) 14-4863. Rockville, MD: Substance Abuse and Mental Health Services Administration.

Taibi, C. (2014, January 9). Dan Rather tried heroin and it gave him "a hell of a headache." Retrieved from http://www.huffingtonpost.com/2014/01/09/dan-rather-heroin_n_4569319.html

Zinberg, N. (1984). *Drug, set, and setting: The basis for controlled intoxicant use.* New Haven, CT: Yale University.

APPENDIX E

PEOPLE CAN MODERATE—IF THEY PREFER IT

W e have driven this point home throughout this text that people can moderate their usage of drugs and alcohol if they want to, but we know that many people are not convinced. Sadly, for these people, fear and self-doubt get in the way of their being able to make an informed, rational decision regarding substance use. That is why we have decided to make a chapter that addresses it directly. There is a prerequisite to this discussion: you must understand points that we've established in earlier chapters before reading this section:

1. Nobody loses control of his or her substance intake after a single drink or hit. (See appendix A.)

2. There is no disease of addiction. (See appendix B.)

3. Substances do not contain a special quality of "addictiveness." (See appendix D.)

4. "Once an addict, always an addict" is simply not true. Most people get over these problems permanently. (See chapter 1 and Appendix C)

5. There is ample evidence that former "addicts/alcoholics" can and do become "moderate" substance users. Keep reading this chapter.

If you understand these five points, then you know there is no such thing as addiction, that there is no such thing as people being pushed by an unseen, unknown force to use substances against their own free will. In *The Freedom Model*, we understand that people are acting of their own choice (free will) to do the things they see as being their best available options for happiness at the time they do them (PDP) according to views held in their own mind that only they have the power and potential to change (mental autonomy).

People drink and drug the way they prefer to, and they can change what they prefer by thinking differently about their options. We have evidence that people do change what they prefer regarding substance use. The most convincing evidence regards alcohol use. Let's start with a study conducted by the NIAAA and the Census Bureau: The 1992 National Longitudinal Alcohol Epidemiologic Survey (NLAES; National Institutes of Health, 1998).

The NLAES was a survey of 43,000 people in the general public from whom they found 4,600 who fit the diagnosis of alcoholism during their lives a year or more prior to the survey. The significance of this is important. Most studies of people with substance use problems come from small samples gathered from only those who show up at treatment facilities or other institutional settings. This study looked beyond those places to get the full breadth of people with substance use problems. It gives a more accurate, nonbiased picture of the full range of people with substance use problems. It analyzes those who seek treatment as well as those who don't. The results from studies like this are more significant and telling than almost any other type of research in the field.

The status at the time of the study of those 4,600 who had ever fit the diagnosis of "alcohol dependence" (i.e., "alcoholic") was as follows:

- 27.8% were drinking in a way diagnosable as "alcohol abuse" or "alcohol dependence"

- 22.3% were abstinent

- 49.9% were "drinking without abuse or dependence" (i.e., drinking moderately)

Yes. Half of the "alcoholics" had become moderate drinkers. This is not an anomaly either. Data collected in a similar survey conducted 10 years later, again by the NIAAA and the Census Bureau, had similar results. The National Epidemiologic Survey on Alcohol and Related Conditions, or NESARC (National Institutes of Health, 2010), found that the status at the time of the study of those who fit the diagnosis of alcohol dependence a year or more prior to the survey was as follows:

- 25% drinking in a way diagnosable as "alcohol dependence"

- 18.2% were abstinent

- 56.8% were drinking without dependence (i.e., drinking moderately)

Two studies, conducted 10 years apart, had similar results. "Alcoholics" can and do become moderate drinkers. Of course they do! There is no experimental evidence to suggest that anyone lacks the ability to drink moderately. Nevertheless, we hear so-called experts repeatedly saying that "some people can moderate, and some people can't." That statement is pure hogwash. Anybody can, but not everyone wants to drink moderately.

We consider these results with alcohol use to be applicable to any other drug. That's not to say that 50% of crack "addicts" will necessarily become moderate crack users; we are simply saying that they *can* become moderate users if they *choose* to. Experiments show that they are in control of their crack use and will choose differently when they see more preferable options. The same is true for any drug, including heroin. Yes, heroin. As we showed you in appendix D, heroin "addicts" can and do become moderate heroin users. The government hasn't collected and presented data as to what percentage tend to moderate. But we can say with full confidence that there is nothing in principle that makes moderation of this drug any less possible than moderation of alcohol. However, it's probably less likely because heroin is illegal and more taboo than alcohol, and for many reasons, people see that quitting altogether is less socially and legally risky than choosing to moderate. Moderation of heroin is also riskier health-wise than alcohol since it is available only on the black market, and therefore purity and content are unknown. Thus, it only makes sense that many would prefer abstinence over moderation of this drug if they decide to change their usage of it. However, this doesn't indicate that people "can't" use it moderately. Just because people don't, doesn't mean they can't.

YOU CAN MODERATE, BUT IS THAT WHAT YOU REALLY WANT TO DO?

Through the entire text of *The Freedom Model*, we have sought to bring you face-to-face with this basic question: What would make you happiest?

When people think they "have to quit," "can't continue drinking/drugging," or "should quit," they are miles away from figuring out what they would *prefer to do*, that which would make them happiest. Instead, they're dealing in false "musts," obligation, and duty. At the end of the day, there is nothing you *must* do, and whatever you believe your duty is, you won't fulfill it unless you prefer or want to fulfill it. That is a fact. That is the PDP at its essence. You will feel motivation (i.e., want, desire, crave, or feel the urge) to do only what you truly believe is your best available option for happiness. You stand the best chance of figuring this out if you fearlessly face all your options and weigh them out honestly and accurately. You cannot do this if you eliminate options based on falsehoods, such as "I am incapable of moderation" or "I might lose control."

Furthermore, cornering yourself into abstinence by holding onto the false belief of "loss of control" can make you feel deprived. From this point of view, you "can't drink moderately" while other people "can," so abstinence becomes your cross to bear—a situation you resent. In fact, abstinence can become a choice that you revel in and enjoy if you choose it without feeling cornered into it. Letting go of the "loss of control" myth allows you to happily choose abstinence, as much as it also allows you to happily choose moderation.

"YEAH, BUT I TRIED BEFORE AND LOST CONTROL"

Nobody loses control of his or her substance use in any meaningful sense. The experimental data does not support such portrayals of any substance use. The classic situation is that an "alcoholic" resolves to have only two drinks on an occasion, but then he continues drinking far beyond that point, maybe all the way up to 10 drinks, until he passes out. This is called a moment of loss of control. He says he couldn't stop drinking. He thinks he wasn't "strong enough" to control his drinking. He says his "judgment goes after I have a few drinks and then I can't make the right choice." None of this portrayal of the situation is scientifically supported.

It helps to get away from substance use for a minute and look at an analogy. Let's say you plan to visit your friend for a few minutes to say hi and check in. You get to talking, and three hours go by. Did you "lose control" of your conversation? Were you *unable* to stop talking? Were you too weak to control yourself? When we look at this in the same terms, we see the absurdity. The reality is that you enjoyed your visit and chose to keep it going longer than you had originally planned. *You changed your mind.* Even if you had other things you wanted to tend to during that time, you decided that this visit and your conversation were more important to you than your errands in that moment.

Now, let's go back to the intention to have two drinks, which then turns into 10 drinks. This situation is almost identical in principle. You change your mind along the way, deciding that you'd rather keep drinking than do anything else. It is often accompanied by the thought *Fuck it; I'll have another* (please excuse our language, but you know it's true).

This can certainly play out in other ways. You may decide to do only a moderate amount of cocaine today. But then, you decide to do it again tomorrow, and the next day, and the next day. You have now used cocaine on more consecutive days than you originally had planned. Again, you were doing what you wanted to do the next day and so on. You didn't lose control, you freely made your choices each day, and you could have chosen differently. You would have chosen differently *if you had preferred to.*

In hindsight, you may look at these episodes and regret them. You may think they are not worth whatever their ultimate price turns out to be. Okay, now you can think deeper about what you might like better (i.e., *prefer*) going forward. You might choose to use cocaine on one day, and then, the next day, when the thought occurs to you to use it again, you might choose to think something like this: *I had my fill yesterday, and when I keep doing cocaine day after day, I regret how much money I've spent and feel like I've wasted time. I can be happy not doing it today and can use that time and energy to do other things I care about. It might be sort of fun, but I'm not going to do it today.*

And that's it. That is thinking differently and making a different decision. Of course, there are infinite variations of thoughts that people could go through to make different decisions. That's normal life stuff. We can't tell you what to think or what will convince you that a different decision is preferable. Only you can figure out what those things are for yourself. All we can say is that, for you to make a different decision than you usually make, you need to see your options differently. You need to see a different decision as preferable.

If it's that you overdo it in the moment, then you may think something like *Will another drink really make me feel any better tonight, or will I enjoy myself more if I just switch to water now?* You may not *know* the answer to that, but you may decide that it's worth not taking another drink tonight as an experiment to find out whether you really can have a more enjoyable time with less alcohol. You may find that you enjoy drinking less more than drinking a lot, and a discovery of a satisfying adjustment in drinking is made. Or you may find that drinking at lower levels is just a tease and not satisfying to you at this point in your life. This may bring you to another decision point next time you consider drinking, where you think *Two drinks weren't satisfying last time, but the 10 drinks I usually need to reach satisfaction isn't worth the costs of the momentary pleasure it brings—so I'd rather not drink at all. I'd rather be sober than tease myself with two drinks or drink to oblivion.*

Isn't it great to be clear about that? Now, if you choose to abstain, you can be happy and confident in that choice. You don't even have to commit to that for life; you can just say *At this point in my life, I know what I like, and it's either a lot of alcohol or none. I want to learn to enjoy myself without leaning on alcohol.* Or you might realize that you've gotten your fill of alcohol and there's nothing else to be gained from it, so you decide you're done with it for life. You don't have to be a martyr to choose abstinence. This decision can be arrived at by discovering that it is the genuinely happier one for you.

What would make you happiest? That's the question that needs to be answered. Saying to yourself that you *have to quit* doesn't really answer it. You may want to go back to chapter 21 on adjusted substance use to ponder the possibilities available to you. Mentally exploring them may allow you to come to peace with a decision. We are not saying you have to/should try moderation, and we aren't recommending moderation or any substance use whatsoever. We know that our readers would make a variety of choices about future substance use even if we only discussed the option of abstinence. So we are simply recommending that you make those choices with a mind focused on finding the option that will provide you the most happiness so that you can be truly invested in your choices and maximize your personal results.

Some people will find that, when they try reduced substance use, they spend an inordinate amount of time thinking about managing it, planning when to do it and how much, watching the clock, and becoming more obsessed and desiring more substance use. The authors of this book all chose extended periods of abstinence for several years. In that time, we learned not to lean on substances and feel like we "needed" them for anything. We also lost our fear of substances as things that could "readdict" us. We let go of the concepts of relapse and the loss of control. We learned the research that took the power away from substances. Then, when we decided we'd like to use substances moderately, we did so with full confidence and ownership of our choices, and there was no such obsessive thinking. The results have been that we did not choose to drink in problematic ways. We have known many others who've done the same. However, we've also had attendees of our educational programs who immediately chose adjusted substance use with no issues and no period of abstinence. Anything is possible *if you want it.*

THE MYTH OF WILLPOWER

A common misconception of our position that addiction is not a disease is that we're saying it's a matter of willpower. We could write an entire chapter to address this myth; suffice it to say that moderating does not require willpower and those who choose to drink heavily don't lack it. Moderate users of substances want only a moderate amount of substances. For example, they don't want to get obliterated when they drink. Subsequently, they do not have to stop themselves from getting obliterated when they drink. They have a few drinks, and they are satisfied and do not choose to have more. There is no special level of self-control, impulse control, or willpower that they use to moderate their drinking. They genuinely want only a minor buzz from alcohol so they actively choose to drink until they get that buzz without choosing to go any further. Or maybe their moderation is characterized by using only once every few weeks as a special treat for fun. Is this you? Or do you prefer substances as the thing you feel you need to deal with the stress of daily life?

If you come to genuinely believe that a buzz is preferable to obliteration, then you will not choose to get obliterated. It's that simple. If you think of it as a special treat, you will use it occasionally and not have to stop yourself or resist daily urges to do it every day. You will feel the motivation to do it only occasionally.

What often complicates the "decision to moderate" is that people like the idea of being moderate users—the lower costs of such a preference—so they think they want to moderate, yet they still actually prefer being drunk or prefer using it daily for their daily stresses. They like the idea of being a two-drink drinker while wanting the feeling of 10 drinks. So, after two drinks, they say "fuck it" and have another and another until they get the feeling that they really want. They may try to exercise "willpower," which amounts to trying to have the motivation to do what they really do not want to do (which, in this case, is to get only a buzz from two drinks). They tell themselves not to take another drink "or else" some laundry list of negative consequences will occur. They try to deter themselves, trying to muster up every ounce of self-control and willpower they have, but still their preference is to keep drinking.

You cannot do what you do not want to do. If you choose to do something, such as having 10 drinks, it is your will. If you choose to drink for stress every day, it is your will. It is not a failure of willpower or self-control. There is no weakness involved in your decision. There is simply personal judgment involved in the decision—the personal judgment that more drinks will make you more satisfied or that you need daily drinking to deal with stress. You do not have two selves inside you, like a devil and an angel on a cartoon character's shoulders. There is no battle of strength between two parties. There is just one of you making your decisions, coming down on the side of the option that you judge to offer the most satisfaction.

By thinking of our "bad" decisions in terms of weakness, we obscure what is really going on, which is that we think those decisions are what we need most at the time that we make them. We think another drink is what we need to feel good. We think chasing down heroin today is what we need to be comfortable in our own skin. We think an eight-ball of cocaine is what we need to keep the party going or we'll miss out on some essential life experience. I (Steven) defer to my own experience now to say why I do not think weakness is involved. I once walked 13 miles in a snowstorm to shoplift things, sell them, and buy heroin in a neighborhood where the cops were constantly patrolling for someone who looked exactly like me. I strongly defied all sorts of forces that made it next to impossible for me to get the heroin that I wanted on that day. There's no weakness involved there. It is evidence that my will to use heroin was strong. This indicates that I believed heroin was very meaningful to my existence at that time. That is the PDP in action.

What do you want and why do you want it? What do you think it will do for you? These are the questions you need to ask—not whether you have enough willpower or self-control and not whether you "can" moderate. You *can* moderate. But can you genuinely see adjusted substance use (either moderation or abstinence) as the more desirable, happier option? That is where the answer of whether you will do it or not can be found.

Again, and we cannot say it enough times—we are *not* recommending any substance use. We remain neutral and make no prescriptions on levels of use. We do so knowing that you will do what you believe is your happiest option regardless of what we say. Many of you have enough experience with substances and have thought enough about them to know what you genuinely want right now. If you're sure of it, great. You can proceed without shame and regret or deprivation. You don't need special willpower to carry it out whether you choose moderation, abstinence, or your same old style of use. You will carry out your preferred level of use easily.

Only when you are unsure do problems arise. But know this: willpower is not a factor. Clearing up your confusion surrounding your options is what you need. Sometimes, the best way to do that is to just choose abstinence as you think things through; it's certainly the safest option. *It's not safest because it removes the risk of "losing control," because loss of control is a myth.* It's safest because it removes all the very real substance-related risks and costs. You can view this as a period of testing the water and making discoveries, just as you can view embarking on adjusted substance use as a period of testing the water and making discoveries. We cannot and will not say what anyone should do, but if your substance use choices have you on death's door, abstinence for at least some period makes sense.

WHAT ABOUT IMPAIRED JUDGMENT?

Impairment and judgment are terms that get used in confusing ways regarding substance use. People say things like "When I drink, my judgment is impaired, and I can't make the right decisions" or "I buy cocaine, cheat on my wife, or have more drinks than I should." Let us be crystal clear with this example: whether to cheat on your spouse is not rocket science. Nor is it trigonometry. Nor is it even as complicated as parallel parking. It doesn't take much mental power. If you have agreed to a monogamous relationship, then the judgment is already made. It just takes knowing what you already know.

Alcohol is a depressant in that it depresses the activity in our brains. This is the reason people who drink have slowed reaction times and driving while drunk is dangerous. We may not have the sensory power available to us while intoxicated on alcohol to judge when we should hit the brakes on our car. Yet decisions such as this are in an entirely different class than decisions about whether to cheat on a spouse, pick a fight with someone, or call the coke dealer. Again, these are not rocket science level decisions.

People engage in such "poor judgment" when they are intoxicated because they are empowered by the license to misbehave (see chapter 19). The evidence shows that so-called "impaired" moral judgment is not the result of the pharmacological powers of alcohol and there's no reason to believe this is a real effect of any other drug either. We do some of these things when drunk because we want to do them and know we'll get somewhat of a pass if they go wrong and/or we get caught by someone who disapproves. We do some of them because we want to be crazy and push boundaries and act differently than we normally do. But we do not do them because our power of "judgment is impaired." These choices are not matters of rocket science. Nor is the matter of whether another drink is a good idea.

Where impaired judgment might be relevant is when you're dealing with putting together doses of drugs in which a 10th of a gram too much could be fatal. These are calculations that may be too difficult for you to make when intoxicated. As for the example of whether to call the coke dealer after you've had a few drinks, if you've promised your spouse you're done with cocaine or you are on probation and have decided you don't want to risk going to jail, then that decision doesn't take any calculation at all.

We say all this not to convince you to go out and moderate. We say it to convince you to drop the excuses and begin making firm decisions about what you think will make you happiest going forward. Blaming "impaired judgment" just keeps you from reassessing your options and is an excuse in most cases. Do you want to use dangerous levels of opiates? Do you want to buy coke on those wild nights at the strip club? Do you want to down two bottles of wine after work every night? If you develop clear, unconfused opinions on what you think will make you happiest, then in most cases, "impaired judgment" isn't even a relevant issue.

THE BOTTOM LINE

The point here is that people do what they want to do. If what you are doing is not working for you in the bigger picture, accept that it is what you have wanted until this point. You *happily* change what you want to change by openly reassessing your options—not by blaming a fictitious loss of control, lack of willpower, or impaired judgment. You can moderate if it is what you really want. You can change what you really want. You can really want abstinence too.

People often hang onto these imagined weaknesses because they keep them from having to face the facts. They want gimmicks and techniques for "how to moderate" or "control their substance use." These too can only distract you from sorting out your view of your options and finding your happiest choices. There are no gimmicks or techniques needed to abstain or moderate. You just need the belief that they are genuinely your more satisfying options.

Just because some people don't moderate doesn't mean they are incapable. It means they don't want to moderate. They want to use at levels/frequencies that are costly. They think they need it that much and that often to be happy. *They prefer it.*

REFERENCES

National Institutes of Health. (1998, November). Drinking in the United States: Main Findings from the 1992 National Longitudinal Alcohol Epidemiologic Survey (NLAES). *U.S. Alcohol Epidemiological Data Reference Manual, 6*(1). Retrieved from https://pubs.niaaa.nih.gov/publications/nlaesdrm.pdf

National Institutes of Health. (2010, September). Alcohol Use and Alcohol Use Disorders in the United States, A 3-Year Follow-Up: Main Findings from the 2004–2005 Wave 2 National Epidemiologic Survey on Alcohol and Related Conditions (NESARC), *Alcohol Epidemiologic Data Reference Manual*, 8(2), September 2010, NIH Publications No. 10-7677.

AFTERWORD

This is where it all began; the Twin Rivers Retreat. And this is where much of the research continues today. Research is understanding a problem, and then working hard to uncover the truth that spells out a solution to that problem. Sometimes that truth is found by understanding what doesn't work, or what is false, first. While The Freedom Model has been in development for more than three decades, (Jerry Brown began the research in 1985) it was through understanding the falsity of the addiction and recovery constructs that we could bring to light its opposite, and then provide that information to the masses who struggle with substances and their use.

That understanding came about in the early years of the project by gaining a very in-depth understanding of the treatment and AA paradigms and how misleading and damaging the rhetoric surrounding those models was. By living with our guests in that retreat for the first 12 years, Jerry Brown (my research mentor) and I discovered the answer to the Recovery Society models; that being the three attributes of The Freedom Model. The PDP, Free will, and Autonomy did not get exposed easily, and it took many decades to codify our full understanding and implication of these wonderfully empowering human attributes.

No one in the treatment industry, except the two of us, had been willing to understand the problem from this in-depth and personal perspective. This isn't bragging – I say this so you understand how much effort went into seeking the truth. By living, day in and day out with our retreat guests for all those years, we were never given the luxury of not finding an adequate answer to the issue of addiction and the shortcomings of recovery. We had to live with our mistakes even more than our successes. But like anything you immerse yourself in both physically, emotionally and mentally, the truth has a way of bubbling out of the mix if you stick with looking for it long enough. For us, it took 28 years.

Steven Slate and Michelle Dunbar came into the research division near the end of those first 12 years, and were the final ingredients needed in our team to get the proper message on paper. While Jerry and I continued to focus on the foundation of the Model, Steven and Michelle took that theoretical foundation and clarified it by reviewing the research that both challenged and supported the information they were provided. This fleshed out the nuances, and gave it life for the reader and our guests at the retreats. As a result, you now have in your hands, the most researched method for leaving addiction and recovery behind.

So where do we go from here? Well, rest assured, we will continue to refine the Model, and learn more. But more importantly, we will be focusing on making sure anyone who has a drinking or a drug problem will know beyond the shadow of a doubt that all the tools necessary to move past the shackles of addiction and recovery lives within them, and that they can move on to a much better place: a place of true internal freedom!

We know without a shadow of a doubt that you, and anyone else reading this book, are fully capable of overcoming your problems with substance use. The challenge for us as helpers is effectively communicating that, when so many others are trying to convince you that you're helpless. It is our sincere wish that you find your answers with this book alone. However, we still understand the practical obstacles that come up for some people. When your life has become chaotic, it is often hard to take the time to calmly sit down with a book and stop panicking long enough to learn and implement a new solution. The daily grind of staving off withdrawal often leaves little time to focus on learning this solution. The social and family dynamics surrounding a troubled substance user can keep the sense of shame and panic going to a point where it's hard to imagine yourself as anything other than an "addict/alcoholic." Moreover, people have different styles of learning that work best for them. Some do better reading, some can tune out the world and listen to an audiobook or watch some videos, and still others will do best when they can discuss the topics and information they're trying to digest with another human being who understands these issues. Some will do best if they can get away from their chaotic life for a while and focus on figuring out this issue once and for all. It is for this reason that we offer courses on The Freedom Model in many forms, including Personal Instruction, and at the Freedom Model Retreats in Upstate New York.

If you or anyone you know needs help moving past addiction and/or recovery, and you want more information on our residential services at the Freedom Model Retreats or The Freedom Model Private Instruction, visit us at **www.thefreedommodel.org** or call **888-424-2626**.

ABOUT THE AUTHORS

STEVEN SLATE

Steven Slate joined Baldwin Research Institute in 2003 as a Program Instructor at the Freedom Model Retreat, where he also served as the Director and Trainer of new teaching staff. He currently serves as a Research Fellow of Baldwin Research, and as Senior Director of the Freedom Model Private Instruction division of Baldwin Research. His original writing on problematic substance use (at his website thecleanslate.org) has garnered praise from distinguished experts, and appeared in college textbooks on addiction and abnormal psychology from McGraw Hill and Greenhaven Press. Steven spends his free time enjoying theater, bowling, and his undying obsession with classic American Hip Hop, and British Drum and Bass music. He's also a comedic actor, who's been consistently performing on the stages of New York City's improvisational/sketch theaters for more than a decade. He lives, cooks, and travels with his loving partner of twelve years, Greg.

MARK SCHEEREN

Mark Scheeren began researching alcohol and drug use and the treatment industry in 1989. He then co-founded Baldwin Research Institute, Inc. and the Freedom Model Retreats, and is currently the Chairman of Baldwin Research. From 1989 through the spring of 2000 Mark lived with his guests at the retreat in an eleven year on-site observational study to fully understand the constructs of addiction and recovery and to build a solution to upend these destructive cultural constructs. Mark authored the first 12 editions of the *St. Jude Program*; the first non-12 step approach to addiction in the country. During these years Mark and his research mentor, Mr. Jerry Brown, also created and promoted the now famous "Treatment Doesn't Work" public service campaign. Mark is also a leading authority and critic of the 12 step paradigm. The research conducted at Baldwin Research Institute and the Freedom Model Retreat's has been reprinted in the *Opposing Viewpoints Series* as well as *Issues that Concern You* textbook series, and have also been featured in the *Drugs and Society* text as well. Mark has been featured in the New York Post, and OK magazine, among other publications as an addiction and treatment industry expert. Mark's hobbies include reading, hiking, the outdoors, and conservation. Mark's family includes his loving wife of 16 years, Danielle, and their three children, Austin, Gabrielle and Joey.

MICHELLE DUNBAR

Michelle Dunbar has served as Executive Director of Baldwin Research Institute for the last 10 years. She has dedicated her life to finding a solution for substance use problems and began as a volunteer at Baldwin Research in 1992 working directly with the guests. Michelle's undergraduate work was in research psychology, and she joined Baldwin Research officially in 2002 working in the Guest Services office talking with families and individuals seeking help. During her tenure at BRI, Michelle has served as Director of Marketing and Guest Services, a Freedom Model Presenter and Director at the Twin Rivers Retreat, and as the Executive Director. Michelle wrote the *Family Program* and has worked with families extensively through her years with Baldwin Research. Michelle has also worked extensively on the past three curriculum updates. She hosted a blog talk radio show in 2014 and 2015 and was privileged to speak with leading addiction activists, authors and researchers such as Dr. Stanton Peele, Dr. Alan Frances, Monica Richardson and Dr. Carl Hart among others. Michelle is a voracious reader and also enjoys swimming, walking, yoga and spending time with her sons Stephen and Christopher, and her best friend and husband of 25 years, Bob.

Made in the USA
San Bernardino, CA
23 January 2020

63557257R00266